ESSENTIALS OF RENAL PHYSIOLOGY

ESSENTIALS OF RENAL PHYSIOLOGY

Alluru S. Reddi, M.D., Ph.D.

Professor of Medicine
University of Medicine & Dentistry of New Jersey
New Jersey Medical School
Newark, NJ

College Book Publishers, L.L.C.
East Hanover, NJ

Published by College Book Publishers, L.L.C.
P.O. Box 483
East Hanover, NJ 07936

Printed in the United States of America

Library of Congress Catalog Card Number: 98-74967
ISBN: 0-9669823-0-4

This book is dedicated to

Francis P. Chinard, M.D.

Eminent Scholar, Researcher, and Teacher

PREFACE

The purpose of writing this book is to provide the undergraduate medical students and the medical housestaff (Interns and Residents) with a clear and concise explanation of the fundamentals of renal physiology with an approach to an understanding of some clinical problems. For example, both medical students and housestaff find the subject of acid-base physiology and its disturbance and electrolyte problems particularly difficult. This book provides them with basic information in a clear-cut and straightforward manner.

Each chapter is followed by pertinent and important study questions with answers. In addition, board-type questions with explanations are provided for each chapter to increase the knowledge of the student.

This book is different from other available texts in renal physiology in several aspects. First, each chapter is treated succinctly and conceptually with simple figures, flow-diagrams and tables. This avoided detailed explanation of each concept. Second, students can understand the concepts more clearly and organize information more efficiently. This avoids memorization. Third, each basic concept has been explained with a clinical example. This will help the student or the housestaff to apply the principles of basic science to clinical practice in the management of patients with water, acid-base, and electrolyte problems.

This book would not have been completed without the help of many medical students and colleagues, who critically analyzed each chapter for accuracy and adequacy of information. I am thankful to several individuals, particularly Tom Banwell, John Bullock, Amos Gona, Norman Lasker, Arthur Ritter, and Marie Birthwright. I thank Adarsh Gupta for his excellent artwork. Finally, I am grateful to my wife and two daughters for their help and support.

Constructive criticism for improvement of the book is gratefully acknowledged.

CONTENTS

CHAPTER 1

BASIC CONCEPTS OF BODY FLUIDS

Objectives

After reading this chapter, the student should be able to:

1. Define the terms osmolality, osmolarity, osmotic pressure, specific gravity, isotonicity, and oncotic pressure.
2. Describe the percentage distribution of water in various fluid compartments.
3. Explain how fluid shifts occur between extracellular and intracellular compartments in physiologic and pathologic conditions.

Water is the most abundant component of the body. It is essential for life in all human beings and animals. Water is the only solvent of the body in which electrolytes and other substances (solutes) are dissolved. An electrolyte is a substance that dissociates in water into charged particles called **ions**. Positively charged ions are called **cations**. The most important cations in blood are Na^+, K^+, Ca^{2+}, and Mg^{2+}. Negatively charged ions are called **anions**. Examples of anions include Cl^-, HCO_3^-, SO_4^{2-}, HPO_4^{2-}, proteins, and organic substances such as lactate or citrate. Substances such as glucose and urea do not dissociate in water because they have no electric charge. Therefore, these substances are called **nonelectrolytes**.

TERMINOLOGY

Units of Solute Measurement

It is customary to express the concentration of electrolytes in terms of the number of ions, either milliequivalents/liter(L) or millimoles/L. This terminology is especially useful when describing major alterations in electrolytes that occur in response to a physiologic disturbance. It is easier to express these changes in terms of the number of ions rather than in terms of the weight of the ions (milligrams/dL or mg %).

Electrolytes do not react with each other milligram for milligram or gram for gram; rather, they react in proportion to their chemical equivalents. Equivalent weight of a substance is calculated by dividing its **atomic weight** by its **valence.** For example, the atomic weight of Na^+ is 23 and its valence is 1. Therefore, the equivalent weight of Na^+ is 23. Similarly, Cl^- has an atomic weight of 35.5 and valence of 1. Twenty-three grams of Na^+ will react with 35.5 g of Cl^- to yield 58.5 g of NaCl. In other words, one Eq of Na^+ reacts with one Eq of Cl^- to form one Eq of NaCl. Because the electrolyte concentrations of biologic fluids are small, it is more convenient to use **milliequivalents** (mEq). One mEq is 1/1000 of an Eq. One mEq of Na^+ is 23 mg.

So far, we have calculated equivalent weights of the monovalent ions (valence = 1). What about divalent ions? Ca^{2+} is a divalent ion because its valence is 2. Since the atomic weight of Ca^{2+} is 40, its equivalent weight is 20 (atomic weight divided by valence or 40/2 = 20). In a chemical reaction, 2 mEq of Ca^{2+} (40 g) will combine with 2 mEq of monovalent Cl^- (71 g) to yield one molecule of $CaCl_2$ (111 g).

Nonelectrolytes, such as urea and glucose, are expressed as mg/dL. To simplify the expression of electrolyte and nonelectrolyte solute concentrations, **Système International** (SI) **units** have been developed. In SI units, concentrations are expressed in terms of **moles** per liter (mol/L), where a molar solution contains one gram molecular or atomic weight of solute in one liter of solution. On the other hand, a **molal** solution is defined as one gram molecular weight of solute in a kilogram of solvent. A **millimole** (mmol) is 1/1000 of a mole. For example, the molecular weight of glucose is 180. One mole of glucose is 180 g, whereas 1 mmol is 180 mg (180 g/1000 = 180 mg) dissolved in one kilogram of solvent. In body fluids, as stated earlier, the solvent is water.

Conversions

Because electrolytes are expressed in mEq/L and nonelectrolytes, such as glucose and urea, are expressed in mg/dL, the reader should know how to convert mg to mEq or mmol. The formulas shown in Box 1-1 can be conveniently used for these conversions.

Table 1-1 shows conversions of important cations and anions in plasma. The table illustrates that expression of electrolyte concentrations in mEq/L is preferred over other expressions because ions react mEq for mEq, and not mmol for mmol or mg for mg. Furthermore, expressing cations in milliequivalents demonstrates that an equal number of anions in milliequivalents are necessary to maintain electroneutrality, which is an important determinant for ion transport in the kidney.

Box 1-1. How to convert milligrams to milliequivalents and millimoles

$$\text{Equivalent weight} = \frac{\text{Atomic wt.}}{\text{Valence}} \quad (1)$$

$$\text{mEq/liter (mEq/L)} = \frac{\text{mg /dL x Valence x 10}}{\text{Molecular wt.}} \quad (2)$$

(The number 10 is used to convert mg/dL to mg/L)

or

$$\text{mEq/L} = \frac{\text{mg/dL x 10}}{\text{Eq wt.}} \quad (3)$$

$$\text{mmol/L} = \frac{\text{mg/dL x 10}}{\text{Molecular wt.}} \quad (4)$$

$$\text{mg/dL} = \frac{\text{mEq/L x Molecular wt.}}{\text{10 x Valence}} \quad (5)$$

or

$$\text{mg/dL} = \frac{\text{mEq/L x Eq wt.}}{10}$$

Examples

The serum concentration of Na^+ is 326 mg/dL. To convert this value into mEq/L, use formula 2.

$$\text{mEq/L} = \frac{326 \times 1 \times 10}{23} = \text{142 mEq/L}$$

To convert mEq/L into mg/dL, use formula 5.

$$\text{mg/dL} = \frac{142 \times 23}{10} = \text{326 mg/dL}$$

To convert mEq/L into mmol/L, use formula 4.

$$\text{mmol/L} = \frac{326 \times 10}{23} = \text{142 mmol/L}$$

Ca^{2+} is a divalent cation. Its serum concentration is approximately 10 mg/dL. To convert into mEq/L, use formula 2.

$$\text{mEq/L} = \frac{10 \times 2 \times 10}{40} = \text{5 mEq/L}$$

If you want to use formula 3, the Eq wt. of Ca^{2+} is 20 (atomic wt/valence = 40/2 = 20).

$$\text{mEq/L} = \frac{10 \times 10}{20} = \text{5 mEq/L}$$

Serum versus Whole Blood

It is customary to determine the concentration of èlectrolytes in serum or plasma rather than in whole blood, which is a mixture of cells and plasma. In addition, electrolytes are usually expressed as mEq or mmol/L of serum or plasma and not plasma water, which accounts for 91-93% of plasma. A sample of plasma is obtained from whole blood by use of anticoagulants; a serum sample is obtained by allowing serum to separate from whole blood at room temperature. If K^+ concentration is found to be increased in a person with normal renal function, both serum and plasma K^+ are measured to exclude hemolysis. Hemolysis occurs less in a blood sample that contains an anticoagulant; therefore, a spurious elevation in K^+ concentration does not occur. On the other hand, an increase in serum K^+ concentration is often seen because the red cells lyse during centrifugation, releasing K^+ into the serum.

Osmolarity versus Osmolality

When two different solutions are separated by a membrane that is permeable to water but not to solutes, water (fluid) moves through the membrane from a lower to a higher concentrated solution until the two solutions reach equal concentration. This movement is called **osmosis**. Osmosis does not continue indefinitely, but stops when the solutes on both sides of the membrane exert an equal **osmotic force**. This force is called **osmotic pressure**.

Table 1-1. Normal (Mean) plasma electrolyte concentrations

Electrolyte	Mol. Wt.	Valence	Eq.Wt.	Concentrations		
				mg/dL	mEq/dL	mmol/L
Cations						
Na^+	23	1	23	326	142	142
K^+	39	1	39	16	4	4
Ca^{2+} [a]	40	2	20	10	5	2.5
Mg^{2+}	24	2	12	2.5	2	1.0
Total cations	--	--	--	354.5	153	149.5
Anions						
Cl^-	35.5	1	35.5	362	104	104
HCO_3^- [b]	44	--	22	55	25	25
$H_2PO_4^-$, HPO_4^{2-}	31	1.8	17	4	2.3	1.3
SO_4^{2-}	32	2	16	1.5	0.94	0.47
Proteins	--	--	--	7000	15	0.9
Organic acids [c]	--	--	--	15	5.76	5.5
Total anions	--	--	--	7437.5	153	137.17

[a] includes ionized and bound Ca^{2+}; [b] measured as total CO_2; [c] includes lactate, citrate, etc.

The osmotic pressure is the colligative property of a solution. It depends on the number of particles dissolved in a unit volume of solvent and not on the valence, weight, or shape of the particle. For example, an atom of Na^+ exerts the same osmotic pressure as an atom of Ca^{2+} with a valence of 2. Osmotic pressure is expressed as **osmoles** (Osm). One **milliosmole** (mOsm) is 1/1000 of an osmole, which can be calculated for each electrolyte using the following formula:

$$\text{mOsm/L} = \frac{\text{mg/dL} \times 10}{\text{Molecular wt.}}$$

Osmolarity refers to the number of mOsm in 1 L of solution, whereas **osmolality** is the number of mOsm in 1 kg of water. However, osmolality is the preferred physiological term because the colligative property depends on the number of particles in a given weight (kg) of water.

The osmolality of plasma is largely a function of Na^+ concentration and its anions (mainly Cl^- and HCO_3^-) with contributions from glucose and urea nitrogen. Since each Na^+ is paired with a univalent anion, the contribution from other cations such as K^+, Ca^{2+} and Mg^{2+} to the osmolality of plasma is generally not considered. Therefore, the plasma osmolality is calculated by doubling Na^+ and including the contribution from glucose and urea nitrogen (generally expressed as blood urea nitrogen or BUN), as follows:

$$\text{Osmolality (mOsm/kg } H_2O) = 2[Na^+] + \frac{\text{glucose}}{18} + \frac{\text{BUN}}{2.8}$$

where 18 and 2.8 are derived from the molecular weights of glucose and urea, respectively. Because serum glucose and urea concentrations are expressed as mg/dL, it is necessary to convert these concentrations to mOsm/L by dividing the molecular weights of glucose (180) or urea nitrogen (28) by 10. Normal serum values are Na^+= 142 mEq/L; glucose= 90 mg/dL and urea nitrogen= 12 mg/dL. The serum osmolality is:

$$\text{mOsm/kg } H_2O = 2[142] + \frac{90}{18} + \frac{12}{2.8}$$
$$= 284 + 5 + 4 = 293$$

The normal range is between 280 and 295 mOsm/kg H_2O. Inside the cell, the major electrolyte that contributes to the osmolality is K^+.

The term serum or plasma osmolality should be distinguished from the term "effective" osmolality or **tonicity**. Tonicity is determined by the concentration of those solutes that remain outside the cell membrane and cause osmosis. Na^+ and glucose remain in the extracellular fluid compartment (see below) and cause water movement. These solutes are, therefore called **effective osmolytes**, and thus contribute to plasma tonicity. Mannitol, sorbitol, and glycerol also behave as effective osmolytes. On the other hand, substances that can enter the cell freely do not maintain an osmotic gradient for water movement. Urea can penetrate the membrane easily, and therefore does not exert an osmotic force that causes water movement. For this reason, urea is referred to as an **ineffective osmolyte**. Urea, therefore, does not contribute to tonicity. Ethanol and methanol also behave like urea. Tonicity cannot be directly measured, but it is calculated using the following equation:

$$\text{Tonicity (mOsm/kg } H_2O) = 2[Na] + \frac{\text{glucose}}{18}$$

The normal range for effective osmolality is between 275 and 290 mOsm/kg H_2O

Isosmotic versus Isotonic

The term isosmotic refers to identical osmolalities of various body fluids; e.g., plasma versus cerebrospinal fluid. However, when discussing osmolalities of solutions used clinically to replace body fluids, the terms **isotonic, hypotonic** or **hypertonic** are used. A solution is considered isotonic if it has the same osmolality as body fluids. When an isotonic solution is given intravenously it will not cause red blood cells to change in size. However, a hypotonic solution will cause red blood cells to swell and a hypertonic solution will cause red blood cells to shrink. Isotonic solution that is commonly used to replace loss of body fluids is 0.9% NaCl (normal saline).

Urine Specific Gravity versus Urine Osmolality

Clinically, estimation of specific gravity is useful in the evaluation of urine concentration and dilution. It is defined as the ratio of the weight of a solution to the weight of an equal volume of water. The specific gravity of plasma is largely determined by the protein concentration and to a lesser extent by the other constituents. For this reason, plasma is about 8 to 10% heavier than pure distilled water. Therefore, the specific gravity of plasma is 1.008 to 1.010 compared to the specific gravity of distilled water, which is 1.000. Urine specific gravity can range from 1.001 to 1.035. A value of 1.005 or less indicates preservation of normal diluting ability and a value of 1.020 or higher indicates normal concentrating ability of the kidney.

Osmolality measures only the number of particles present in a solution. On the other hand, the specific gravity determines not only the number but weight of the particles in a solution. Urine specific gravity and urine osmolality usually change in parallel. For example, a urine specific gravity of 1.020 to 1.030 is related to a urine osmolality of 800 to 1200 mOsm/kg H_2O. Similarly, the specific gravity of 1.005 is generally equated to an osmolality of less than 100 mOsm/kg H_2O. This relationship between the specific gravity and osmolality is disturbed when the urine contains an abnormal solute, such as glucose or protein. As a result, the specific gravity increases disproportionately to the osmolality. In addition to these substances, radiocontrast material also increases the specific gravity disproportionately.

Measurement of urine specific gravity or osmolality is useful in the assessment of volume status, in the differential diagnosis of acute renal failure (acute rise in serum creatinine and BUN above normal), polyuria (urination of 3-5 L/day) and hyponatremia (serum Na^+ concentration < 135 mEq/L). A volume depleted individual with normal renal function is able to concentrate his or her urine, and, therefore, the specific gravity or osmolality will be greater than 1.020 or 800 mOsm/kg H_2O, respectively.

Oncotic Pressure

Oncotic pressure, also called the **colloid osmotic pressure**, is the osmotic force generated by relatively impermeable solutes such as proteins, which are confined to the plasma. This oncotic pressure is one of the Starling forces involved in fluid movement across the capillaries. The normal oncotic pressure in human plasma ranges from 23 to 28 mm Hg. Of this, 15 to 17 mm Hg are produced by proteins (mostly albumin) and 8-9 mm Hg by cations held in the plasma by the electric charge of the proteins via the Gibbs-Donnan equilibrium.

BODY FLUID COMPARTMENTS

As stated above, the major body fluid is water. In a lean individual, it comprises about 60% of the total body weight. Fat contains less water. Therefore, in obese individuals the water content is 55% of the total body weight. In contrast, a 70-kg lean person contains 42 liters of water (70 x 0.6 = 42 L) This total body water is distributed between two major compartments: the **extracellular fluid** (ECF) and **intracellular fluid** (ICF) compartments. About one-third (20%) of the total amount of water is confined to the ECF, and two-thirds (40%) to the ICF compartment. The ECF compartment, in turn, is divided into the following subdivisions:

1. Plasma
2. Interstitial fluid and lymph
3. Bone and dense connective tissue water
4. Transcellular (cerebrospinal, pleural, peritoneal, synovial, and digestive secretions)

Of these subdivisions, the plasma and interstitial fluids are the two most important because of constant exchange of fluid and electrolytes between them. Plasma and interstitial fluid are separated by the capillary endothelium. Plasma circulates in the blood vessels, whereas the interstitial fluid bathes all tissue cells except for the formed elements of blood. For this reason, **Claude Bernard**, the French physiologist, called the interstitium "the true environment of the body" (**milieu interieur**). Figure 1-1 summarizes the distribution of water in various body fluid compartments.

Measurement of Body Fluid Compartments

The measurements of total body water and the volumes of various body fluid compartments can be determined indirectly by the principle of dilution using marker substances. The markers used are physiologically inert and metabolically inactive but can be easily measured by colorimetry or quantitated by radioactivity. Interstitial water content is calculated as the difference between plasma and extracellular water, whereas the intracellular water content is derived from the difference between total body water and extracellular water.

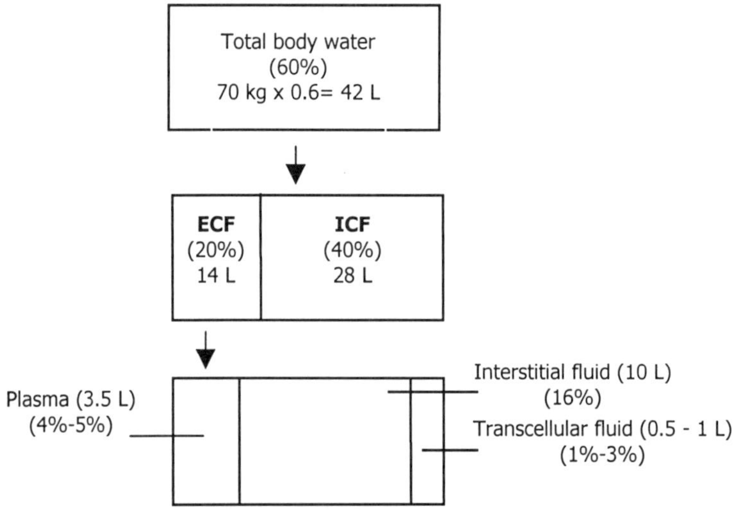

Figure 1-1. Distribution of water in various body fluid compartments: ECF = extracellular fluid; ICF = intracellular fluid. A 70-kg lean man has 42 L of water, assuming the total body water content is 60% of the body weight (70 x 0.6 = 42 L).

The procedure for measuring these volumes is simple. If a marker labelled X is given to the subject and allowed to equilibrate between various compartments, the volume of distribution of that marker in the compartment can be calculated using the following formula:

$$\text{Volume of compartment} = \frac{\text{Quantity X given - Quantity X excreted}^{a}}{\text{Concentration of X in compartment}}$$

[a] *Most of the markers are excreted in the urine whose concentration can be measured easily.*

Several markers that have been used clinically to determine volumes of various body fluid compartments are listed in Table 1-2. However, these measurements are not performed routinely in clinical practice.

Table 1-2. Markers used for measurement of body fluid compartments

Compartment	Marker
Total Body Water	Antipyrine Deuterium oxide (D_2O) Tritiated water (^3HHO)
Extracellular Fluid	Inulin Mannitol Raffinose $^{24}Na^+$ $^{36}Cl^-$ $^{35}SO_4^{2-}$
Plasma	^{131}I-albumin Evans blue (T-1824) ^{51}Cr-erythrocytes
Interstitial	None
Intracellular	None

COMPOSITION OF THE FLUID COMPARTMENTS

The important electrolyte composition of each of the major body fluid compartments is shown in Table 1-3, and can be summarized as follows:

1. ***Na^+ is the most abundant cation and Cl^- and HCO_3^- are the most abundant anions in the ECF compartment.***
2. ***Although the ionic composition is slightly different between plasma and interstitial fluid, it is essentially identical. The only major difference is the presence of proteins (15 mEq/L) in the plasma. The proteins are responsible for the slightly unequal distribution of ions between these two compartments due to the Gibbs-Donnan equilibrium.***
3. ***The composition of the ICF compartment varies from one tissue to another. Compared to the ECF compartment, K^+ is the most abundant cation and organic phosphate and proteins are the most abundant anions in the ICF compartment. Na^+ concentration is low. This asymmetric distribution of Na^+ and K^+ across the cell***

membrane is maintained by the enzyme, Na/K-ATPase (Chapter 6).

4. ***Compared to electrolytes, the composition of the nonelectrolytes, such as urea nitrogen and glucose, constitute only a minor portion of the total solute concentration in both compartments.***
5. ***Despite the differences in ionic composition between ECF and ICF compartments, the cationic charges are equal to the anionic charges within each compartment. This charge balance is called electroneutrality.***
6. ***The difference in concentration of solutes between ECF and ICF compartments is maintained because of 1) Gibbs-Donnan equilibrium; 2) selective permeability characteristics of plasma membranes; 3) specific membrane transporters or pumps (Chapter 6); and 4) binding of certain ions to intracellular proteins and other organic substances.***

Table 1-3. Electrolyte composition of fluid compartments

Electrolyte	Plasma (mEq/L)	Interstitial fluid (mEq/L)	Intracellular fluid (skeletal muscle) (mEq/L)
Cations			
Na^+	142	144	14
K^+	4	4	140
Ca^{2+}	5	2.5	4
Mg^{2+}	2	1.5	35
Total	153	152	193
Anions			
Cl^-	104	114	2
HCO_3^-	25	30	8
$H_2PO_4^-$, HPO_4^{2-}	2.3	2	40
SO_4^{2-}	0.94	1	20
Proteins	15	0	55
Organic acids	5.76	5	68
TOTAL	153	152	193

Water Movement Between ECF and ICF Compartments

In a healthy individual, the ECF and ICF are in osmotic equilibrium. If this equilibrium is disturbed, water moves from the area of lower solute concentration to the area of greater solute concentration in order to re-establish the osmotic equilibrium. The **Darrow-Yannet** diagram illustrates this point (Figure 1-2). Let us assume that an individual weighs 70 kg and has an osmolality of 280 mOsm/kg H_2O in both ECF and ICF compartments and his total body water is 60% of the body weight. What happens to osmolality and water distribution in each compartment if we add 210 mmol of NaCl without water to the ECF? Since NaCl dissociates into Na^+ and Cl^-, it contributes an additional 420 mOsm to ECF. This addition raises the osmolality of the ECF which then causes water to move from the ICF to the ECF. This movement of water results in a transient dilution of the ECF, while the ICF becomes more concentrated. Subsequent physiologic adjustments result in an osmotic equilibrium. Note that the total fluid volume has not changed, only that the ECF has expanded at the expense of the ICF. These changes are illustrated diagrammatically in Figure 1-2.

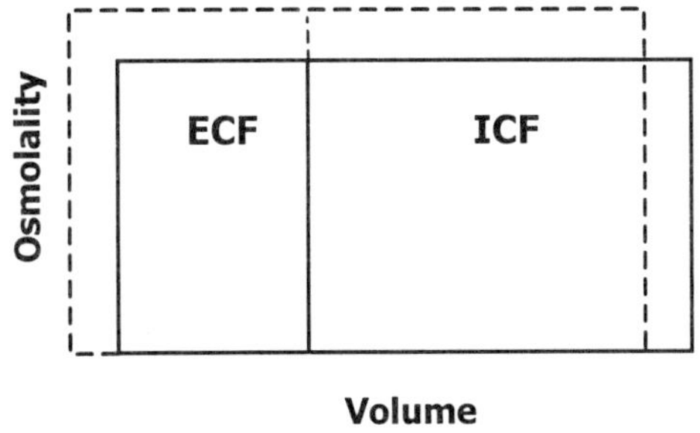

Figure 1-2. Darrow-Yannet diagram showing fluid and osmolality changes in the ECF and ICF compartments. Initial state is shown by a solid line and final state by a dashed line. Width represents the volume of the compartments, and height represents osmolality.

Thus, the addition of 420 mOsm to the ECF causes the osmolality to increase from 280 to 290 mOsm/kg H_2O (Total body mOsm/Total body water = (42 L x 280= 11,760 + 420) 12,180/42 L = 290 mOsm). Also, the ECF volume increases from 14 L to 15 L. ECF volume is calculated as follows:

ECF volume = Total body water - new ICF volume

where new ICF volume = ICF mOsm (28 L x 280 mOsm)/new osmolality
= 7840/290 = 27 L

Therefore, the ECF volume = 42 - 27 = 15 L.
This means that 1 L of water moved from ICF to ECF compartment.

Let us use another example. What would happen if 1 L of water is added to the ECF? Initially, this additional 1 L of H_2O would not only increase the ECF volume but it would also decrease its osmolality from 280 to 261 mOsm/kg H_2O. (Total ECF mOsm/ECF water content= 3920/15 = 261 mOsm). Since the ICF osmolality is higher than this new ECF osmolality, water will move into the ICF until a new osmotic equilibrium is reached. As a result, the ICF volume also increases. The net result is an increase in volume and a decrease in osmolality in both compartments. These changes are shown in Figure 1-3.

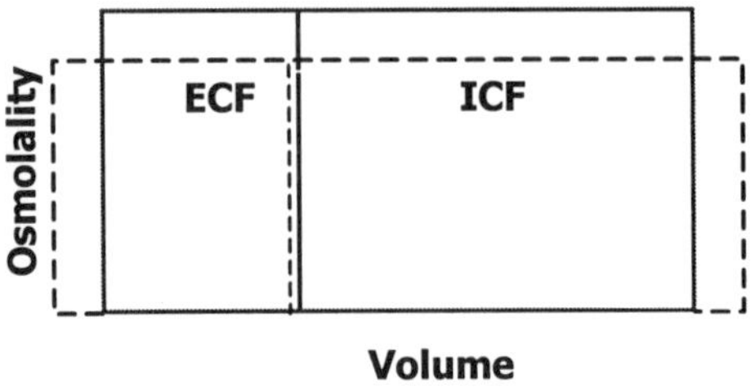

Figure 1-3. Darrow-Yannet diagram showing volume and osmolality changes in normal state (solid line) and following addition of 1 L of water to the ECF (dashed line).

Thus, addition of 1 L of water to ECF decreases the final osmolality to 273 mOsm/kg H_2O (Total body mOsm/New total body water = 11,760/43 = 273 mOsm) and increases water content in the ICF by 0.72 L and ECF by 0.28 L. (ICF mOsm/New osmolality = 7840/273 = 28.72 L). It should be noted that these changes are minimal in an individual with a normal renal function, since the kidneys compensate for these changes by excreting excess water in order to maintain fluid balance.

What would happen if 1 L of isotonic (0.9%) NaCl is added instead of pure water to ECF? Since 0.9% saline is isotonic, it does not cause water movement. Therefore, body osmolality does not change. However, this isotonic NaCl will remain in the ECF and cause its expansion, as shown in Figure 1-4.

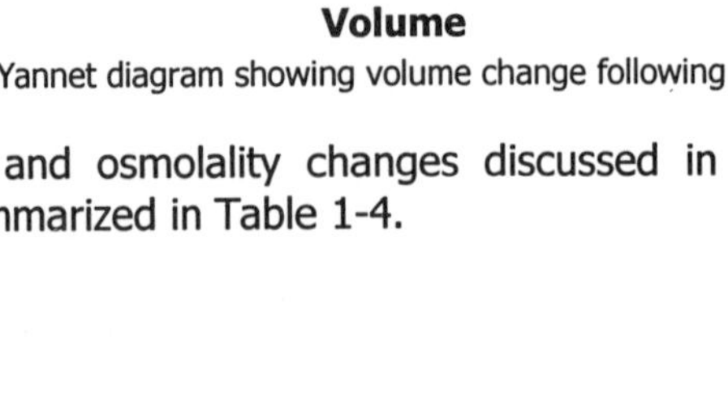

Figure 1-4. Darrow-Yannet diagram showing volume change following addition of 1 L of isotonic NaCl.

The volume and osmolality changes discussed in the previous three examples are summarized in Table 1-4.

Table 1-4. Volume and osmolality changes following NaCl tablets, water, and isotonic NaCl addition to ECF

Substance added	ECF volume	ICF volume	Body fluid osmolality
NaCl tablets	↑	↓	↑
Water	↑	↑	↓
Isotonic saline	↑	NC	NC

NC = no change

NONPATHOLOGICAL CONDITIONS INFLUENCING THE VOLUME OF TOTAL BODY WATER

Several physiological conditions affect total body water content and its compartments. Some of these conditions are discussed below.

Age and Gender

The amount of total body water decreases with age. In a newborn infant, total body water accounts for about 70-75% of body weight. Female infants have 5% less water than male infants. This percentage decreases to 50% at age 60, which is due to changes in bone density, as well as a decrease in total body muscle mass and an increase in percentage of fat.

Obesity

Fat cells contain less water than other cells. An inverse relationship exists between fat content and total body water content: the greater the adipose tissue mass, the less is the water content. A slight increase in total body water distribution has been reported in obese individuals following weight loss due to dietary restriction.

Malnutrition

Malnutrition secondary to starvation has been shown to increase total body water, presumably due to loss of body fat.

Dehydration

Dehydration has been shown to cause a decrease both in ECF and ICF water content, as well as total body water content.

Pregnancy

The amount of total body water increases throughout normal pregnancy. This increase is attributed to the water content of amniotic fluid, placenta, fetus, and expanded plasma volume.

SUMMARY

1. The major body fluid is water. In a lean subject, it comprises about 60% of the total body weight. Total body water is divided between the ECF (one-third) and ICF (two-thirds) compartments. The ECF compartment consists of two major subcompartments: plasma and interstitial fluid.
2. Markers such as antipyrine, inulin, and ^{131}I-albumin are used for measurements of total body water, extracellular fluid and plasma compartments, respectively.
3. Na^+ is the most abundant cation and Cl^- and HCO_3^- are the most abundant anions in the ECF compartment. In contrast, K^+ is the most abundant cation and organic phosphate and proteins are the major anions in the ICF compartment. The asymmetric distribution of Na^+ and K^+ across the cell membrane is maintained by the enzyme, Na/K-ATPase.
4. Water can diffuse freely between the ECF and ICF compartments and also between plasma and interstitial fluid compartments. This movement is controlled by the osmotic pressure gradients between different compartments. An isotonic solution does not cause osmosis, whereas a hypotonic or hypertonic solution causes osmosis.

STUDY QUESTIONS

Case 1

A 30-year-old man volunteers for determination of the sizes of his body fluid compartments. He receives an intravenous injection of a solution containing 2.4 g of inulin, 400,000 CPM of ^{131}I-albumin, and 5.2 g of antipyrine. Two hours later, 10 ml of blood is drawn from the antecubital vein and centrifuged to obtain plasma. One ml of plasma is removed and found to contain 100 CPM, 0.1 mg of inulin and 0.1 mg of antipyrine. The subject urinates 100 ml of urine which contains 10 mg/ml inulin and 10 mg/ml antipyrine.

Question 1. Calculate the sizes of the following compartments.

A. total body water
B. extracellular fluid volume
C. plasma volume
D. interstitial fluid volume
E. intracellular fluid volume

Answer:
For measurement of the size of any compartment, use the following formula:

$$\text{Volume of compartment} = \frac{\text{Quantity of marker given - Quantity of marker excreted}}{\text{Concentration of marker in compartment}}$$

A. Total body water (TBW)

The marker used for measurement of TBW is antipyrine. By substituting the values into the formula, we obtain:

$$TBW = \frac{5200 \text{ mg} - 1000 \text{ mg}^{*}}{0.1 \text{ mg}} = 42{,}000 \text{ ml or } 42 \text{ L}$$

* Total amount in 100 ml of urine

B. Extracellular fluid volume (ECV)

Inulin is used as a marker for ECV.

$$ECV = \frac{2400 \text{ mg} - 1000 \text{ mg}}{0.1 \text{ mg}} = 14{,}000 \text{ ml or } 14 \text{ L}$$

C. Plasma volume (PV)

^{131}I-albumin is used as a marker for PV

$$PV = \frac{400{,}000 \text{ CPM}}{100 \text{ CPM}} = 4000 \text{ ml or } 4 \text{ L}$$

D. Interstitial fluid volume (ISF)

ISF = ECV – PV = 14 - 4 = 10 L

E. Intracellular fluid volume (ICF)

ICF = TBW - ECF = 42 - 14 = 28 L

Case 2

A 28-year-old insulin-dependent diabetic male patient was admitted to the hospital because of nausea, vomiting, and abdominal pain. His weight was 60 kg and the initial laboratory values were:

Na^+ = 146 mEq/L
K^+ = 5 mEq/L
HCO_3^- = 10 mEq/L
BUN = 70 mg/dL
Glucose = 540 mg/dL

Question 1. Calculate this patient's plasma osmolality and explain his fluid shift.

Answer: Plasma osmolality is calculated by using the following formula:

$$\text{Plasma osmolality (mOsm/kg } H_2O) = 2[\text{Plasma } Na^+] + \frac{\text{Glucose}}{18} + \frac{\text{BUN}}{2.8}$$

$$= 2[146] + \frac{540}{18} + \frac{70}{2.8} = 347 \text{ mOsm/kg } H_2O$$

Because plasma osmolality is elevated, water initially moves out of cells, i.e., from the ICF to the ECF and causes expansion of the latter until a new steady state is reached.

The patient was treated with insulin and isotonic NaCl. The blood chemistry was:

Na^+ = 140 mEq/L
K^+ = 4.2 mEq/L
HCO_3^- = 20 mEq/L
BUN = 40 mg/dL
Glucose = 180 mg/dL

Question 2. Explain the impact of BUN on fluid shift.

Answer: Although plasma osmolality is still elevated, no fluid shift will occur on account of BUN. The lack of fluid shift is due to its ineffectiveness as an osmole; i.e., urea crosses the cell membrane easily and does not establish a concentration gradient.

Question 3. Calculate this patient's plasma tonicity (effective plasma osmolality).

Answer: Tonicity is a measure of the osmotically active particles from Na^+ and glucose. Therefore, the serum concentration of BUN is not included in the calculation. The plasma tonicity is:

$$2[140] + \frac{180}{18} = 290 \text{ mOsm/kg } H_2O$$

Case 3

A 30-year-old patient with AIDS was admitted for weakness, weight loss, fever, nausea, vomiting, and mental irritability. His blood pressure was low. The diagnosis of Addison's disease (a disease caused by the deficiency of the corticosteroid hormones hydrocortisone and aldosterone produced by the adrenal cortex) was made. Admitting laboratory values were:

Na^+ = 120 mEq/L
K^+ = 6 mEq/L
Cl^- = 100 mEq/L
HCO_3^- = 12 mEq/L
BUN = 70 mg/dL
Glucose = 60 mg/dL

Question 1. Explain the fluid shift in this patient.

Answer: This patient lost more NaCl than water from the ECF compartment due to aldosterone deficiency. As a result, his plasma osmolality is low. Decreased plasma osmolality causes water to move from the ECF to the ICF compartment. The net result is the contraction of ECF volume and expansion of ICF volume and reduction in osmolality, as shown in the figure below:

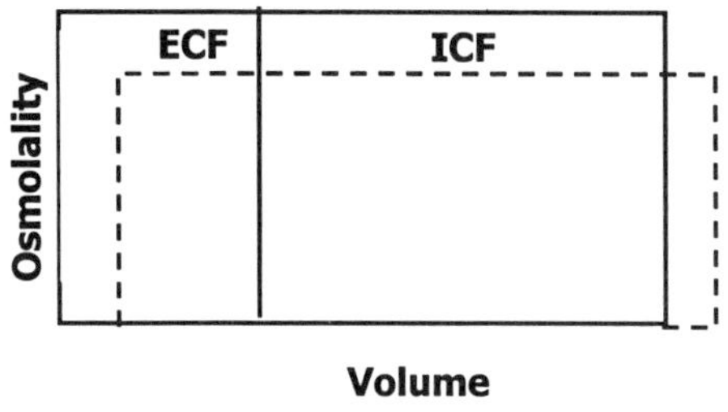

(Initial state is represented by solid line and final state by dashed line)

Case 4

A patient on maintenance hemodialysis (a technique, generally called artificial kidney, used to remove nitrogenous wastes from the blood and excess water from the body as a treatment for patients with kidney failure) three times a week for kidney failure is admitted with shortness of breath and a weight gain of 22 lbs. He weighed 50 kg after his last treatment 6 days ago. His serum chemistry is as follows:

	After dialysis	On admission
Na^+	140 mEq/L	135 mEq/L
K^+	3.6 mEq/L	5.8 mEq/L
HCO_3^-	28 mEq/L	18 mEq/L
Cl^-	100 mEq/L	106 mEq/L
BUN	40 mg/dL	120 mg/dL
Creatinine	8 mg/dL	12 mg/dL
Effective osmolality	290 mOsm/kg H_2O	282 mOsm/kg H_2O

Question 1. Calculate the following after dialysis and on admission.

A. Total body water
B. ICF volume
C. ECF volume
D. Total body effective osmoles
E. ICF effective osmoles
F. ECF effective osmoles
G. Serum glucose concentration

Answer:

<u>After Dialysis</u>

A. Total body water comprises 60% of body weight. Of this, 40% is in the ICF and 20% is in the ECF compartment. Total body water (0.6 x 50 kg)=30 L
B. ICF volume (0.4 x 50 kg) = 20 L
C. ECF volume (0.2 x 50 kg) = 10 L
D. Total body effective osmoles (290 x 30 L) = 8,700 mOsm/kg H_2O
E. ICF effective osmoles (290 x 20 L) = 5,800 mOsm/kg H_2O
F. ECF effective osmoles (290 x 10 L) = 2,900 mOsm/kg H_2O
G. Serum glucose concentration = 180 mg/dL

Only Na^+ and glucose are used to calculate the effective osmolality. Since Na^+ concentration is 140 mEq/L, its contribution is 280 mOsm. The remaining 10 mOsm are contributed by glucose (1 mOsm = 18 mg or 10 mOsm = 180 mg/dL).

<u>On Admission</u>

A. Total body water (0.6 x 60 kg[a]) = 36 L
B. ICF volume (0.4 x 60 kg) = 24 L
C. ECF volume (0.2 x 60 kg) = 12 L
D. Total body effective osmoles (280 x 36 L) = 10,080 mOsm/kg H_2O
E. ICF effective osmoles (280 x 24 L) = 6,720 mOsm/kg H_2O
F. ECF effective osmoles (280 x 12 L) = 3,360 mOsm/kg H_2O)

Serum glucose concentration = 216 mg/dL (1 mOsm = 18 mg or 12 mOsm = 216 mg/dL)

[a]The gain of 22 lbs. is equal to gaining 10 kg. Therefore, the body weight on admission is 60 kg.

SUGGESTED READING

1. Fanestil, D.D. Compartmentation of body water. In: Clinical Disorders of Fluid and Electrolyte Metabolism. 5th edition. R.G. Narins (ed.). McGraw-Hill, New York, 1994; pp. 3-20 (*An excellent discussion on body fluid compartments and their measurements with a clear description of Gibbs-Donnan equilibrium*).
2. Yoshika, T., Iitaka, K. and Ichikawa, I. Body fluid compartments. In: Pediatric Textbook of Fluids and Electrolytes. I. Ichikawa (ed.). Williams and Wilkins, Baltimore, 1990; pp.14-20 (*A summary of various body fluid compartments, their composition and measurements*).

CHAPTER 2

STRUCTURE AND FUNCTION OF THE KIDNEY

Objectives

After reading this chapter, the student should be able to:

1. List the various functions of the kidney.
2. Describe the gross and microscopic structure of the kidney.
3. List the various segments of the nephron.
4. Describe the structural components of the glomerulus and functions of the basement membrane.
5. Discuss the functions of the following nephron segments: proximal tubule, loop of Henle, distal tubule, and collecting duct.
6. Discuss the distribution of aquaporins in various segments of the nephron.
7. Describe the structure and function of the juxtaglomerular apparatus.
8. Describe the blood and nerve supply to the kidney.
9. Define micturition and discuss the innervation of the urinary bladder.

The kidneys perform three major functions. As regulatory organs, the kidneys precisely control the composition and volume of the body fluids and maintain acid-base balance by varying the excretion of water and solutes. As excretory organs, the kidneys remove various nitrogenous metabolic end products in the urine. In general, the kidneys filter blood in the glomerulus to form a protein-free ultrafiltrate. This ultrafiltrate passes through the various tubular segments where reabsorption of essential constituents and secretion of unwanted products occur. As endocrine organs, the kidneys produce important hormones, such as renin, erythropoietin, and active vitamin D_3. In addition, the kidneys are a major site for degradation of various endogenous and exogenous compounds. In order to understand these functions, it is essential to examine the gross and microscopic structure of the kidneys.

GROSS ANATOMY

The kidneys are paired, bean-shaped structures located retroperitoneally in the lumbar region, one on either side of the vertebral column. The upper pole of the kidney is at the level of the twelfth thoracic vertebra, and the lower pole lies close to the third lumbar vertebra. The lateral edge of the kidney is convex, while the medial aspect is concave with a notch called the **hilum**. The hilum receives the blood and lymphatic vessels, the nerves, and the ureter. The hilum contains a cavity, the **renal sinus**, where the ureter expands to form the **renal pelvis**. The normal adult kidney is about 11-12 cm long, 5-7 cm wide, and 2-3 cm thick, and it weighs 125 to 170 g. The kidneys in females are smaller than in males. The left kidney is slightly larger than the right kidney, and the weight of both kidneys correlates best with the body surface area. Since the kidneys are in contact with the diaphragm, they move with respiration. Each kidney is enveloped in a fibrous capsule (renal capsule), which is surrounded by a layer of fat called perirenal fat.

Each kidney is composed of the **parenchyma** and the **collecting system**. On a sagittal section of the kidney, the parenchyma consists of an **outer cortex** and an **inner medulla** (Figure 2-1). The medulla is divided into 10 to 18 conical **pyramids**. From the base of each pyramid, 400-600 elongated projections called **medullary rays** penetrate the cortex. The cortex extends from the medulla to the renal capsule and includes the regions between the pyramids. The medulla is divided into an outer (toward the cortex) and an inner medulla (toward the pelvis).

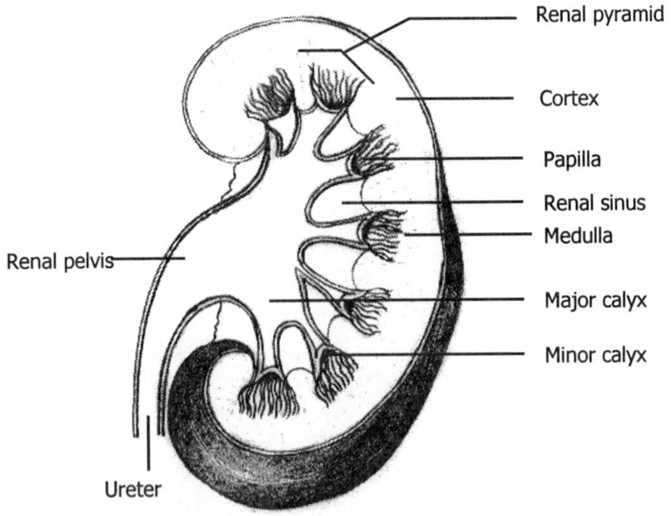

Figure 2-1. Sagittal section of the kidney (Modified with permission from Sweny, P., Farrington, K. and Moorhead, J.F. The Kidney and its Disorders. Blackwell Scientific Publications, Oxford, 1989).

The collecting system includes the **calyces**, **renal pelvis**, and the **ureters**. Calyces are funnel-shaped structures into which the renal pyramids drain. Within each kidney, 2 to 3 major calyces give rise to 8 to 10 minor calyces. The tips of the pyramids form the **renal papillae**, which enter the minor calyces. The major calyces unite to form the renal pelvis. The renal pelvis drains into the ureter, which connects the kidney to the bladder.

MICROSCOPIC ANATOMY

Nephron

The basic structural and functional unit of the kidney is the **nephron** (Figure 2-2).

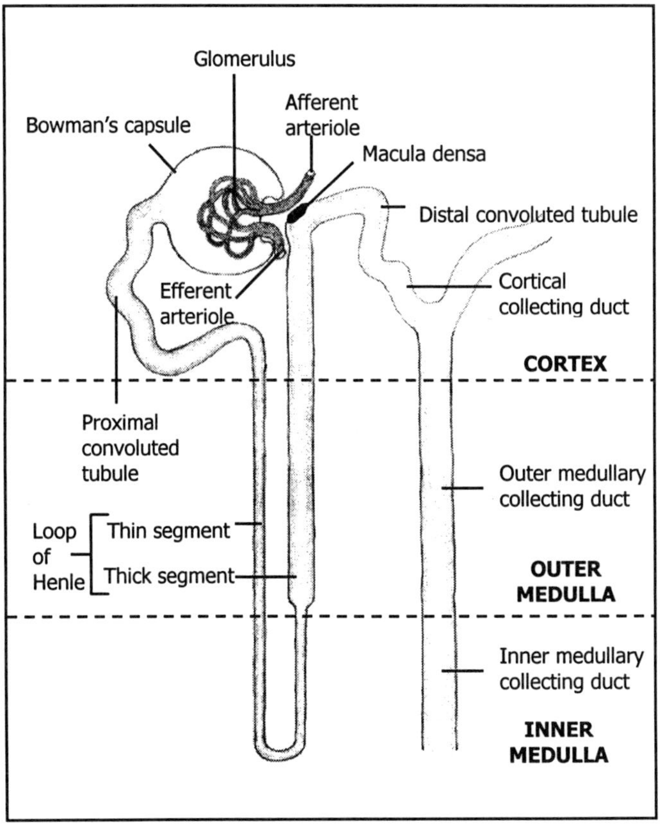

Figure 2-2. The nephron and the collecting duct.

There are about 600,000 (range 300,000 to 1,200,000) nephrons in each kidney. Each nephron contains specialized cells that filter the plasma, then selectively remove, reabsorb, and secrete a variety of substances into the urine. The nephron consists of a **renal corpuscle**, the **proximal tubule**, the **loop of Henle**, and the **distal tubule**. The **collecting duct** is not part of the nephron because it is embryologically derived from the **ureteric bud**, whereas the nephron is derived from the **metanephric blastema**. However, the collecting duct is commonly included in the nephron because of its related function. Table 2-1 lists segments of the nephron and the collecting system.

Table 2-1. Segments of the nephron and collecting system (Adapted with permission from Kriz, W. and Bankir, L. A standard nomenclature for structures of the kidney. Am. J. Physiol. 254: F1-F8, 1988).

I. **Nephron**
  A. **Renal Corpuscle**
    - Glomerulus
    - Bowman's capsule
  B. **Tubule**
    1. Proximal tubule
      - Convoluted part (pars convoluta)
      - Straight part (pars recta)
    2. Intermediate tubule
      - Descending part or thin descending limb of Henle's loop
      - Ascending part or thin ascending limb of Henle's loop
    3. Distal tubule
      - Straight part or thick ascending limb of Henle's loop (medullary and cortical part; the latter includes the macula densa)
      - Convoluted part

II. **Collecting duct system**
  A. **Connecting tubule**
  B. **Collecting duct**
    1. Cortical collecting duct
    2. Outer medullary duct
    3. Inner medullary duct

Depending on the length of Henle's loop, the nephrons are classified either as **long-looped** or **short-looped** (Figure 2-3). Most of the nephrons that originate from the corticomedullary junction (called juxtamedullary nephrons) have long loops and bend back in the inner medulla. Nephrons with short loops (or cortical nephrons) generally originate from superficial and midcortical glomeruli and have loops that bend back in the outer medulla. In humans, short-looped nephrons are about 7 times more numerous than long-looped nephrons. Although both types of nephrons are morphologically similar, they are functionally different. Short-looped nephrons mainly participate in Na^+ regulation, while long-loop nephrons are involved in concentrating urine. It is interesting to note that the ability to concentrate urine depends mainly on the relative length of the medulla rather than on the length of Henle's loop.

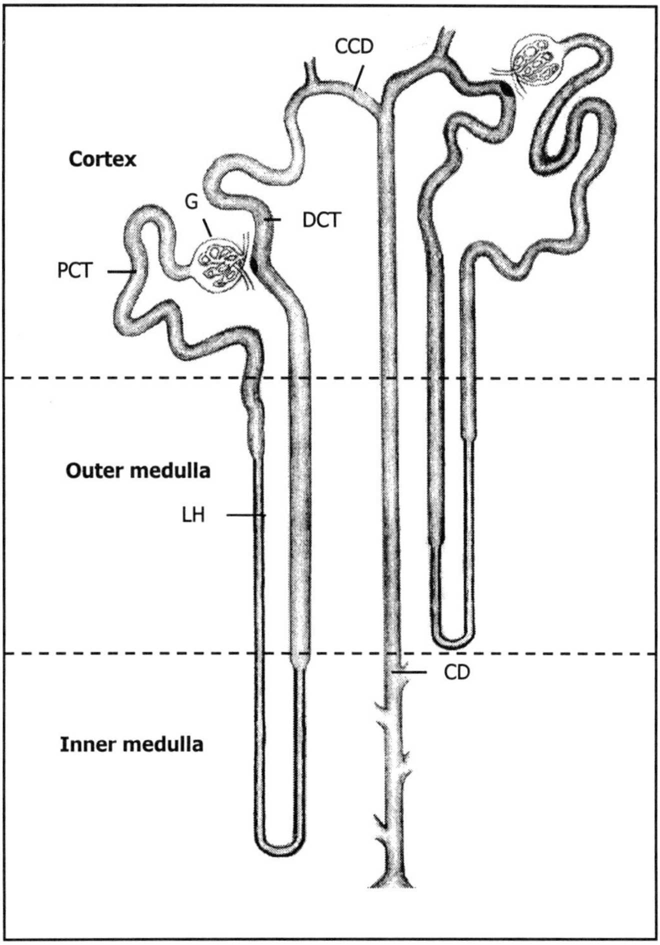

Figure 2-3. Schematic representation of a short-looped and a long-looped (juxtamedullary) nephron. G = glomerulus; PCT = proximal convoluted tubule; LH = loop of Henle; DCT = distal convoluted tubule; CCD = cortical collecting duct; CD = collecting duct (Modified with permission from Kriz, W. and Bankir, L. A standard nomenclature for structures of the kidney. Am. J. Physiol. 254: F1-F8, 1988).

Renal Corpuscle

The renal corpuscle consists of the **glomerulus** and **Bowman's capsule** (Figure 2-4A and B). Generally the term "glomerulus" is widely used for the entire corpuscle. The glomerulus is composed of a capillary network lined by an inner thin layer of endothelial cells; a central region of mesangial cells surrounded by collagen-like mesangial matrix, and an outer layer of visceral epithelial cells. The endothelial and epithelial cells are separated by the glomerular basement membrane (GBM) (Figure 2-4C).

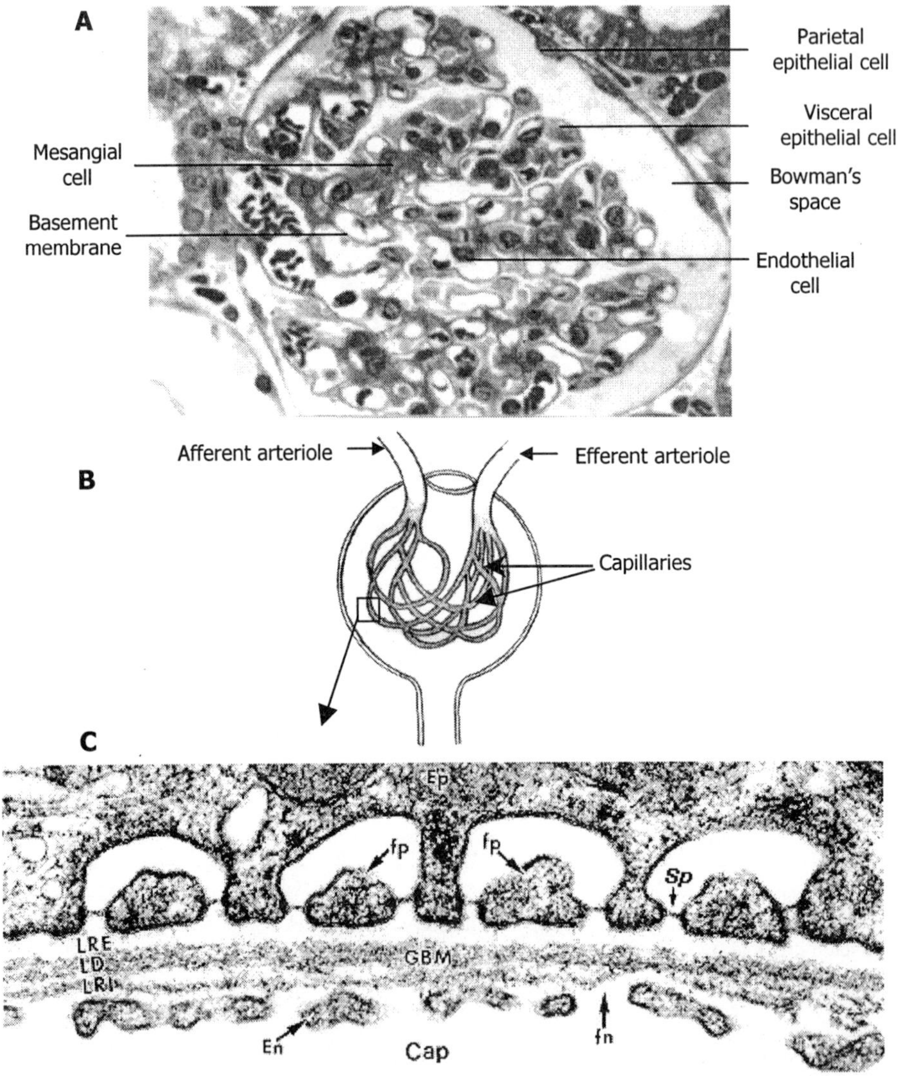

Figure 2-4. A. Light micrograph of a normal human glomerulus. X 250 (Courtesy of Dr. M.Y. Khan). B. Schematic illustration of the glomerulus. C. Electron micrograph of the glomerular capillary wall showing foot processes (fp) of visceral epithelial cell (Ep) with slit pore (Sp), glomerular basement membrane (GBM), and fenestrated (fn) endothelium (En). LRE = lamina rara externa; LD = lamina densa; LRI = lamina rara interna; Cap = capillary lumen. X 60,000 (Courtesy of Dr. Y.S. Kanwar).

The GBM is a dense fibrillar structure, which is the only anatomical barrier between blood and urine. It is composed of three layers of different electron density: a dense middle layer called the lamina densa, and two layers of lower electron density on either side of the lamina densa, usually referred to as the lamina rara interna and lamina rara externa (Figure 2-4C). Biochemical studies of the GBM showed that it contains predominantly type IV collagen, proteoglycans, and laminin. Collagen provides the structural framework, whereas proteoglycans, such as heparan sulfate, confer a negative charge to the GBM. Because of this negative charge, filtration of albumin is curtailed (see Chapter 4). Laminin interacts with type IV collagen and heparan sulfate. It also has the ability to promote cell adhesion, growth, and tissue differentiation. The Bowman's capsule, which is a double-walled cup surrounding the glomerulus consists of an outer layer of parietal epithelial cells. Between the visceral epithelial and parietal epithelial cells is a space called **Bowman's space** or **urinary space**. The glomeruli are located exclusively in the cortex, which undergo pathologic changes in several disease conditions (see Clinical Applications for details).

The term glomerular mesangium refers to the mesangial cells and their surrounding area, which is composed of collagen-like mesangial matrix. The glomerular mesangium provides structural support for the glomerular capillary walls (Figure 2-5). The mesangial cells behave like smooth muscle cells, and possess contractile and phagocytic properties. In addition, the mesangial cells synthesize several vasoactive agents and growth factors. The mesangial cells contract and relax in response to vasoactive agents and growth factors, and thus play an important role in glomerular filtration (Chapter 4).

The renal corpuscle is responsible for the ultrafiltration of the blood, which is the first step in urine formation. In this process, medium-and small-sized molecules are allowed to pass through into the Bowman's space, while large-size molecules, such as proteins, are left behind. To enter the Bowman's space, the ultrafiltrate passes through the fenestrae (spaces between the endothelial cells), the basement membrane, and the slit pores of the foot processes (cytoplasmic projections of the visceral epithelial cell) (Figure 2-4C).

Proximal Tubule

The proximal tubule is the continuation of the parietal epithelium of Bowman's capsule. It consists of a convoluted part, **the pars convoluta** and a straight part, the **pars recta**. The proximal tubule is lined by cuboidal or columnar cells with a brush border on their luminal surface (Figure 2-6). The brush border consists of millions of microvilli which markedly increase the surface area available for the absorption of tubular fluid. The epithelial cells have well developed basal foldings at the basolateral surface with abundant,

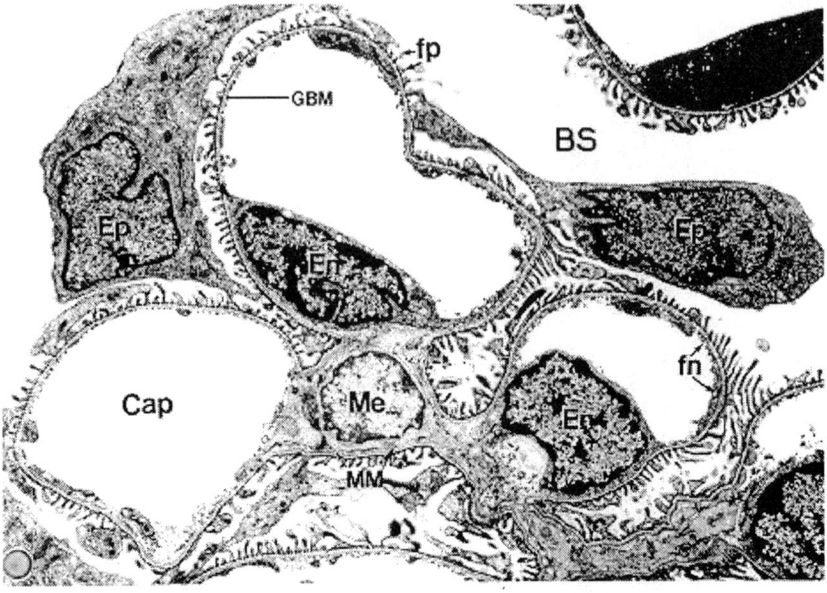

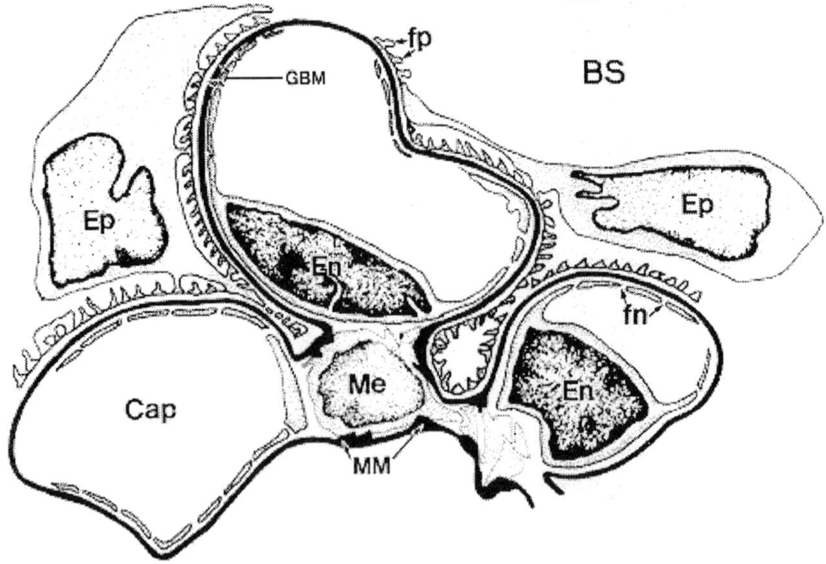

Figure 2-5. A. Electron micrograph of portion of glomerulus showing anatomical relationships of visceral epithelial cell (Ep), endothelial cell (En), mesangial cell (Me) with glomerular basement membrane (GBM) and mesangial matrix (MM). GBM is lined outside by foot processes (fp) and inside by fenestrated (fn) endothelial linings. Cap = capillary with lumen; BS = Bowman's space. X 6,000. B. Schematic drawing of A (Courtesy of Dr. Y.S. Kanwar).

vertically-oriented, elongated mitochondria. This arrangement of mitochondria is characteristic of epithelia involved in active transport. Adjacent cells are joined by a three-part junctional complex: (1) the apical component of the junctional complex (tight junction or zonula occludens); (2) the intermediate junction, or zonula adherens; and (3) the desmosomes or macula adherens. These junctional complexes not only hold adjacent cells together but also provide a space called the **lateral intercellular space** between cells. The three part junctional complex facilitates transport of solutes and water through cells (transcellular transport) or between cells (paracellular transport) or both (Chapter 6). The proximal tubule reabsorbs about 60% of the ultrafiltrate. Several electrolytes (Na^+, K^+, Cl^-, HCO_3^-, Ca^{2+}, HPO_4^{2-}), amino acids, glucose and water are reabsorbed in pars convoluta of the proximal tubule (Chapter 7). Secretion of organic acids and bases seems to occur mostly in the pars recta. It is this portion of the proximal tubule that is susceptible to injury to nephrotoxins such as heavy metals and drugs.

Thin Limb of Henle's Loop

The pars recta of the proximal tubule continues into the medulla as the thin descending limb of Henle's loop. The loop then bends back and becomes the thin ascending limb of Henle's loop. The length of the descending limb depends on the origin of the glomerulus. For example, short-looped nephrons originating from either the superficial or midcortical region have short, thin descending limbs that extend only into the outer medulla. Long-looped nephrons originating from the corticomedullary border have long, thin descending limbs extending into the inner medulla.

Histologically, **four** types of epithelial cells have been described in the thin limb of Henle's loop (Figure 2-6). **Type I** cells are found only in the thin descending limb of short-looped nephrons. **Type II** epithelium is found in the thin descending limb of long-looped nephrons in the outer medulla, and **Type III** epithelium is found in the inner medulla. The thin ascending limb and the hairpin bend of long-looped nephrons contain **Type IV** cells.

Studies in animals have revealed structural and functional differences among these types of cells. Type I epithelium is thin; it has few microvilli, and cellular organelles are sparse. Type II epithelium contains many short microvilli, prominent mitochondria, and other organelles. It also has paracellular channels. Type III cells have a simpler structure than Type II cells. They have few microvilli and cellular organelles. Type IV epithelium lacks surface microvilli but contains a few cellular organelles. Both Type I and Type II epithelial cells are highly permeable to water. Permeability to Na^+ and Cl^- is higher in Type II than in Type I cells. In contrast, Type I cells are more permeable to urea. The epithelium of the thin ascending limb, composed mainly of type IV cells, is largely impermeable to water, but highly permeable to Na^+ and Cl^-.

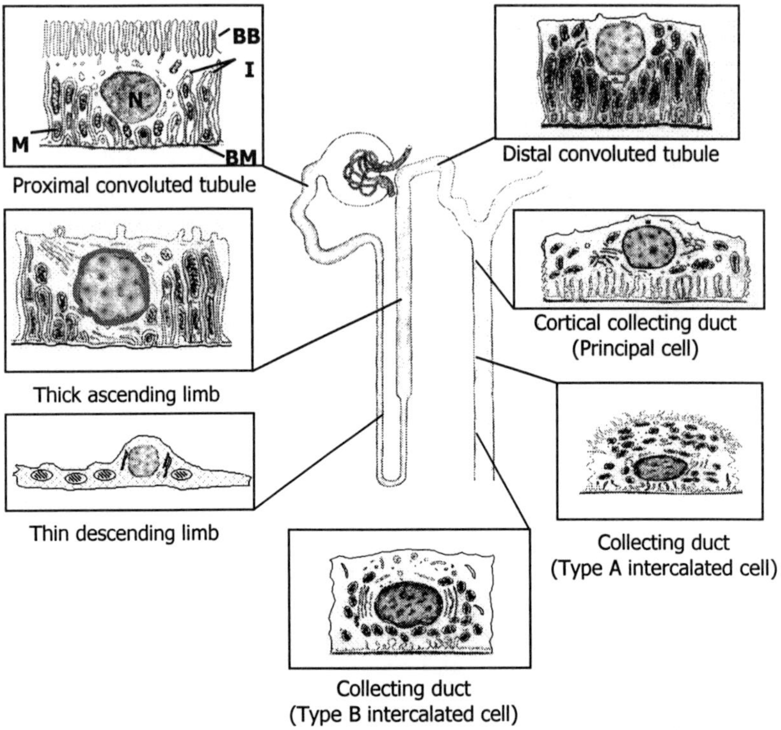

Figure 2-6. Schematic representation of a nephron and ultrastructure of tubular epithelial cells. BB = brush border; N = nucleus; BM = basement membrane; M = mitochondrion; I = invaginations.

The thin descending limb is more permeable to water and less permeable to NaCl. As a result, water moves into the interstitium and makes the ultrafiltrate more concentrated than in the proximal tubule. In contrast, the thin ascending limb is impermeable to water, but permeable to NaCl. Therefore, the ultrafiltrate becomes dilute and the medullary interstitium hypertonic. Thus, the thin descending and ascending limbs participate in the countercurrent multiplication of the urinary concentration process (Chapter 9).

Distal Tubule

The distal tubule includes the thick ascending limb of Henle's loop and the distal convoluted tubule. The thick limb runs from the medulla into the cortex up to its parent glomerulus, where it forms the **macula densa**. The distal convoluted tubule extends from the macula densa to the collecting duct. The cells of the two segments of the distal tubule are morphologically similar. Both segments are lined by columnar epithelium with prominent mitochondria (Figure 2-6). The basolateral membrane has extensive invaginations. In contrast to the proximal tubule, the luminal surface of the distal tubule has no brush border.

The thick ascending limb of Henle's loop is responsible for the reabsorption of Na^+, K^+, and Cl^- in the ratio of 1:1:2 (Chapter 7). The reabsorption of these electrolytes is dependent on the Na/K-ATPase located in the basolateral membrane. NaCl reabsorption also occurs in the distal convoluted tubule; energy for this transport is provided from the hydrolysis of ATP by the basolateral Na/K-ATPase activity. Both segments of the distal tubule are normally impermeable to water and thus the fluid formed in the distal tubule is hypotonic. The impermeability of the distal tubule to water, combined with active transport of Na^+ and Cl^- out of the thick ascending limb, makes the medullary interstitium hypertonic (Chapter 9). Immunocytochemical studies have shown the presence of **Tamm-Horsfall** protein in the luminal surface of the thick ascending limb of Henle's loop. This mucoprotein is the constituent of hyaline cast present in normal urine.

Connecting Tubule

The connecting tubule connects the distal convoluted tubule with the collecting duct. In the rat, this tubule is composed of at least four types of cells: **connecting tubule** cells, **distal convoluted tubule** cells, **intercalated** cells and **principal** cells. The connecting tubule cells are tall with an apical nucleus and few mitochondria. They seem to be involved in K^+ secretion, which is partly regulated by mineralocorticoids.

Collecting Duct

Depending on its location in the kidney, the collecting duct can be divided into the **cortical**, **outer medullary,** and **inner medullary** portions. The epithelium of the collecting ducts contains two types of cells: **principal** or **light** (65%) and **intercalated** or **dark** (35%) cells (Figure 2-6). The principal cell is the predominant type of cell lining the collecting duct system. It has a light-staining cytoplasm with a few randomly scattered mitochondria. The basal membrane of principal cells has numerous infoldings that do not enclose mitochondria. The intercalated cell has a dense-staining cytoplasm with numerous mitochondria and other organelles. Two types of intercalated cells, **type A** and **type B**, have been described in the rat (Figure 2-6).

In the cortical collecting duct, principal cells are responsible for K^+ secretion and Na^+ reabsorption. This function is only partly regulated by aldosterone, because some of the cells are capable of K^+ secretion in the absence of this hormone. Type A intercalated cells are involved in H^+ ion secretion and HCO_3^- reabsorption, whereas the type B cell is responsible for HCO_3^- secretion. However, both cell types contain carbonic anhydrase (Chapters 7 and 11).

The outer medullary collecting duct also contains **principal** (70%) and **intercalated** (30%) cells. The principal cells in this duct are taller and contain fewer cellular organelles than the principal cells in the cortical collecting duct. The ultrastructure of the intercalated cells is similar in both segments of the collecting duct. Studies have shown that principal cells possess Na/K-ATPase and may be involved in Na^+ reabsorption. These cells seem to play no role in K^+ secretion. Type A intercalated cells are involved in H^+ ion secretion in this segment as well.

Biochemical studies in the rat and rabbit have shown that segments of both cortical and outer medullary collecting ducts contain H/K-ATPase. This enzyme system is involved in H^+ ion secretion and K^+ reabsorption.

The inner medullary collecting duct is composed of **principal** (90%) and **intercalated** (10%) cells. The ultrastructure of these cells is similar to those in the outer medulla. Several studies have shown that the inner medullary collecting duct is involved in the reabsorption of Na^+, Cl^-, K^+, urea, and water. H^+ ion secretion also occurs in this segment. Salt and water transport in this segment is partially regulated by **atrial natriuretic peptide** (ANP) hormone. While the major function of the cortical collecting duct is the secretion of K^+, the outer and inner medullary collecting ducts play an important role in urine acidification (Chapter 11).

Transport of water occurs in all segments of the collecting duct in the presence of the **antidiuretic hormone** (ADH), or **vasopressin**. The apical (luminal) epithelium is impermeable to water in the absence of ADH. Thus, the presence of ADH produces hypertonic (concentrated) urine, whereas its absence results in hypotonic (dilute) urine (see Chapter 9). The cortical and outer medullary collecting ducts are impermeable to urea, whereas the inner medullary collecting duct is freely permeable to urea. This arrangement is a prerequisite for urea recycling that occurs between the collecting duct and thin limb of Henle's loop to maintain medullary hypertonicity (Chapter 9).

DISTRIBUTION OF AQUAPORINS (AQPs) IN THE NEPHRON

AQPs are recently discovered water channel proteins that are responsible for water transport across water permeable epithelial cells in the nephron and other organs. To date, ten AQPs have been identified. Of these, six AQPs, termed AQP-1 through AQP-4, AQP-6, and AQP-7 have been identified in the kidney (Figure 2-7). AQP-1 is expressed in the proximal tubule and the descending limb of Henle's loop at both the apical and basolateral membranes. It is also present in the descending vasa recta. AQP-1 is absent in the thin and thick ascending limbs of Henle's loop where the water permeability is low. AQP-2 is present in the apical membrane of the principal cells of the cortical, outer medullary and inner medullary collecting duct and in cells of the inner medullary collecting duct. Recently, the presence of AQP-2 has been demonstrated in the connecting tubule. AQP-3 is expressed predominantly in the basolateral membrane of the principal cells of the collecting duct from cortex to the tip of papilla, whereas AQP-4 is present in the basolateral membrane of the principal cells of the inner medullary collecting duct. AQP-6 is present only in the kidney cortex and medulla. The exact function of this AQP is unknown. AQP-7 is localized at brush border of the proximal straight tubule, and it may involve in water and urea transport. Of the six AQPs, only AQP-2 is regulated by ADH. This hormone stimulates the synthesis and insertion of AQP-2 into the apical membrane of the principal cell to promote water permeability (see Chapter 10).

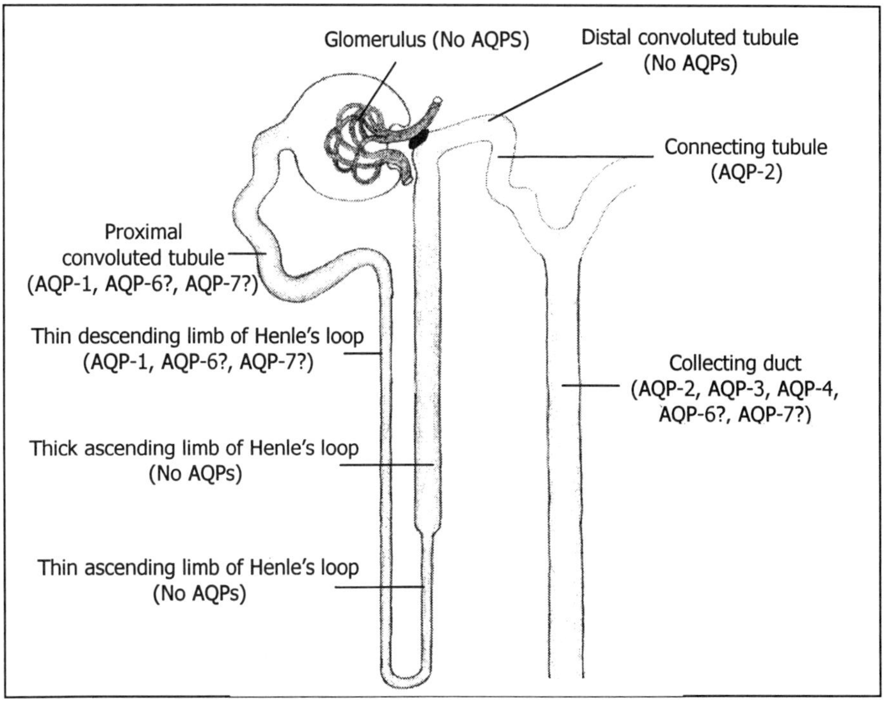

Figure 2-7. Distribution of aquaporins (AQPs) in various segments of the nephron and the collecting duct.

THE JUXTAGLOMERULAR APPARATUS (JGA)

As it passes through the cortex, the ascending limb of the Henle's loop comes very close to the vascular pole of its own glomerulus to form the JGA . The JGA includes four components: the **macula densa** (specialized cellular structure of the terminal cortical thick ascending limb), the terminal portion of the **afferent arteriole**, the first portion of the **efferent arteriole**, and the **extraglomerular mesangial** (Goormaghtigh or lacis) **cells** located between the two arterioles and macula densa (Figure 2-8).

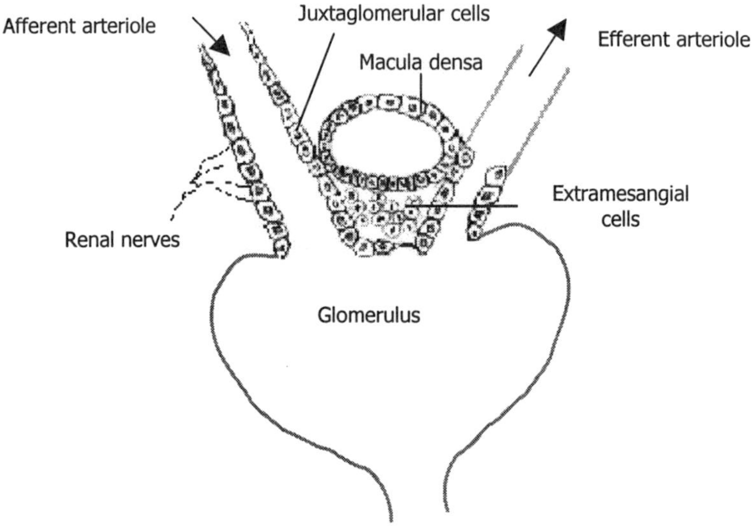

Figure 2-8. The relationship of the juxtaglomerular apparatus and the macula densa.

The extraglomerular mesangial cells are similar in ultrastructure to glomerular mesangial cells. The afferent, and to a lesser extent, the efferent arterioles possess granule-containing "epitheloid" cells called **juxtaglomerular cells.** These cells produce the hormone **renin**. The function of the extra-glomerular mesangial cells is not clearly understood. However, it is believed that these cells mediate the signals from the macula densa and transmit them to both the granular cells of the arterioles and mesangial cells of the glomerulus. The mesangial cells contain **myofilaments** (actin), which contract in response to angiotensin II. The JGA is richly supplied by adrenergic nerve fibers, which stimulate renin secretion via an α-adrenergic receptor. The JGA, particularly the macula densa, plays an important role in the feedback mechanism in the autoregulation of renal blood flow and glomerular filtration rate.

Figure 2-9 summarizes the anatomic and functional relationships of the various segments of the nephron, discussed so far.

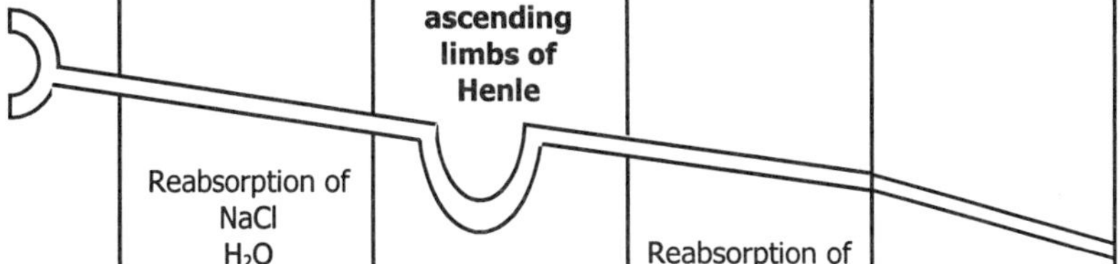

Glomerulus	Proximal tubule	Thin descending and ascending limbs of Henle	Distal tubule	Collecting duct
Ultrafiltration	Reabsorption of NaCl H_2O K^+ glucose amino acids PO_4^{3-} HCO_3^- Ca^{2+} Mg^{2+} urate urea Secretion of H^+ NH_4^+ organic anions organic cations	Transport of Na^+ H_2O Reabsorption of H_2O	Reabsorption of NaCl K^+ Ca^{2+} Mg^{2+} NH_4^+ Maintenance of medullary hypertonicity Secretion of renin Formation of *Tamm-Horsfall* protein	Reabsorption of NaCl K^+ H_2O Secretion of H^+ K^+ NH_3

Figure 2-9. Schematic representation of nephron segments showing the structural-functional relationships.

BLOOD SUPPLY TO THE KIDNEY

The kidney is usually supplied by one renal artery arising from the abdominal aorta. After or before entering the hilum, the renal artery divides into an **anterior** and a **posterior** division, both of them give rise to a total of 5 **segmental** arteries (referred to as the apical, upper, middle, lower, and posterior segmental arteries). The segmental arteries are **end** arteries, and occlusion of a single artery results in infarction of the area supplied. These segmental branches form the **interlobar** arteries in the renal sinus, which then enter the renal columns adjacent to the renal pyramids (Figure 2-10).

At the base of the pyramids, these interlobar arteries follow the curvature of the kidneys to form **arcuate** arteries. From these arteries arise **interlobular** arteries that course radially through the cortex toward its surface. The interlobular arteries give rise to the **afferent** arterioles, which divide into 5 to 8 lobules and form the **glomerular capillaries**. The loops of these capillaries reunite to form the **efferent** arteriole of the glomerulus. The efferent arteriole leaves the glomerulus as a short unbranched segment before it branches into capillaries. These capillaries, which supply blood to the proximal and distal tubules of the cortex, are known collectively as the **peritubular** capillary network. The efferent arterioles of glomeruli located in the juxtamedullary cortex and near the medullary region not only supply blood to their own tubules but also run deep into the medulla. These long, thin vessels are called **arteriolae rectae**, or **straight** arterioles. They form a loop with **straight venules** or **venulae rectae** of the medulla to form the **vasa recta** of the kidney. Thus, the blood supply to the medulla is entirely derived from the efferent arterioles of the juxtamedullary glomeruli.

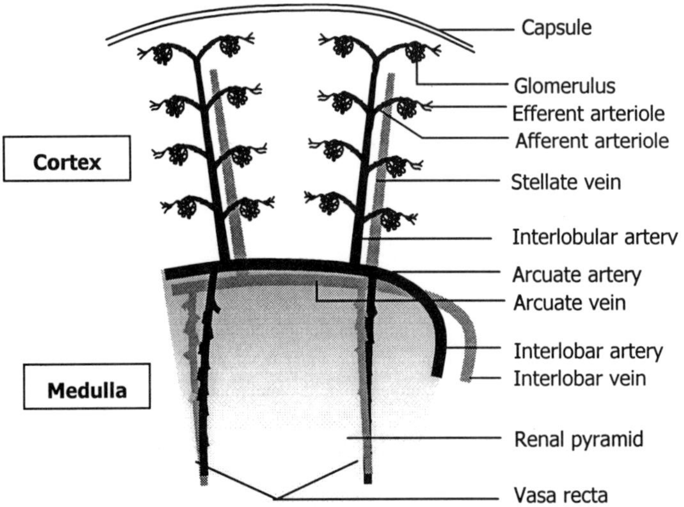

Figure 2-10. Blood supply to the kidney. Arcuate artery and vein are seen in the border between the cortex and medulla (Modified with permission from Kriz, W. and Bankir, L. A standard nomenclature for structures of the kidney. Am. J. Physiol. 254: F1-F8, 1988).

The capillaries of the outer cortex converge to form the **stellate** veins which drain into the **interlobular** veins. Blood from these veins drain into the **arcuate** veins and then into the **interlobar** veins. The interlobar veins form the **renal** vein through which the blood leaves the kidney.

NERVE SUPPLY TO THE KIDNEY

The kidney is supplied by autonomic nerve fibers largely arising from the celiac plexus. These nerve fibers run around the renal artery, its various branches, the JGA, and the tubules. Stimulation of these autonomic nerve fibers releases **norepinephrine**. In addition, **dopamine** has also been identified. Increased sympathetic activity has been shown to cause release of renin, reabsorption of

Na^+ by renal tubules, and regulation of the glomerular filtration rate. No **cholinergic** fibers within the renal parenchyma have been identified.

LYMPHATICS OF THE KIDNEY

Renal lymphatics consist of a capsular and a hilar or parenchymal network. The lymphatic vessels within or beneath the renal capsule drain into subcapsular lymphatic channels that lie close to the interlobular arteries. In the renal cortex, the lymphatic vessels begin as capillaries around the interlobular artery which drain into the arcuate and interlobular lymphatic vessels and finally into hilar vessels. The latter are joined by capsular lymphatic vessels to form 4 - 5 trunks that follow the renal vein and end in the lateral **aortic** nodes. The medulla lacks a lymphatic system.

MICTURITION

Once urine is formed, it is transported from the renal pelvis to the bladder via ureters. The bladder consists of a **body** whch stores the urine and a **neck,** which connects with the urethra (Figure 2-11). Involuntary passage of urine from the bladder to the urethra is prevented by two sphincters: the **internal** and **external sphincters**. The body and internal sphincter are composed of smooth muscle called the **detrussor muscle**, whereas the external sphincter consists of **striated muscle.**

Both the sympathetic and parasympathetic nerves innervate the bladder. The efferent fibers of the parasympathetic nervous system originate from S_2 to S_4 of sacral segments of the spinal cord and innervate the detrussor muscle of the body and internal sphincter through the **pelvic nerve**. The sympathetic efferent neurons arise from L1 and L2 segments of the spinal cord and travel through the **hypogastric nerve** to innervate the detrussor muscle of the body and internal sphincter. This innervation is mediated by α_1- and β_2- receptors.

The external sphincter receives its input from sacral somatic segments S_2 and S_3 and travel through the **pudendal nerve** (Figure 2-11). Sympathetic and parasympathetic afferent fibers arise from the bladder and internal sphincter and carried via hypogastric and pelvic nerves. The afferent fibers sense the bladder fullness and transmit to the spinal cord and higher centers in the brain.

The pudendal nerve also carries sensory afferent fibers. Stimulation of the pelvic nerve causes contraction of the detrussor muscle in the body and relaxation of the internal sphincter. This results in emptying of the bladder, which is called **micturition**. Opposite effects occur when hypogastric nerve is stimulated. For example, stimulation of α_1-receptors causes contraction of the internal sphincter, whereas β_2-receptor stimulation causes relaxation of the detrussor muscle of the body. The result is urine storage.

Micturition is a reflex that involves all levels of the nervous system. The micturition reflex is characterized by a coordination of detrussor muscle contraction and relaxation of urethral sphincters. This peripheral reflex arc is centered in the sacral segments of the spinal cord, which is, in turn, under the control of the central nervous system. In the adult, micturition is under the control of the cerebral cortex. It can either inhibit or facilitate micturition. The process of micturition starts when sensory input indicating bladder fullness reaches the cerebral cortex. It then alerts the **micturition center** located in the **pons** to commence voiding. The pontine micturition center sends messages to the S_2 to S_4 segments of the spinal cord where efferent fibers of the parasympathetic nerves lie. Stimulation of these fibers causes contraction of the detrussor muscle and relaxation of the urethral sphincters, resulting in voiding. Although the urge to void starts with accumulation of 150-200 ml, emptying of the bladder does not start until the urine volume reaches approximately 400 ml.

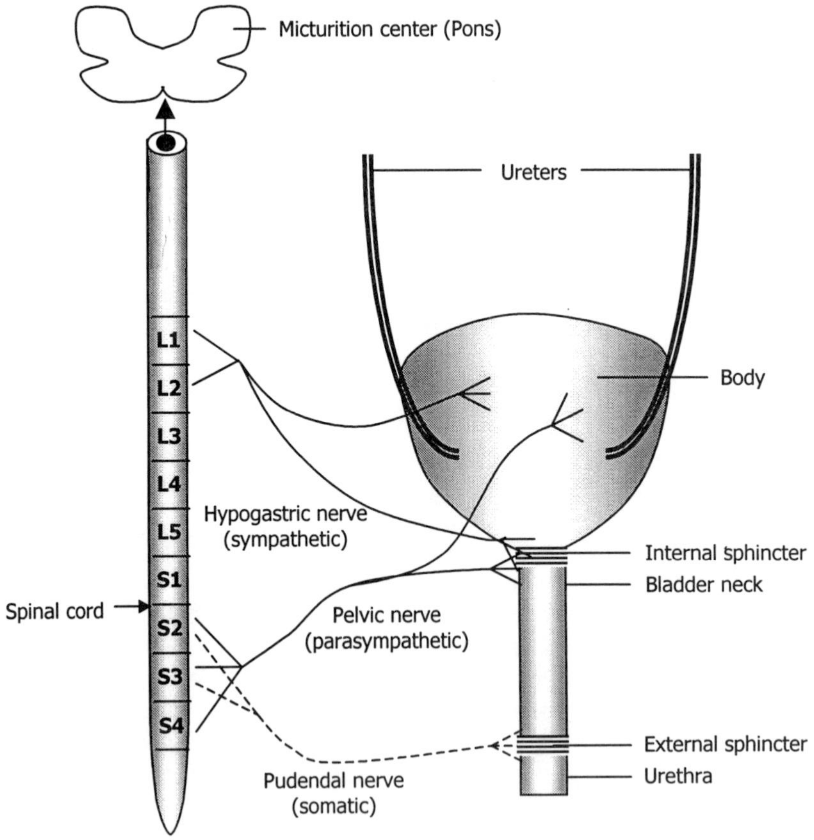

Figure 2-11. Schematic illustration of the urinary bladder and its innervation.

CLINICAL APPLICATIONS

Several congenital or developmental anomalies of the kidney have been described. These anomalies have both clinical and therapeutic implications. Three types of developmental abnormalities have been described: abnormalities in size and number, abnormalities in location, and development of cysts in the kidney.

Renal **agenesis** refers to the complete absence of renal development. Bilateral agenesis (complete absence of both kidneys) is observed in stillborn fetuses and is a rare condition. Unilateral or solitary kidney occurs in 1 out of 500-1000 people. Individuals with a single kidney are usually asymptomatic. The solitary kidney is usually larger than 12 cm due to compensatory hypertrophy and is commonly discovered accidentally on routine physical examination or as a result of an investigation for other conditions. Up to 10% of individuals have duplications of the renal pelvis and collecting system.

Ectopia means abnormal location of the kidney. In simple ectopia, the kidney is located near or in the pelvis and can be easily palpated. Crossed ectopia is a condition in which the kidney with its ureter from one side crosses to the other side and may fuse with the normally placed kidney. Because of this rotation, urine flow may become obstructed. **Horseshoe kidney** is another example of ectopia. It occurs in 1 out of 400 people. Horseshoe kidney is formed because of the fusion of two kidneys at the lower pole and distortion of the ureters. Individuals with horseshoe kidneys are at increased risk for infection and stone formation.

Cystic diseases of the kidney are common in both the pediatric and adult populations. Fifty percent of people over the age of 50 will have 1 or 2 cysts in their kidneys. These are clinically silent. The most common cystic disorder is **polycystic kidney disease** (PKD). There are two forms of PKD. Autosomal dominant PKD is typically found in adult subjects, whereas autosomal recessive PKD is expressed at birth and is lethal. The cysts are located throughout the nephron and the kidneys are greatly enlarged. The kidneys are easily palpable on physical examination. In adults, PKD causes urinary tract infection, hypertension, and renal failure. **Medullary cystic kidney** disease is another disorder leading to renal failure in young adults. **Medullary sponge kidney** is characterized by the presence of cysts in the terminal collecting duct. Patients with this condition do not develop renal failure, but they are at risk for urinary tract infection and kidney stone formation.

The size of the kidneys can be assessed by any one of the following four methods: (1) x-ray of the kidney, ureter, and bladder (KUB); (2) renal ultrasound; (3) intravenous pyelogram (IVP); and (4) renal scan. Based on these procedures, the size of the kidneys can be evaluated as normal, large, or small. Several diseases, as shown below, can cause large or small kidneys.

Large (>12 cm)	Small (<10 cm)
Solitary kidney	Chronic glomerulonephritis
Polycystic disease	Chronic hypertension
Diabetes	Bilateral renal artery stenosis
Amyloidosis	Congenital hypoplasia
Acute renal failure	
Infiltrative kidney (lymphoma)	

The mesangial cells play a central role in the progression of glomerular disease. First the mesangial cell number may increase more than the normal number of two or three cells. This process is called **mesangial hypercellularity**, and the associated clinical sign with this hypercellularity is **hematuria** (blood in urine). Second, the mesangial cell may secrete excess mesangial matrix, resulting in **mesangial sclerosis.** Expansion of mesangial matrix may encroach on glomerular capillary lumina, causing a reduction in its size. This reduction in size of lumina may cause a reduction in glomerular filtration surface area and eventually a decrease in glomerular filtration rate (GFR). In diabetes mellitus, an inverse relationship between the mesangial matrix expansion and GFR has been demonstrated. Third, the mesangial cells play an important role in the development of immune complex-mediated glomerular diseases. Once the immune complexes are deposited in the mesangium, they trigger inflammatory reactions and cause glomerular disease.

The endothelial cells also undergo pathologic changes, and cause glomerular capillary occlusion. Similarly, the foot processes of the visceral epithelial cell undergo fusion in conditions of heavy proteinuria (see below). Abnormalities of the glomerular basement membrane (GBM) are frequent in many glomerular diseases. In several diseases of the kidney, the GBM appears thick. This thickness is due to excess deposition of collagen, as in diabetes mellitus, or immune complexes, as in membranous nephropathy.

Clinically, the glomerular diseases can be divided into two major syndromes: **nephrotic** and **nephritic**. Patients with nephrotic syndrome have proteinuria (heavy protein in the urine), hypoalbuminemia (low serum concentration of albumin), hypercholesterolemia (high serum concentration of cholesterol), lipiduria (lipid in the urine), and edema (fluid in the interstitial compartment) (see Chapter 8). These abnormalities are largely due to biochemical and morphologic changes in the GBM. Diabetes mellitus is an example of nephrotic syndrome. The nephritic syndrome presents predominantly with hematuria. Acute post-infectious glomerulonephritis is an example of nephritic syndrome. Most of the glomerular diseases slowly progress to **chronic renal failure**, which is defined as a gradual increase in serum creatinine and BUN concentrations over months to years. In contrast, **acute renal failure** is defined as an abrupt increase in serum creatinine and BUN concentrations over a period of days to few weeks. Acute renal failure may be due to tubular necrosis of the nephron segments, particularly the proximal and distal tubules.

Urinary incontinence refers to the involuntary leakage of urine or loss of voluntary control of micturition. It is traditionally classified into **stress incontinence** (involuntary loss of urine during physical activity), **urge incontinence** (urine loss due to outflow obstruction), **overflow incontinence** (constant urine leak due to chronic urinary retention), **total incontinence** (urine leak during day and night time without normal voiding), and **functional incontinence** (voiding without regard to social norms of time and place). Incontinence is caused by either detrussor muscle abnormalities or sphincter abnormalities or a combination of both.

The prevalence of incontinence increases with age. In people over age 65, the prevalence is 15 to 30%. Involuntary contractions of the bladder are common even in continent and neurologically intact elderly.

SUMMARY

1. The kidneys are paired organs located retroperitoneally in the lumbar region. Each kidney has an outer cortex and an inner medulla. The medulla is, in turn, divided into an outer medulla and an inner medulla.
2. The functional unit of the kidney is the nephron. Each kidney contains about 600,000 nephrons. The nephron consists of a renal corpuscle, the proximal tubule, the loop of Henle, the distal tubule, and the collecting duct.
3. The renal corpuscle consists of the glomerulus and Bowman's capsule. Blood is filtered in the glomerulus to form protein-free ultrafiltrate, which is the first step in urine formation. About 60% of this ultrafiltrate is reabsorbed in the proximal tubule. The loops of Henle participate in countercurrent multiplication of urine concentration. The collecting duct plays an important role in K^+ secretion and urine acidification. Reabsorption of water occurs in the collecting duct in the presence of ADH.
4. The juxtaglomerular apparatus consists of the renin-producing granular cells in the afferent arteriole, the macula densa, and the extraglomerular cells. The macula densa plays an important role in the feedback mechanism in the autoregulation of renal blood flow and glomerular filtration rate.
5. Micturition is a process of emptying the bladder, which is under the control of spinal cord, micturition center in the pons and cerebral cortex.

STUDY QUESTIONS

Case 1

A 40-year-old man was found to have hypertension, palpable kidneys and many red blood cells in his urine (hematuria) on routine physical examination. He states that his father has hypertension and is on dialysis (artificial kidney) for kidney failure.

Question 1. Explain the reason for this patient's hypertension and hematuria.

Answer: Based on his family history and physical examination, the patient is likely to have autosomal dominant polycystic kidney disease. In this condition, the kidneys are generally large and can be palpated on physical examination. Hypertension and hematuria are common signs of polycystic kidney disease. Cystic diseases constitute the fourth cause for end stage renal failure, requiring either maintenance dialysis or kidney transplantation for survival.

Case 2

A 30-year-old male is brought to the trauma center after a motor vehicle accident. A CT scan of the head showed an injury to the cerebral cortex, and the brain stem was intact.

Question 1. What would happen to his bladder function?

Answer: Any injury above the micturition center of the pons causes bladder spasticity. Symptoms vary from urinary retention, urgency, frequency, and incontinence. Sacral spinal cord reflex arc remains intact.

Question 2. How is an ultrafiltrate formed?

Answer: An ultrafiltrate is essentially plasma minus protein. It is formed when blood is filtered at the glomerulus into the Bowman's space through the glomerular capillary. This glomerular capillary consists of an inner layer of endothelial cells, an outer layer of visceral epithelial cells, and a central region of mesangial cells with collagen-like mesangial matrix. Between the endothelial and epithelial cells is the glomerular basement membrane.

Question 3. Match each tubular segment in Column A with a likely function from Column B.

Column A	Column B
1. Pars convoluta	a. Involved in feedback mechanism that regulates RBF and GFR
2. Pars recta	b. More permeable to water than NaCl
3. Thin descending Henle's loop	c. Urine acidification
4. Thick ascending Henle's loop	d. Secretion of organic acids and bases
5. Macula densa	e. Reabsorption of Na^+, K^+, and Cl^- in the ratio of 1:1:2
6. Cortical collecting duct	f. Reabsorption of most of Na^+ and amino acids
7. Medullary collecting ducts	g. Secretion of K^+

Answers: 1 = f; 2 = d; 3 = b; 4 = e; 5 = a; 6 = g; 7 = c.

Question 4. What would happen to the bladder control if the spinal cord is injured at S_2 to S_4 sacral segments?

Answer: Injury to the spinal cord at S_2 to S_4 segments results in a flaccid neuropathic bladder, characterized by urinary retention, loss of voluntary detrussor contractions and diminished external sphincter muscle tone. Urinary incontinence does not generally occur in these patients.

SUGGESTED READING

1. Schnabel, E. and Kriz, W. Structure of the kidney. In: Textbook of Nephrology. 3rd edition. S.G. Massry and R.J. Glassock (eds.). Williams & Wilkins, Baltimore, 1995; pp. 10-34 (*This chapter provides a brief review of the microscopic structure of the kidney with detailed description of the histology of the tubular epithelium*).
2. Tischer, C.C. and Madsen, K.M. Anatomy of the kidney. In: The Kidney. 5th edition. B.M. Brenner (ed.). W.B. Saunders Company, Philadelphia, 1996; pp. 3-75 (*This chapter contains a detailed description of structural and functional relationships of the kidney with innumerable anatomical and histological illustrations of the kidney and tubular epithelium*).

CHAPTER 3

AN OVERVIEW OF RENAL HORMONES

Objectives

After reading this chapter, the student should be able to:

1. List the hormones that are produced by the kidney.
2. Discuss the renal actions of the following hormones: renin, angiotensin II, aldosterone, erythropoietin, vitamin D_3, adenosine, prostaglandins, nitric oxide, bradykinin, atrial natriuretic peptide, endothelin, parathyroid hormone, and antidiuretic hormone.
3. Describe how disease conditions influence actions of the above hormones.

There is a close relationship between the kidneys and hormones. First, the kidney produces several hormones. Of particular importance are **renin**, **erythropoietin**, active **vitamin D_3**, **prostaglandins**, **adenosine, nitric oxide, kinins**, **endothelin,** and **urodilatin**. Second, the kidneys metabolize many hormones (e.g., polypeptide hormones, steroid hormones, thyroid hormones) to inactive metabolites, and third, several hormones are important modulators of renal function and fluid and electrolyte balance both in physiologic and pathophysiologic conditions (e.g., atrial natriuretic peptide, parathyroid hormone, antidiuretic hormone, aldosterone). In this chapter, only those hormones produced by the kidney and some hormones with actions on the kidney are discussed.

HORMONES PRODUCED BY THE KIDNEY

Renin-Angiotensin-Aldosterone System

The hormone renin is produced by the juxtaglomerular cells of the afferent arteriole in the juxtaglomerular apparatus (JGA) in response to various stimuli. It is released into the circulation and acts on **angiotensinogen**, that is made primarily in the liver, to form **angiotensin I** (AI). AI, a decapeptide, is converted to **angiotensin II** (AII), an octapeptide, by **angiotensin converting enzyme**. This enzyme is present on the endothelial surface of all capillaries and is widely distributed in many tissues. AII is the most active product of the renin-angiotensin system, and it exerts its biologic effects by binding to specific receptors. Two types of AII receptors have been identified: AT_1 and AT_2 receptors. Many effects of AII are mediated via AT_1 receptors. The physiologic role of AT_2 receptor is not clearly defined. AII has several functions (Figure 3-1). The most important are that it stimulates **aldosterone** secretion and it is a potent vasoconstrictor. In addition, it stimulates catecholamine release, causes Na^+ retention by the proximal tubule, and stimulates thirst. In the renal circulation, it causes preferentially vasoconstriction of the efferent arteriole. At high concentrations, AII also causes vasoconstriction of the afferent arteriole. AII plays an important role in the autoregulation of glomerular filtration rate (GFR) and renal blood flow (RBF). AII is further metabolized to AIII by aminopeptidase A (not shown in Figure 3-1).

The major stimuli for renin release are (1) a decrease in mean arterial pressure; (2) an increase in catecholamine release; and (3) NaCl concentration in the macula densa. In addition, a number of clinical conditions and drugs influence circulating renin levels (Table 3-1).

Recent evidence suggests that renin and AII are produced in a variety of tissues, including the kidney, heart, liver, brain, and blood vessels. The tissue renin plays an important role in physiologic as well as pathologic conditions.

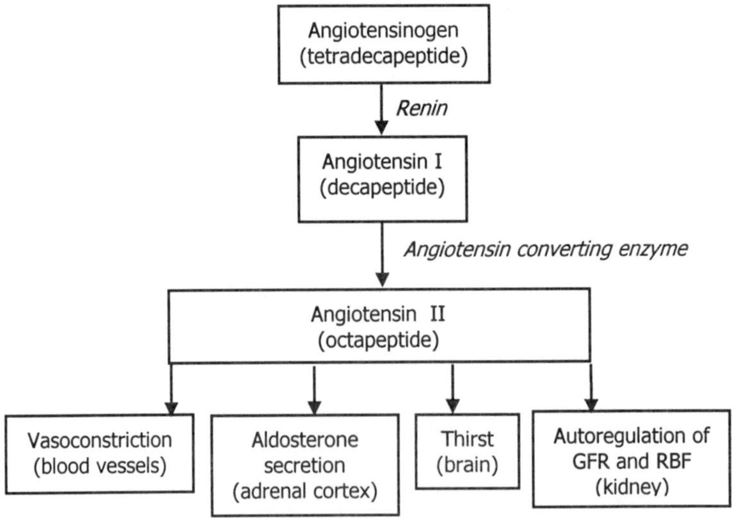

Figure 3-1. The renin-angiotensin-aldosterone system.

Aldosterone

Aldosterone, as the name implies, is a steroid hormone synthesized by the zona glomerulosa cells of the adrenal cortex. The secretion of aldosterone is regulated by AII, K^+, atrial natriuretic peptide (ANP), and adrenocorticotrophic hormone. ANP inhibits aldosterone secretion; the other factors stimulate aldosterone secretion.

Table 3-1. Effect of various disease states and drugs on plasma renin activity

Increase	Decrease
Renovascular hypertension	Primary aldosteronism
Malignant hypertension	Licorice ingestion
Addison's disease	Nonsteroidal anti-inflammatory drugs
Hemorrhage	β-blockers
Diuretics	Atrial natriuretic peptide
Angiotension converting enzyme-inhibitors	Vasopressin
Prostaglandins E_2 and I_2	Adenosine

The kidney is the principal target for aldosterone action. It promotes Na^+ reabsorption and K^+ secretion in principal cells of the cortical collecting duct. At the basolateral membrane, aldosterone stimulates Na/K-ATPase, which removes Na^+ ions from the cell and transports them into the blood. Aldosterone also stimulates secretion of H^+ ions in type-A intercalated cells.

Clinically, excessive aldosterone activity causes Na^+ retention, kaliuresis (loss of K^+ in urine), and metabolic alkalosis. Conversely, aldosterone deficiency is associated with urinary loss of Na^+, hyperkalemia, and metabolic acidosis. A syndrome similar to aldosterone deficiency may be caused by aldosterone antagonists such as **spironolactone**, a K^+-sparing diuretic (see Chapter 19). Also, **angiotensin converting enzyme-inhibitors** cause hypoaldosteronism, and produce a clinical syndrome similar to aldosterone deficiency.

Erythropoietin (EPO)

EPO is a glycoprotein. It is synthesized by the peritubular interstitial cells of the corticomedullary junction. Hypoxia is the most potent stimulus for EPO production, which results from either anemia or ischemia to the kidney. EPO acts on the so-called colony-forming units of erythroid cells to stimulate erythropoiesis (formation of red blood cells). EPO also stimulates the release of reticulocytes into the blood. A number of factors have been shown to stimulate EPO production. These factors include prostaglandins, vasopressin, free oxygen radicals, and androgens. Nonsteroidal anti-inflammatory drugs (NSAIDs) block EPO production following hypoxic stimulation. Also, adenosine and some cytokines (interleukin-1 and tumor necrosis factor α) inhibit EPO production. Extrarenal production of EPO has been demonstrated primarily in the liver due to hypoxia. In an adult, about 90% of EPO production occurs in the kidney and the remaining 10% in the liver.

Patients with **chronic renal failure** have low levels of EPO. As a result, these patients develop anemia. Parenteral administration of EPO to selected patients has been shown to improve anemia and quality of life.

Vitamin D

The naturally occurring vitamin D precursor in animals is **7-dehydrocholesterol**, which is present in the skin (Figure 3-2). Ultraviolet radiation to the skin converts this precursor to **cholecalciferol** or **vitamin D_3**. Vitamin D_3 can also be obtained from the diet. Vitamin D_3 undergoes hydroxylation in the liver to form **25-hydroxycholecalciferol**, which is further hydroxylated in the kidney to form **1,25-dihydroxycholecalciferol** (1,25-$(OH)_2D_3$) or **calcitriol**. This metabolite is the most active form of vitamin D in the body. The enzyme responsible for this hydroxylation is called **25-hydroxycholecalciferol-1 α-hydroxylase**. Parathyroid hormone, hypophosphatemia, and hypocalcemia stimulate, whereas hyperphosphatemia, hypercalcemia, and glucocorticoids inhibit the synthesis of 1,25-$(OH)_2D_3$.

The major actions of calcitriol are on the small intestine, bone, and kidney. In the intestine, it stimulates the absorption of Ca^{2+}, phosphate (PO_4^{3-}) and Mg^{2+}, but the effect on Ca^{2+} absorption is more pronounced. The effects on bone are not clearly understood. However, 1,25-$(OH)_2D_3$ stimulates bone resorption (release of Ca^{2+} and PO_4^{3-}) in the presence of parathyroid hormone. In the kidney, 1,25-$(OH)_2D_3$ increases renal tubular Ca^{2+} and PO_4^{3-} reabsorption. In addition to these effects, 1,25-$(OH)_2D_3$ suppresses parathyroid hormone by its action on specific receptors in the parathyroid gland.

A major fraction of 25-dihydroxycholecalciferol is also converted in the kidney and other tissues to **24, 25-dihydroxycholecalciferol**. The role of this metabolite is still not clearly understood (see Figure 3-2).

Vitamin D metabolism is altered in renal failure. The formation of 1,25-$(OH)_2D_3$ decreases as the GFR starts to decline. The decrease in 1,25-$(OH)_2D_3$ formation leads to decreased absorption of Ca^{2+} in the gut causing hypocalcemia. The resultant hypocalcemia stimulates parathyroid hormone secretion. PO_4^{3-} retention also occurs with a decrease in 1,25-$(OH)_2D_3$. The net effect of these abnormalities in vitamin D metabolism is **renal osteodystrophy**, a bone disease seen in patients with renal failure. Renal osteodystrophy improves with oral administration of 1,25-$(OH)_2D_3$.

Prostaglandins (PGs)

PGs are called **autocoids** because they are produced at or near their site of action. The kidney is a major organ for PG production. Important sites of PG production include renal vascular endothelium, glomerular cells, and cortical and medullary collecting ducts. PG synthesis is several-fold higher in the medulla than in the cortex. The converse is true for PG degradation. PGs are formed from arachidonic acid, which is derived from phospholipids of cell membranes

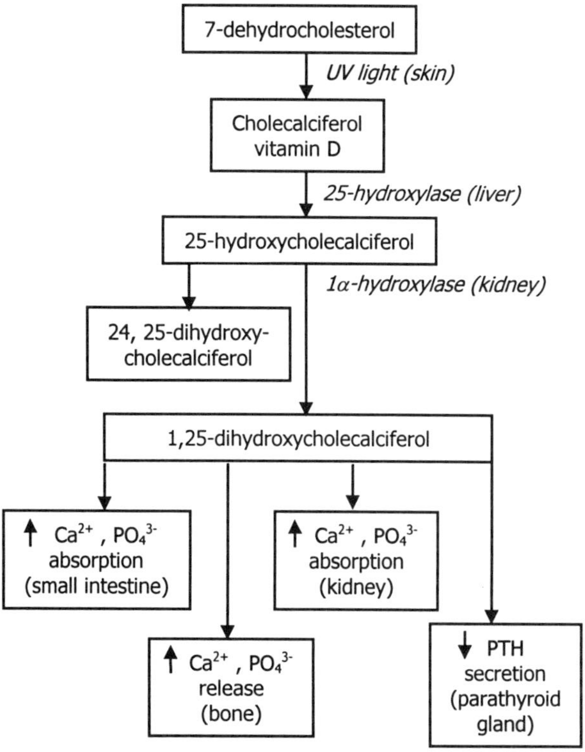

Figure 3-2. Metabolism of vitamin D and its actions.

and the diet. Arachidonic acid undergoes **lipoxygenase**, **cyclooxygenase** and **cytochrome P450 monooxygenase** pathways. Leukotrienes are formed through lipoxygenase pathway. The microsomal cytochrome P450 enzyme system generates a wide variety of oxygenated products. PGs are formed through the cyclooxygenase pathway (Figure 3-3). Cyclooxygenase converts arachidonic acid to two intermediary **endoperoxides** (PGG_2, PGH_2), which then give rise to prostanoids (PGE_2, $PGF_{2\alpha}$, PGD, PGI_2 or prostacyclin) and thromboxane A_2 (T_xA_2).

PGs have both vasodilatory and vasoconstrictive properties. Under normal physiologic conditions, PGs have minimal effects on the kidney. However, under pathophysiologic conditions (hemorrhage, congestive heart failure or volume depletion), vasodilatory PGs (PGE_2, PGI_2) counteract the effects of AII and catecholamines. Table 3-2 shows the actions of PGs in the kidney. NSAIDs, such as indomethacin or ibuprofen, counteract PG actions through the inhibition of cyclooxygenase

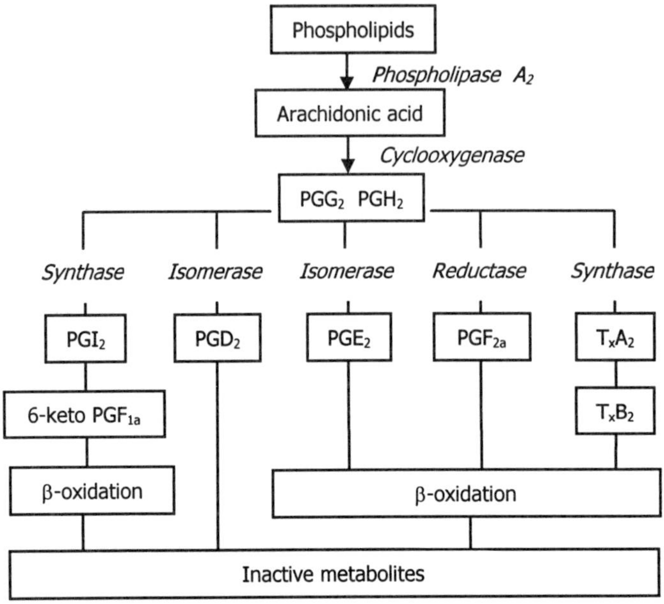

Figure 3-3. Biosynthesis of prostaglandins.

Table 3-2. Pertinent physiologic actions of prostaglandins (PGs) in the kidney

PGs	Renal function	Mechanism
PGE_2, PGI_2	↑ RBF	Renal vasodilation
Thromboxane A_2	↓ RBF and GFR	Renal vasoconstriction
PGE_2	↑ Na^+ excretion	Increase in filtered load of Na^+ and inhibition of Na^+ transport in MTALH and collecting duct
PGE_2	↑ Water excretion	Antagonizes the ADH-stimulated adenylate cyclase
PGE_2, PGI_2	↑ Renin production	Stimulate JGA to release renin
PGE_2, PGI_2	↑ Erythropoietin secretion	Stimulate adenylate cyclase

MTALH = medullary thick ascending limb of Henle's loop; ADH = antidiuretic hormone; RBF = renal blood flow; GFR = glomerular filtration rate; JGA = juxtaglomerular apparatus.

Adenosine

Adenosine is formed intracellularly from adenosine monophosphate (AMP) during hypoxia by the enzyme 5′-nucleotidase. It then passes through the cell membrane and regulates a variety of physiologic functions such as cardiac rate, vascular smooth muscle tone, renal hemodynamics, and Na^+ transport. Adenosine acts through two types of receptors: A_1 and A_2. In the kidney, extracellular production of adenosine from AMP has also been demonstrated. Both A_1 and A_2 receptors are distributed throughout the nephron and blood vessels. Infusion of adenosine into the renal artery causes initially a reduction and then an increase in RBF. This reduction in RBF is due to vasoconstriction of the afferent arteriole. On the other hand, adenosine causes a decrease in GFR, renin as well as EPO production. At lower doses, adenosine produces marked water and Na^+ excretion. It is postulated that adenosine participates in the regulation of GFR by tubuloglomerular feedback mechanism (see Chapter 4).

Nitric Oxide (NO)

NO is released from vascular endothelium. It is also called endothelium-derived relaxing factor. NO is a vasodilator. In the kidney, it is produced by vascular endothelium and mesangial cells. NO increases RBF and GFR. The latter effect is related to an increase in glomerular capillary ultrafiltration coefficient (K_f) (see Chapter 4). Na^+ excretion is promoted by NO, which is due to inhibition of AII action on Na^+ reabsorption in the proximal tubule.

Chronic inhibition of NO production leads to hypertension, glomerular sclerosis and proteinuria. Dietary supplementation with L-arginine from which NO is synthesized prevents all these changes.

Kallikrein-Kinin System

Bradykinin represents this hormone system. Infusion of bradykinin into the renal artery causes vasodilation of afferent and efferent arterioles and increases RBF. There is no effect on GFR. Bradykinin also induces Na^+ and water excretion. The kinins have been shown to counteract the effects of the action of antidiuretic hormone (ADH) and stimulate the production of vasodilatory PGs and renin. It appears that renal kinins mediate their effects directly and also indirectly through interaction with the renin-AII-aldosterone, PGs, and ADH systems.

Endothelin (ET)

ET is a 21-amino acid peptide released by vascular endothelial cells. It is a powerful vasoconstrictor of vascular smooth muscle and mesangial cells. Its release is stimulated by thrombin. Three ETs have been identified: ET-1, ET-2, and ET-3. The physiologic functions of these three ETs do not vary significantly, but their potencies in eliciting vascular smooth muscle contraction vary significantly. In the kidney, ET is produced by glomerular capillaries, glomerular epithelial, endothelial, and mesangial cells as well as inner medullary collecting duct cells.

Most of the physiologic functions have been studied with ET-1. The actions of ET-1 can be summarized as follows: (1) it causes contraction of the vascular smooth muscle cell and first briefly lowers then raises blood pressure; (2) it increases contractility of the heart; (3) it increases renal vascular resistance and thereby reduces RBF and GFR; (4) the decrease in GFR is associated with a decrease in K_f; and (5) doses of ET-1 that do not impair GFR may promote Na^+ excretion.

HORMONES WITH ACTIONS ON THE KIDNEY

Atrial Natriuretic Peptide (ANP)

ANP, although not synthesized by the kidney, has several important actions on kidney function. Active ANP is a 28-amino acid peptide and is the major circulating form. It is synthesized and stored in the atrial muscle cells. Volume expansion or atrial stretch stimulates the release of ANP. Accordingly, pathophysiologic conditions associated with volume expansion, such as congestive heart failure, severe liver failure, or renal failure, have high circulating levels of ANP. Pregnancy is also associated with high circulating levels of ANP. Plasma levels of ANP are also elevated in patients with atrial arrhythmias. Even eating an ounce of potato chips can cause an increase in plasma ANP levels.

The actions of ANP in the body are opposite to those of ET-1. ANP reduces systemic blood pressure, primarily by decreasing cardiac output and peripheral vascular resistance. ANP decreases sympathetic nervous system activity, which, in turn, diminishes cardiac contractility. In the kidney, ANP causes renal afferent arteriolar dilatation and efferent arteriolar constriction. These effects enhance GFR. ANP has been shown to inhibit Na^+ reabsorption in the proximal tubule and inner medullary collecting duct. In the latter segment of the nephron, ANP antagonizes the action of ADH and inhibits water reabsorption. Thus, ANP promotes natriuresis and diuresis. ANP inhibits aldosterone secretion indirectly by inhibiting renin and directly by inhibiting adrenal glomerulosa cells. Inhibition of aldosterone also promotes Na^+ excretion, and lowers blood pressure.

Urodilatin is a hormone that belongs to the ANP family of peptides. It is discussed in this section because of its similar actions with ANP. Urodilatin consists of 32 amino acids, and originally isolated from urine. It differs from ANP in several aspects. First, urodilatin contains an additional four amino acid extension at the N-terminus. This extension renders urodilatin resistant to degradation by the neutral endopeptidase. Second, urodilatin is synthesized by the intercalated cells of the cortical collecting duct. Third, urodilatin is not present in plasma either in physiologic or pathologic conditions. However, the effects of urodilatin on the kidney are similar to those of ANP. Urodilatin increases RBF. GFR may or may not be increased. Urodilatin inhibits NaCl and water reabsorption in the medullary portion of the collecting duct.

Parathyroid Hormone (PTH)

Active PTH is a large polypeptide containing 84 amino acids. PTH is secreted by the parathyroid gland. The secretion of PTH is primarily regulated by extracellular ionized Ca^{2+}. As little as a 10% increase or a decrease in the plasma Ca^{2+} concentration inhibits or stimulates PTH secretion. Other modulators of PTH secretion are 1,25-$(OH)_2D_3$ and Mg^{2+}. 1,25-$(OH)_2D_3$ and hypomagnesemia inhibit both the secretion and synthesis of PTH. PTH acts on the kidney and bone. It also has an indirect action on the intestine. In the kidney, PTH stimulates Ca^{2+} reabsorption in the distal nephron and inhibits PO_4^{3-} reabsorption and stimulates the synthesis of 1,25-$(OH)_2D_3$ in the proximal tubule. The major action of PTH on bone is stimulation of osteoclast function to release Ca^{2+} and PO_4^{3-} (bone resorption). In the intestine, PTH promotes Ca^{2+} reabsorption through the mediation of 1,25-$(OH)_2D_3$. The effects of PTH on the kidney and bone are illustrated in Figure 3-4.

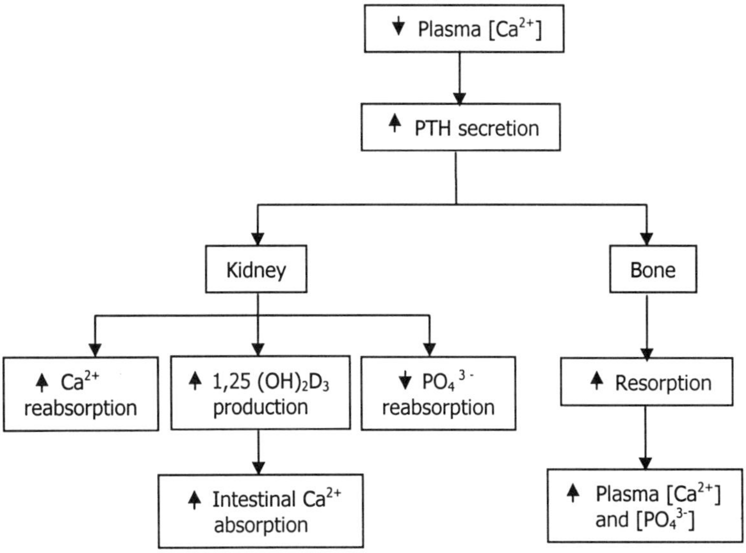

Figure 3-4. Effect of parathyroid hormone (PTH) on calcium and phosphate metabolism. [Ca^{2+}] or [PO_4^{3-}] = plasma calcium or phosphate concentrations.

Antidiuretic Hormone (ADH)

ADH, also called arginine vasopressin (AVP), is synthesized by the supraoptic and paraventricular nuclei of the hypothalamus. It is secreted as a prohormone, which is composed of three components: ADH, neurophysin, and glycopeptide. This prohormone is transported to the posterior pituitary gland where it is cleaved to form ADH and neurophysin. The fate of glycopeptide is unknown. The major physiologic stimulus for ADH release is plasma osmolality. In addition, a number of nonosmotic stimuli release ADH.

The main actions of ADH are on the kidney. It increases water permeability in the cortical and medullary collecting ducts and plays an important role in urinary concentration and dilution (see Chapter 9). ADH also increases NaCl reabsorption in the medullary thick limb of Henle's loop. Studies in rats have shown that intravenous infusion of AVP reduces K_f possibly due to contraction of mesangial cells. At higher concentrations, AVP causes an increase in systemic blood pressure. Details of ADH actions are discussed in Chapter 10.

SUMMARY

1. The kidney is the main source of renin, erythropoietin, and active vitamin D_3. Hormones such as prostaglandins, adenosine, nitric oxide, and endothelin are produced by the kidney and also other parts of the body. Degradation of several hormones occurs in the kidney.
2. Renin acts on angiotensinogen to form angiotensin I, which is converted into angiotensin II (AII) by angiotensin converting enzyme. AII is a potent vasoconstrictor. It also stimulates aldosterone secretion.
3. Erythropoietin stimulates red cell production. Hypoxia is the potent stimulus for EPO production. Active vitamin D_3 promotes Ca^{2+} and PO_4^{3-} absorption by the kidney and small intestine. It also causes bone resorption to release Ca^{2+} and PO_4^{3-}.
4. Adenosine and nitric oxide cause an increase in RBF. GFR is decreased by adenosine and increased by nitric oxide. Prostaglandins such as PGE_2, PGI_2, and bradykinin cause an increase in RBF and GFR. Thromboxane A_2 and endothelin-1 lower RBF and GFR.
5. Hormones, such as atrial natriuretic peptide (ANP), parathyroid hormone (PTH), and antidiuretic hormone (ADH), are not produced by the kidney, but play an important role in renal hemodynamics, and Ca^{2+} and PO_4^{3-}, and water metabolism. ANP increases GFR and Na^+ excretion. PTH acts on the kidney by stimulating tubular reabsorption of Ca^{2+} and synthesis of active vitamin D_3. It also causes bone resorption releasing Ca^{2+} and PO_4^{3-} into circulation. Urodilatin, produced by the kidney, belongs to the family of ANP peptides. It inhibits NaCl and water reabsorption in the medullary portion of the collecting duct. ADH plays an important role in urinary concentration and dilution.

STUDY QUESTIONS

Case 1

A 50-year-old female with noninsulin-dependent diabetes mellitus was found to have 150 mg of albumin in the urine. She was started on an angiotensin converting enzyme-inhibitor (ACE-I). Plasma renin and angiotensin I (AI) are elevated, whereas the levels of angiotensin II (AII) are decreased.

Question 1. Discuss the impact of decreased AII levels on blood pressure and aldosterone secretion.

Answer: The ACE-inhibitors inhibit the conversion of AI to AII. As a result, the renin and AI levels are increased. Since AII is more potent than AI or renin, it lowers blood pressure despite an increase in renin and AI levels. Aldosterone secretion is also decreased.

Case 2

A patient with cirrhosis of the liver is treated with large doses of indomethacin for knee pain. One month later, the patient complains of nausea, vomiting, and shortness of breath. He has also gained 5 pounds.

Question 1. Discuss the effects of indomethacin on RBF and GFR.

Answer: Nonsteroidal anti-inflammatory drugs such as indomethacin inhibit cyclooxygenase, and thereby reduce the production of vasodilatory prostaglandins (PGE_2 and PGI_2). As a result, renal vasoconstriction occurs, which decreases both RBF and GFR.

Question 2. What effect does indomethacin have on aldosterone secretion?

Answer: Indomethacin inhibits renin production. As a result, aldosterone secretion is decreased.

Question 3. Discuss the role of excess aldosterone secretion.

Answer: Aldosterone promotes K^+ secretion in principal cells of the cortical collecting duct. It also promotes Na^+ and water reabsorption, resulting in mild expansion of the extracellular fluid compartment. This volume expansion causes a decrease in renin production. Because of Na^+ and water retention, patients with excess aldosterone levels develop hypertension.

Question 4. Answer the following True or False statements:

1. Eating an ounce of potato chips increases circulating atrial natriuretic peptide (ANP) levels.
2. Endothelin-1 increases RBF and GFR.
3. Adenosine decreases renin and erythropoietin production.
4. Nitric oxide promotes Na^+ excretion by antagonizing the effects of AII.
5. Hypoxia reduces synthesis of adenosine and erythropoietin.
6. Delivery of NaCl to the macula densa reduces renin release.
7. Bradykinin increases GFR.
8. Chronic inhibition of nitric oxide reduces blood pressure.
9. ANP lowers renin and aldosterone production.

Answers: 1. True; 2. False; 3. True; 4. True; 5. False; 6. False; 7. False; 8. False; 9. True.

SUGGESTED READING

1. Gunning, M.E., Ingelfinger, J.R., King, A.J. and Brenner, B.M. Vasoactive peptides and the kidney. In: The Kidney. 5th edition. B.M. Brenner (ed.). W.B. Saunders Company, Philadelphia, 1996; pp. 627-712 (*A detailed review of several hormones and their effects on renal hemodynamics, fluid, and electrolyte metabolism*).
2. Lakkis, F.G., Nassar, G.M. and Badr, K. Hormones and the kidney. In: Diseases of the Kidney. 6th edition. R.W. Schrier and C.W. Gottschalk (eds.). Little, Brown and Company, Boston, 1997; pp. 251-292 (*Another extensive review of hormones on renal hemodynamics and tubular transport in physiologic and pathophysiologic conditions*).

CHAPTER 4

RENAL BLOOD FLOW AND GLOMERULAR FILTRATION

Objectives

After reading this chapter, the student should be able to:

1. Discuss the quantity and distribution of blood supply to the kidney and how renal blood flow differs from that of other major organs.
2. Describe the factors that influence the glomerular filtration of molecules.
3. Discuss the mechanism by which albumin leaks through the glomerular basement membrane.
4. Discuss the determinants of glomerular filtration rate.
5. Define the terms filtration equilibrium, filtration fraction, autoregulation, the Laplace equation.
6. Discuss the myogenic and tubuloglomerular feedback theories.
7. List and describe the various factors that influence afferent and efferent arteriolar resistances, renal blood flow, glomerular filtration rate, and glomerular ultrafiltration coefficient.

The formation of urine by the kidneys involves three basic mechanisms. First, a portion of blood that flows through the glomerular capillaries is filtered into the Bowman's space to form an ultrafiltrate. This process is called **glomerular filtration**. The composition of ultrafiltrate is similar to that of plasma except for protein and any substances bound to protein. Second, reabsorption of water and solutes occurs as the ultrafiltrate passes through the tubules. Third, secretion of some solutes, including H^+ ions and metabolic waste products, occurs in the tubules. **Renal blood flow** (RBF) through the renal arteries serves all three of these mechanisms.

RENAL BLOOD FLOW (RBF)

The vascular supply of the kidney was discussed in Chapter 2. The kidneys receive about 20% of the cardiac output. In a 70-kg person, this percentage amounts to 1200 ml of blood per minute (assuming a cardiac output of 6 liters/min). The kidneys weigh approximately 300 g, and therefore the RBF is 4 ml/min/gram. This blood flow is 5 to 20 times greater than the flow to most other organs of the body. About 90% of this blood flow goes to the renal cortex and the remaining 10% to the medulla. The low blood flow to the medulla is necessary to maintain its hyperosmolar environment. Despite the high blood flow to the kidney, its oxygen consumption rate per gram tissue is less than that of heart muscle. The major energy-requiring process in the kidney is the transport of Na^+ ; it has been estimated that 1 mmol of oxygen is needed for reabsorption of about 25 mEq of Na^+. It is the tubular transport of Na^+ that is the primary determinant of the rate of O_2 consumption. Since the cortical blood flow is about 9 times higher than the medullary blood flow, O_2 consumption is similarly higher in the cortex than in the medulla.

The difference between the arterial and venous O_2 content in the human kidney is approximately 1.5 ml/dL of blood, which is the smallest arteriovenous O_2 difference of the major organ systems. Unlike other organs, where blood flow is related to the O_2 requirements of the organ, in the kidney, the O_2 consumption is a function of blood flow.

Blood flow to the kidney is determined, in accordance with Ohm's law, by two factors: (a) effective renal perfusion pressure, and (b) the vascular resistance. Changes in either of these factors cause changes in the RBF. Both the afferent and efferent arterioles as well as interlobular arteries offer resistances and therefore regulate blood flow. These resistances, in turn, are influenced by neural and humoral factors, drugs, and intrinsic renal factors. In general, the RBF regulates glomerular filtration. Therefore, it is, essential to consider the effect of various vasoactive substances on these two renal functions together. First, let us see how ultrafiltration occurs in the glomerulus.

GLOMERULAR FILTRATION

The filtration of plasma occurs at the glomerulus. The plasma passes through the glomerular basement membrane (GBM), which is the only anatomical barrier between plasma and urine. The structural components of the glomerulus and the barriers for filtration are shown in Figure 4-1 and also in Chapter 2. The GBM does not allow plasma proteins, such as albumin to pass through it. Also, solutes that are bound to plasma proteins do not pass through the GBM. The ultrafiltrate that reaches the Bowman's space is devoid of protein.

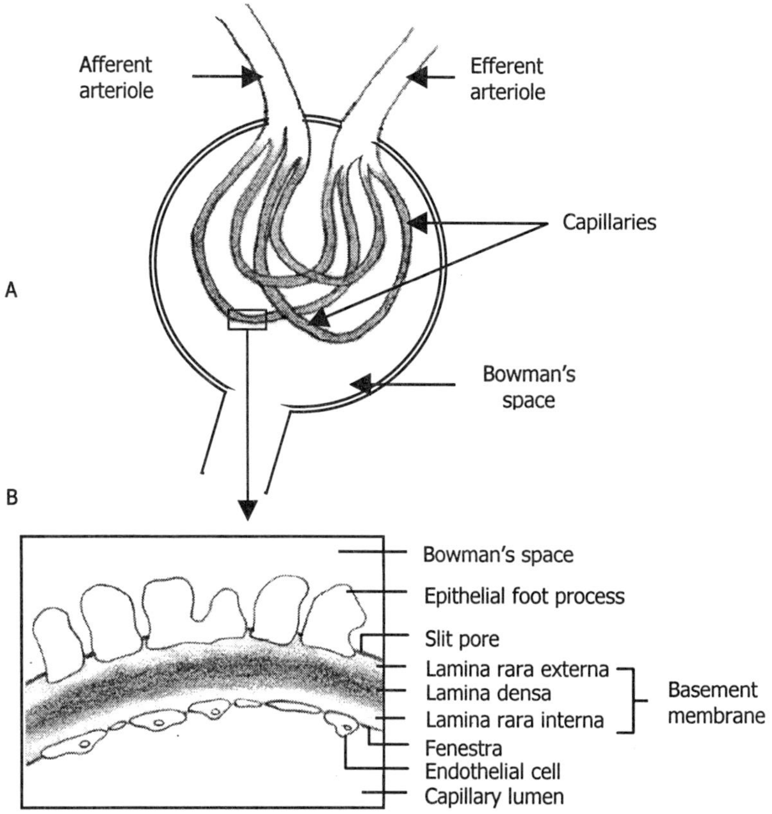

Figure 4-1. Schematic illustration of the glomerulus with afferent and efferent arterioles (A) and the glomerular capillary showing basement membrane (B).

FACTORS INFLUENCING THE FILTRATION OF MOLECULES

The filtration of molecules through the GBM depends on their shape, size, and ionic charge. Linear, flexible molecules (dextran, for example) can penetrate the GBM more easily than globular molecules (albumin).

The effect of size and charge on the rate of filtration was initially demonstrated using dextran. Dextran is a polysaccharide available in various sizes and charges. It is filtered by the glomerulus but is neither secreted nor reabsorbed by the tubules. Therefore, the urinary excretion of dextran is a function of filtration by the glomerulus. Figure 4-2 illustrates the filterability of dextran as related to size as well as charge.

The numbers on the ordinate indicate the relative degree of filterability. Molecules with a number of 1.0 are freely filtered, and those with less than 1.0 are progressively restricted. The size of the molecules is presented as the effective molecular radius (Stokes-Einstein radius) on the abscissa. As the size of the molecular radius of various dextrans increases, passage through the GBM becomes progressively restricted. Thus, filtration of dextran molecules with radii less than 20Å is not restricted, whereas molecules with radii greater than 42Å are completely restricted. The filterability of a positively charged dextran (cationic dextran) at any given molecular radius is higher than a negatively charged, similar sized dextran (anionic dextran). In other words, positively charged molecules pass through the GBM much more readily than negatively charged molecules.

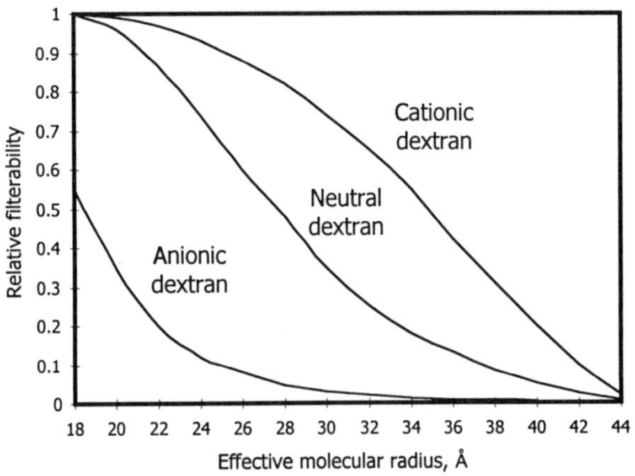

Figure 4-2. Relative filterability of neutral, anionic, and cationic dextrans as a function of effective molecular radius (Å=Angstroms)(Modified from Bohrer, M.P., Baylis, C., Humes, H.D., et al., Permselectivity of the glomerular capillary wall. Facilitated filtration of circulating polycations. Reproduced from The Journal of Clinical Investigation, 1978, 61:72-78, by copyright permission of The American Society for Clinical Investigation).

Albumin has a molecular weight of 69,000 daltons with a radius of 35.5Å. It carries a negative charge at physiologic pH. Biochemically, the GBM is composed of collagen and heparan sulfate proteoglycan; the latter confers a negative charge to the GBM. Since albumin is large and also anionic, its filterability is further restricted due to the repulsion by the negative charge on the GBM. If the negative charge on the GBM is lost, albumin can leak through the GBM and appear in the urine. This is exactly what happens in diabetes and other glomerular diseases that are characterized by proteinuria.

DETERMINANTS OF GLOMERULAR FILTRATION

The rate at which ultrafiltration occurs per unit time is called the **glomerular filtration rate** (GFR). The forces that govern the GFR are determined by the **Starling principle** in a manner similar to that which occurs in the systemic circulation. Four major forces determine the rate of GFR:

1. The hydraulic (hydrostatic) pressure within the glomerulus (P_{Gc}).
2. The hydraulic (hydrostatic) pressure within the Bowman's space (P_{Bs}).
3. The colloid oncotic pressure within the glomerular capillary (π_{Gc}).
4. The colloid oncotic pressure within the Bowman's space (π_{Bs}).

The first force tends to push fluid across the GBM, whereas the second and third forces oppose ultrafiltration (Figure 4-3). π_{Gc} is principally due to albumin. Since the filtrate entering the Bowman's space is albumin-free, π_{Bs} is virtually negligible. Therefore, the major opposing oncotic force for ultrafiltration is π_{Gc}.

Another determinant of ultrafiltration is the **glomerular filtration coefficient** (K_f), which is the product of the hydraulic water permeability (water pores per surface area, L_p) and the total filtering surface area (A); therefore, K_f equals L_pA. In other words, L_pA is the total membrane porosity available for water flow.

Based upon the above determinants, GFR of either a single nephron or all nephrons can be defined as K_f multiplied by the sum of the Starling forces:

$$\mathbf{GFR = K_f\,(P_{Gc} - P_{Bs} - \pi_{Gc})}$$

From micropuncture studies performed on rats, the following values are representative pressures for Starling forces (see Table 4-1):

P_{Gc} = 45 mm Hg
P_{Bs} = 10 mm Hg
π_{Gc} = 20 mm Hg
π_{Bs} = 0 mm Hg

The **net filtration pressure** (P_f), which is defined as the amount of pressure that is needed to push the fluid across the glomerular capillary (Figure 4-3), is:

$$P_f = (P_{Gc} - P_{Bs} - \pi_{Gc}) \text{ or } (45\text{-}10\text{-}20) = 15 \text{ mm Hg}$$

Thus, the GFR can be expressed as:

$$GFR = K_f \times P_f$$

In contrast to other systemic capillaries such as the muscle, the π_{GC} in glomerular capillaries from one end to the other is not constant. The reason

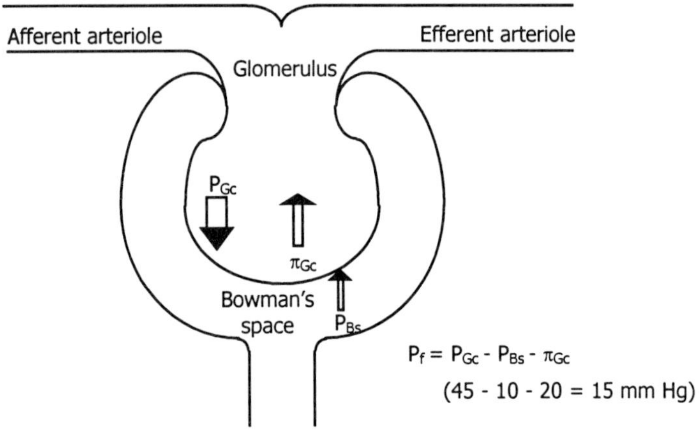

Figure 4-3. Diagrammatic representation of the glomerular capillary showing the Starling forces for ultrafiltration. The major force favoring ultrafiltration is the P_{Gc} (hydraulic pressure in the capillary), and opposing forces are π_{Gc} (oncotic pressure in the capillary) and P_{Bs} (hydraulic pressure in the Bowman's space). The net ultrafiltration pressure (P_f) is the overall pressure needed to push the fluid across the capillary into the Bowman's space. Numbers in parentheses indicate the representative pressures in the rat.

for this change in π_{Gc} is that as plasma water is filtered along the length of the capillary, the concentration of albumin, which is not filtered, progressively increases. In the rat, for example, the π_{Gc} is 20 mm Hg at the beginning of the capillary, whereas at the end it is 35 mm Hg (Table 4-1). Because of this progressive increase in π_{Gc}, the P_f gradually decreases to a point where filtration ceases. This is called the **filtration equilibrium** (Figure 4-4).

Table 4-1. Hydraulic, colloid oncotic and net filtration pressures (mm Hg) in the afferent and efferent arterioles of the glomerular capillary in the rat. (Adapted with permission from Deen, W.M., Robertson, C.R. and Brenner, B.M., Glomerular ultrafiltration. Fed. Proc. 33: 14-20, 1974).

Pressures	Afferent end	Efferent end
P_{Gc}	45	45
P_{Bs}	10	10
π_{Gc}	20	35
P_f	15	0

The filtration in glomerular capillaries is several times higher than in other systemic capillaries. Not all the plasma that flows through the glomerulus is filtered. This is due to the filtration equilibrium. Normally only about 20% of the plasma that flows through the glomerular capillary is filtered into Bowman's space. This amount is called the **filtration fraction**, which is calculated as GFR/RPF x 100. (filtration fraction is discussed in more detail in Chapter 5.) In reality, about 180 L/day of plasma are filtered in the glomerulus. This amounts to 125 ml/min (180 liters divided by the minutes per day; i.e., 1440), which is the GFR in an adult.

REGULATION OF RBF AND GFR

Under physiologic conditions, minor changes in GFR do occur. These changes are due to changes in afferent and efferent arteriolar resistances,

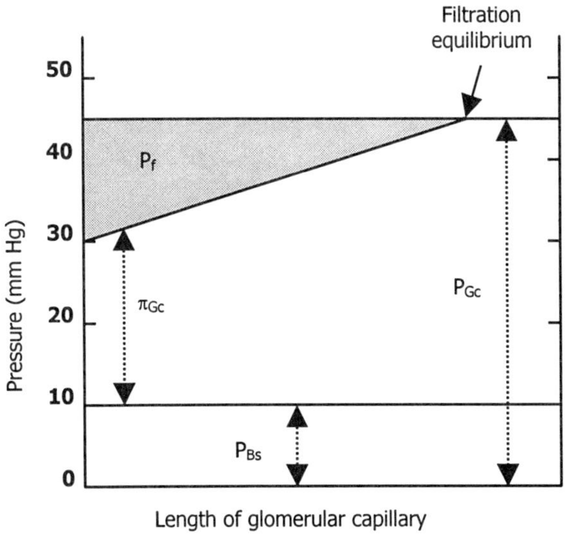

Figure 4-4. Starling forces involved in glomerular ultrafiltration in the rat. Note that the P_{Gc} and P_{Bs} remain constant at the beginning and end of the capillary. However, the π_{Gc} progressively increases along the length of the capillary until no ultrafiltration occurs (filtration equilibrium). The shaded area represents the net filtration pressure (P_f).

which primarily affect P_{Gc}. An increase in afferent arteriolar resistance (R_A) reduces renal blood flow, which in turn decreases P_{GC} and thus GFR. A decrease in R_A causes opposite effects. Moderate constriction of the efferent arteriole raises P_{Gc} and thus GFR. A decrease in efferent arteriolar resistance (R_E) by vasodilation decreases P_{Gc} with a reduction in GFR (Figure 4-5). Changes in R_A and R_E result from vasoactive agents and altered sympathetic tone (Table 4-2). Changes in Starling forces other than P_{Gc} also affect RBF and GFR, as shown in Figure 4-5. The mesangial cells play an important role in GFR by influencing the K_f. Contraction of these mesangial cells by vasoconstrictors causes a decrease in K_f and thus GFR. On the other hand, vasodilators cause relaxation of the mesangial cells and an increase in K_f. This results in an increase in GFR. Thus, the contractile and relaxant properties of the mesangial cell make it an ideal candidate to regulate GFR.

The above discussion indicates that the RBF is an important regulator of GFR. It then follows that both RBF and GFR, with certain exceptions, are regulated by the same mechanisms. The following section discusses intrinsic renal mechanisms, followed by other factors that regulate RBF and GFR (Table 4-2).

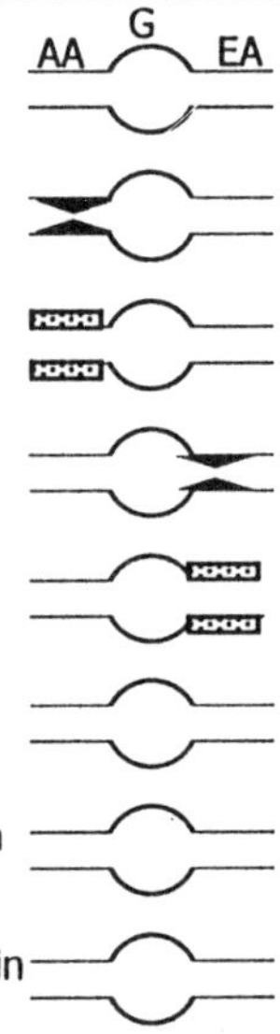

Conditions	P_{Gc}	RBF	GFR
Normal	N	N	N
Constriction of afferent arteriole	↓	↓	↓
Vasodilation of afferent arteriole	↑	↑	↑
Constriction of efferent arteriole	↑	↓	↑
Vasodilation of efferent arteriole	↓	↑	↓
Acute increase in π_{Gc}	↑	NC	↑
Acute decrease in π_{Gc}	↑	NC	NC
Chronic increase in P_{Bs}	↓	↓	↓

Figure 4-5. Effect of afferent (AA) and efferent (EA) arteriolar resistances and Starling forces (π_{Gc} and P_{Bs}) on glomerular hydraulic pressure (P_{Gc}), RBF and GFR. G = glomerulus; NC = no change.

Autoregulation

The kidneys maintain a constant RBF and GFR over a wide range of systemic blood pressures, usually between 80 and 180 mm Hg (Figure 4-6). Because this maintenance also occurs in a denervated or isolated perfused kidney, the mechanisms involved are probably intrinsic to the kidney. This ability of the kidney to regulate itself is called **autoregulation**. Two major theories have been proposed to explain autoregulation: the **myogenic** and **tubuloglomerular feedback** theories.

The myogenic theory follows the Laplace equation, which states that the wall tension (T) in the renal artery is the product of the transmural hydrostatic pressure difference [pressure inside the artery (P_i) minus the pressure outside artery, i.e., interstitial pressure (P_o)] and the radius (r) of the vessel. Therefore:

$$T = r\,(P_i - P_o)$$

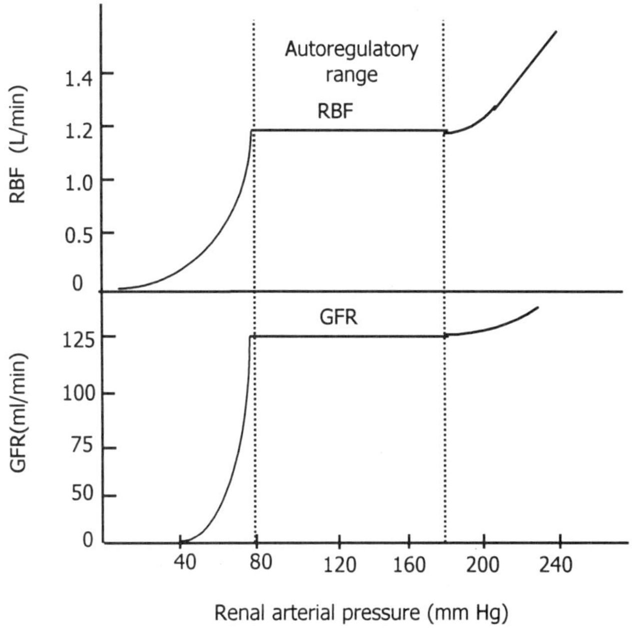

Figure 4-6. Autoregulation of renal blood flow (RBF) and glomerular filtration rate (GFR). Note the autoregulation for RBF is between 80 and 180 mm Hg of arterial pressure.

According to this equation, wall tension increases when the transmural pressure difference increases. However, according to myogenic theory, wall tension as well as RBF and GFR, are maintained at constant levels when the transmural pressure difference increases. The mechanism is explained as follows (Figure 4-7). When perfusion pressure (P_i) increases with a consequent increase in blood flow, the radius (r) of the artery decreases due to vasoconstriction. As a result, the RBF and GFR remain constant. Conversely, when P_i decreases or the blood flow decreases, the r increases due to arteriolar dilatation. Consequently, the RBF and GFR are maintained near normal. Studies have indicated that the properties of the myogenic theory are confined to the afferent arteriole. It has been shown that constriction of the afferent arteriole due to increased RBF is related to enhanced Ca^{2+} entry into the vascular smooth muscle cell of the arteriole.

In summary, the myogenic theory states that the vascular smooth muscle contracts when the transmural pressure difference increases across the afferent arteriole due to high blood flow, and relaxes when the transmural pressure difference decreases. These changes in vascular smooth muscle contractility in response to transmural pressure differences allow the RBF, and subsequently GFR remain relatively constant.

Table 4-2. Effects of various hormones and other factors on renal hemodynamics

Agents	R_A	R_E	RBF	GFR	K_f
Vasoconstrictors					
Angiotensin II	↑	↑↑	↓	NC(↓)	↓
Norepinephrine	↑	↑	↓	NC(↓)	↓
Parathyroid hormone	NC	NC	NC	↓	↓↓
Vasopressin	NC	NC	NC	NC	↓
Endothelin-1	↑	↑	↓	↓	↓
Adenosine	↑ then ↓	↑	↓ then ↑	↓	NC
Thromboxane A_2	↑	↑	↓	↓	NC(↓)
Vasodilators					
Nitric oxide	↓	↓	↑	↑	↑
Prostaglandin E_2, I_2	↓	↓	↑	NC(↑)	↓
Atrial natriuretic peptide	↓	↑	NC	↑	↑
Bradykinin	↓↓	↓	↑	NC	↓
Acetylcholine	↓	↓	↑	NC	↓
Histamine	↓↓	↓	↑	NC	↓
Glucocorticoids	↓	↓	↑	↑	NC
Dopamine (Low dose)	↓	↓	↑	↑	NC

R_A and R_E := afferent and efferent arteriole resistances; RBF = renal blood flow; GFR = glomerular filtration rate; K_f = glomerular filtration coefficient; ↑ = mild increase; ↑↑ = moderate increase; ↓ = mild decrease; ↓↓ = moderate decrease; NC = no change.

The myogenic theory leaves two important questions unanswered: (1) How are changes in perfusion pressure sensed by the afferent arteriole? and (2) How does wall tension cause appropriate changes in the radius of the arteriole?

The tubuloglomerular feedback (TGF) theory has been suggested as an alternative to the myogenic theory (Figure 4-8). This theory works as follows: Increased arterial pressure leads to a transient increase in RBF and GFR. This increase in GFR causes an increase in tubular fluid flow containing Na^+ and Cl^- to the distal tubule. The macula densa senses this increase in tubular fluid flow and activates appropriate effector mechanisms to raise R_A. The increase in R_A in turn, lowers RBF and GFR to the required level. Conversely, a decrease in arterial pressure causes RBF and GFR to decrease. This decrease in RBF and GFR decreases the delivery of fluid to the macula

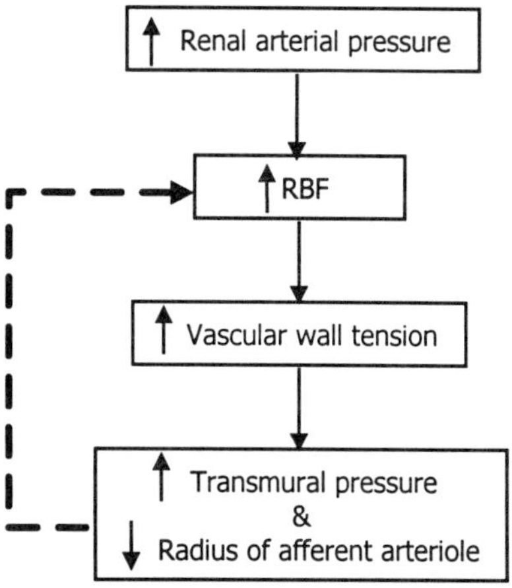

Figure 4-7. Myogenic theory. Broken arrow indicates negative feedback on RBF.

densa, which causes a decrease in R_A. The resultant vasodilation raises RBF and GFR to a homeostatic level.

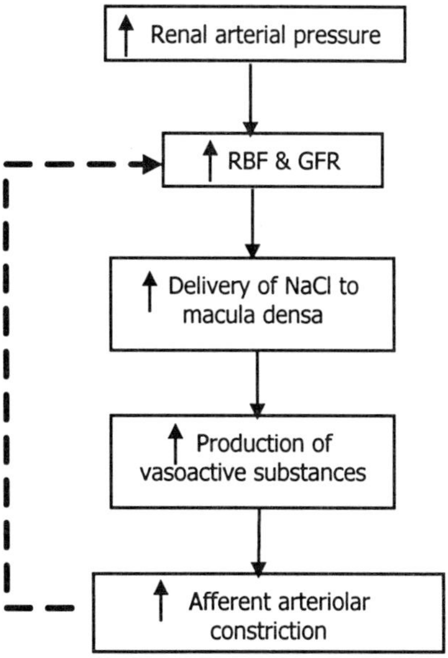

Figure 4-8. Tubuloglomerular feedback system. Broken arrow indicates negative feedback on RBF and GFR.

TGF is a complex but protective intrarenal mechanism that maintains RBF and GFR. The mediators of this mechanism, however, are incompletely understood. Proposed mediators include cytosolic Ca^{2+} in the smooth muscle cells of the afferent arteriole, thromboxane, nitric oxide, and adenosine. An increase in distal delivery of fluid releases adenosine, which produces an adenosine-mediated afferent arteriolar vasoconstriction causing a reduction in GFR. When fluid delivery is reduced, opposite effects seem to occur, which return the GFR to normal.

Neural Factors

Both afferent and efferent arterioles are innervated by sympathetic neurons that release norepinephrine. Stimulation of these neurons increases R_A and R_E with a consequent decrease in RBF and GFR. Under basal conditions, renal nerve activity is so low that GFR is unaffected. However, under conditions of stress, renal nerve activity is stimulated, and RBF as well as GFR decrease. Renal denervation has been shown to improve RBF and GFR during stress but not during normal conditions.

Dopamine, a precursor of norepinephrine, is a vasodilator with significant effects on renal hemodynamics (R_A, R_E, RBF, GFR, and K_f). In the kidney, it is synthesized by proximal tubular cells. Dopamine exerts its effects by binding to its receptors. Two types of receptors have been identified: DA_1 and DA_2. Infusion of low dose dopamine increases RBF and GFR through its DA_1 receptor-mediated vasodilatory effects. Both R_A and R_E are decreased with no change in K_f. Higher concentrations of dopamine have been shown to produce the opposite effects on renal hemodynamics.

Hormonal Factors

A number of factors and hormones other than norepinephrine have been shown to have variable effects on renal hemodynamics in both humans and animals. These effects are summarized in Table 4-2, and a brief description of each of these hormones and factors is given below (see Chapter 3 for more details). From Table 4-2, it is evident that changes in preglomerular and postglomerular resistances (R_A and R_E, respectively) cause changes in RBF, whereas changes in K_f cause a change in GFR. However, in the absence of a change in K_f, an increase in RBF results in an increase in GFR.

Angiotensin II (AII)

Infusion of pressor doses of AII causes an increase in R_A and R_E, and a decrease in RBF and K_f. However, the increase in R_E is greater than the increase in R_A, so that P_{GC} is increased. Because of this increase in P_{GC}, the

GFR is maintained normal or slightly decreased despite a decrease in RBF and K_f.

Parathyroid Hormone (PTH)

PTH has been shown to cause a decrease in GFR without a change in RBF. This decrease in GFR is attributed to a marked reduction in K_f.

Vasopressin

Vasopressin does not affect either RBF or GFR. However, it causes a reduction in K_f, which is due to contraction of mesangial cells.

Endothelin-1 (ET-1)

ET-1 is a potent vasoconstrictor of both afferent and efferent arterioles, and causes a decrease in RBF and GFR. A marked decrease in K_f due to mesangial cell contraction has been observed following ET-1 infusion into the rat.

Adenosine

Intrarenal infusion of adenosine causes a transient decrease followed by a slight increase in RBF. However, GFR remains markedly reduced secondary to a reduction in P_{GC}.

Nitric Oxide (NO)

NO is a potent vasodilator. It has a half-life of 3-5 seconds. Because of this short half-life, the effects of NO on renal hemodynamics have been indirectly studied by the administration of a competitive inhibitor of its production. This inhibitor is called N-monomethyl-L-arginine (L-NMMA). The administration of L-NMMA to normal rats causes an increase in R_A and R_E and a decrease in K_f, resulting in a decrease in RBF and GFR. This suggests that the endogenous NO increases RBF and GFR by decreasing R_A, R_E, and increasing K_f. The major role of NO in vivo is to counteract the effects of AII and norepinephrine.

Prostaglandins (PGs)

Vasodilatory PGs (PGE_2, PGI_2) lower R_A and R_E, and increase RBF without affecting GFR. The lack of effect on GFR is due to marked reduction in K_f. On the other hand, vasoconstrictive PGs (thromboxane A_2) may lower RBF and GFR.

Atrial Natriuretic Peptide (ANP)

ANP decreases R_A and increases R_E, resulting in an increase in P_{Gc} and GFR. K_f is also increased. However, ANP seem to have no effect on RBF.

Bradykinin

Bradykinin is a renal vasodilator. It decreases R_A more than R_E, and causes a marked increase in RBF. However, there is no change in GFR because of a decrease in K_f.

Acetylcholine (ACh)

Ach, like bradykinin, is a vasodilator. It causes a decrease both in R_A and R_E with a large increase in RBF. However, GFR is not increased due to marked decline in K_f.

Histamine

Histamine is released by mast cells and also synthesized by glomerular cells. It decreases R_A more than R_E, with the resultant increase in RBF. Histamine does not increase GFR because of a substantial reduction in K_f.

Glucocorticoids

Glucocorticoids cause significant reductions both in R_A and R_E, resulting in an increase in RBF. GFR also increases because of no change in K_f.

SUMMARY

1. The kidneys receive about 20% of the cardiac output. About 90% of this renal blood flow (RBF) goes to the cortex and the remaining 10% to the medulla. RBF is under the control of afferent and efferent arteriolar resistances.
2. As the RBF reaches the glomerular capillaries, a portion of it is filtered into Bowman's space to form an ultrafiltrate. This process is called glomerular filtration, which is accomplished by the Starling forces across the glomerular capillaries. The ultrafiltrate contains no proteins. Filtration of proteins, particularly albumin, is restricted by the negative charge present on the glomerular basement membrane.

3. Generally RBF regulates glomerular filtration rate (GFR). The kidneys maintain a constant RBF and GFR over a wide range of systemic blood pressures by a phenomenon called autoregulation. Two intrinsic processes that are involved in autoregulation are the myogenic and tubuloglomerular feedback mechanisms. These mechanisms in varying combination change the afferent arteriolar tone in the regulation of RBF and GFR.
4. Both RBF and GFR are also influenced by various factors such as hormonal and neural factors, including drugs.

CLINICAL APPLICATIONS

A number of renal diseases as well as nonrenal disorders can affect RBF and GFR. Nonrenal disorders such as hemorrhagic hypotension and congestive heart failure (reduced cardiac output) cause R_A to increase, which leads to a decrease in RBF. In congestive heart failure, the GFR remains normal or is only minimally decreased, which causes the filtration fraction to increase.

In acute renal failure, the RBF is reduced by about 30% - 40%; however, the GFR decreases by more than 75%, leading to a decrease in the filtration fraction. Conversely, in chronic renal failure, the RBF decreases substantially, whereas the GFR is relatively preserved. GFR remains normal for a time because R_E increases, causing the surviving nephrons to hyperfunction. As time passes, however, the number of hyperfunctioning nephrons is greatly reduced and the GFR is no longer maintained. At this time, the patient requires dialysis for survival.

In urinary tract obstruction, the RBF increases initially because of increased production of vasodilatory prostaglandins. A few hours later, RBF begins to decrease due to an increase in R_A. GFR also decreases due to a fall in P_f.

High-protein intake (>1 g/kg) has been shown to cause renal vasodilation, which in turn increases both RBF and GFR. Renal vasodilation may be due to vasodilatory prostaglandins, nitric oxide, and the pancreatic hormone glucagon. Chronic ingestion of a high-protein diet may induce structural changes in the kidney. These changes may progress to sclerosis if the kidney has some underlying injury. Conversely, long-term consumption of a low-protein diet has been shown to cause a decrease in RBF and GFR.

Diabetes mellitus is another condition in which RBF and GFR are abnormally high at the onset of the disease. Low-protein diets and angiotensin converting enzyme-inhibitors have been shown to reduce both RBF and GFR and protect the kidney from structural damage.

In nephrotic syndrome (loss of urinary protein > 3.5 g/day), albumin is lost in the urine, causing hypoalbuminemia. Hypoalbuminemia causes a decrease in π_{GC}, resulting in an increase in P_f. Theoretically, the GFR should increase. However, because of a decrease in K_f, the GFR may remain normal or even low. Following an infusion of albumin, the GFR increases slightly because of an increase in K_f. How changes in plasma oncotic pressure cause changes in K_f are incompletely understood.

Normal aging and pregnancy also influence RBF and GFR. RBF decreases progressively with age. This decrease is attributed to an increase in vascular resistance of both afferent and efferent arterioles caused by atherosclerosis. Similar to RBF, the GFR also declines with age. It has been shown that the decrease in GFR averages 1 ml/min per year between 40 and 80 years of age. Despite this decrease in GFR, the serum creatinine remains within normal range because of age-related reduction in muscle mass. The decline in RBF is greater than that of GFR, so the filtration fraction increases with age.

In normal pregnancy, the RBF increases strikingly in early and mid-pregnancy and decreases slightly after the 36th gestational week. However, the GFR increases progressively throughout gestation. These changes result in a decrease in filtration fraction during early pregnancy and a slight increase during late pregnancy or at term (Table 6-3). The mechanisms responsible for increases in both RBF and GFR remain incompletely understood. However, increased cardiac output, enhanced secretion of vasodilatory prostaglandins as well as several humoral factors produced during pregnancy have been implicated.

STUDY QUESTIONS

Question 1. What would happen to RBF and GFR acutely if a patient sustains a bleeding injury that decreases systolic blood pressure by 25 mm Hg? Also explain what happens to RBF and GFR in severe hypotension.

Answer: In acute arterial hypotension of mild degree, the RBF decreases proportionately to the decrease in arterial pressure. This is due to stimulation of both the sympathetic nervous system and the renin-angiotensin system. The release of norepinephrine causes the afferent arteriole to constrict, which increases R_A, and thus decreases RBF. However, the increase in angiotensin II (AII) causes efferent arterioles to constrict which increases P_{GC}. As a result, the GFR remains normal or slightly decreased, but the filtration fraction increases.

If the patient develops severe hypotension, both RBF and GFR decrease due to severe renal ischemia. RBF and GFR may remain low for a considerable period of time even if arterial pressure is increased and volume depletion, if any, corrected. This suggests that profound renal vasoconstriction is responsible for the slow return of RBF and GFR.

Case 1

A 55-year-old male is diagnosed with congestive heart failure and is treated with digoxin and an angiotensin converting enzyme-inhibitor. Because of pain due to leg edema, he is given ibuprofen for 4 weeks. He becomes progressively hypertensive and his leg edema worsens. At this point, he seeks medical help. His serum chemistry at the time of admission and 6 weeks previously are as follows:

	Admission	6 weeks previously
Na^+	128 mEq/L	135 mEq/L
K^+	5.2 mEq/L	4.2 mEq/L
Cl^-	109 mEq/L	100 mEq/L
HCO_3^-	15 mEq/L	24 mEq/L
Creatinine	3.5 mg/dL	1.2 mg/dL
BUN	70 mg/dL	20 mg/dL
Glucose	110 mg/dL	110 mg/dL

Question 1. Explain why this patient's creatinine and BUN, which were normal 6 weeks previously are elevated at the time of admission.

Answer: In patients with congestive heart failure, cardiac output decreases. Since 20% of cardiac output goes to the kidneys, the amount of blood flow to these organs is also decreased. Furthermore, these patients have stimulated sympathetic outflow, which causes renal afferent arteriolar constriction. Renal arteriolar constriction decreases RBF. However, as stated earlier, the GFR remains normal or slightly decreased so that the filtration fraction is increased. Also, renal vasodilatory prostaglandins are produced in response to norepinephrine. These prostaglandins minimize renal ischemia. Nonsteroidal anti-inflammatory drugs such as ibuprofen abolish the protective effect of vasodilatory prostaglandins. As a result, renal vasoconstriction persists, which subsequently decreases RBF. Since GFR depends on RBF, prolonged renal ischemia reduces GFR as well. For this reason, the creatinine and BUN are elevated in this patient, which were normal 6 weeks prior to ibuprofen intake.

Question 2. Explain what happens acutely to RBF and GFR when salt intake is excessive.

Answer: Excess salt intake causes a transient increase in extracellular volume, which raises cardiac output. Because the sympathetic nervous system and renin-angiotensin system are inhibited, RBF and GFR increase. An increase in the tubular load of Na^+ and Cl^- contributes to decreased tubular reabsorption and, hence, increased excretion. Increased excretion restores euvolemia.

SUGGESTED READING

1. Hura, C. and Stein, J.H. Renal blood flow. In: Handbook of Physiology, section 8: Renal Physiology. E.E. Windhager (ed.). Oxford University Press, New York, 1992; pp. 1129-1184 (*An in-depth review of measurements of renal blood flow and its regulation*).
2. Maddox, D.A. and Brenner, B.M. Glomerular ultrafiltration. In: The Kidney, 5th edition. B.M. Brenner (ed.). W.B. Saunders Company, Philadelphia, 1996; pp. 286-333 (*A detailed and authoritative review of glomerular filtration and its regulation*).
3. Arendshorst, W.J. and Navar, L.G. Renal circulation and glomerular hemodynamics. In: Diseases of the Kidney. 6th edition. R.W. Schrier and C.W. Gottschalk (eds.). Little, Brown and Company, Boston, 1997; pp. 59-106 (*A succinct review of renal circulation and glomerular filtration and their regulation*).

CHAPTER 5

ESTIMATION OF GFR AND RBF: CLEARANCE TECHNIQUES

Objectives

After reading this chapter, the student should be able to:

1. Discuss the concept of clearance.
2. Describe the methods of determining glomerular filtration rate, creatinine clearance, renal plasma flow, renal blood flow, and effective renal blood flow.
3. Evaluate the relationship between the serum creatinine concentration and creatinine clearance.

CONCEPT OF RENAL CLEARANCE

Clearance is not a biological process, but a theoretical concept. As blood passes through the kidneys, some of the dissolved constituents (solutes) are removed and excreted in the urine. The plasma is thus "cleared" of some solutes in the process of urine formation. Removal of solutes from blood occurs by filtration through the glomerular capillaries or by secretion into the tubular lumen. Some solutes, after entering the tubular lumen either by filtration or secretion, are then actively reabsorbed. The net clearance of these solutes is thus greatly reduced.

If a solute is filtered but neither reabsorbed nor secreted by the tubules the amount excreted in the urine will be equal to the amount that is filtered per unit time. If the concentration of that solute is measured in plasma and urine and the volume of urine generated per unit time is also known, the filtration rate of that solute can easily be calculated. This rate, which we have termed GFR, is conventionally expressed in ml/min or, rarely, liters/day.

ESTIMATION OF GFR

Inulin Clearance

Let us see how GFR is measured. Because the body does not produce any substance that is filtered but neither secreted nor reabsorbed, it is necessary to synthesize such a substance. This substance is then introduced into the body, preferably by the parenteral route, to measure GFR. In order to qualify as a marker for GFR, such a substance must: (1) be physiologically inert and nontoxic; (2) be completely filterable at the glomerulus and not protein-bound; (3) not be secreted or reabsorbed; (4) not be metabolized or synthesized by the kidney; and (5) not alter GFR. **Inulin** (*not* insulin) is a fructose polymer that meets all of these criteria. Once infused into the blood, inulin is filtered at the glomerulus, and the amount of inulin excreted into the urine per minute is equal to the amount that was filtered per minute (Figure 5-1). If the concentration of inulin is measured in the plasma and urine and the amount of urine formed per minute is known, then the clearance (C) or filtration rate of inulin can be calculated by the following formula:

$$C = \frac{UV}{P}$$

where U = urine concentration of inulin (mg/ml); V = urine volume (ml/min); P = plasma concentration of inulin (mg/ml).

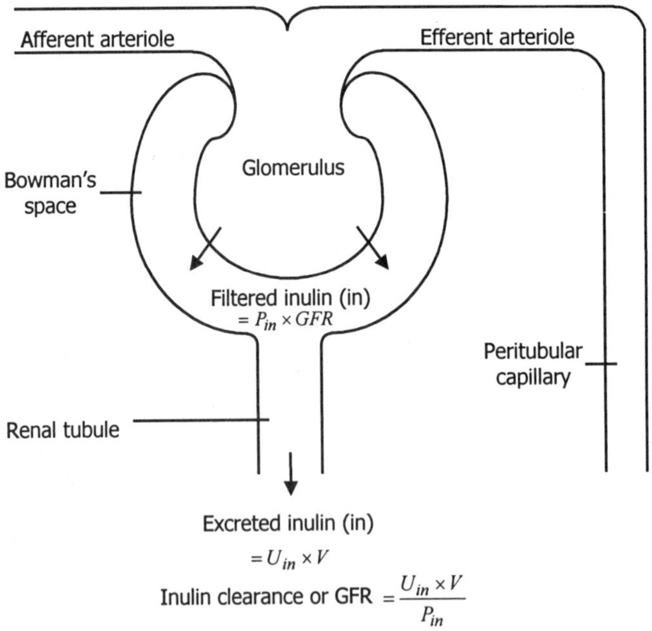

Figure 5-1. Illustration to demonstrate how inulin is handled by the kidney. Inulin is filtered and excreted but is neither reabsorbed, secreted nor metabolized by the kidney. P_{in} or U_{in} = plasma or urine inulin concentration, respectively; V = urine flow rate; GFR = glomerular filtration rate.

Suppose inulin were infused intravenously into a vein and its concentration in urine and plasma were 60 mg/mL and 0.5 mg/ml, respectively, and the urine volume flow were 1 ml/min. The clearance of inulin is therefore:

$$C = \frac{60\ \text{mg/ml} \times 1\ \text{ml/min}}{0.5\ \text{mg/ml}} = 120\ \text{ml/min}$$

This calculation reveals that 120 ml of plasma is cleared of inulin per minute, or 120 ml of plasma per minute must have been filtered at the glomerulus. In other words, this clearance is equal to the GFR of 120 ml/min or 173 liters/day (120 ml/min x 1440 min/day).

Creatinine Clearance

In clinical practice, inulin infusion and its measurements are rather cumbersome and time-consuming. Therefore, other methods of estimating GFR, such as those listed in Table 5-1, have been tried. Of these, estimation of **creatinine clearance** has become the standard procedure for measurement of GFR in subjects with normal renal function.

Creatinine is derived from muscle creatine by nonenzymatic dehydration. If muscle mass is decreased, as in old age, malnutrition, or muscle dystrophy, creatinine production is decreased. Creatinine is filtered at the glomerulus and appears in the urine. In healthy adults, the urinary creatinine ranges from 20-25 mg/kg/day in males and 15-20 mg/kg/day in females. To calculate creatinine clearance, urine is collected over a 24-hour period, and a single blood sample is drawn for creatinine determination. Urine creatinine determination is also needed to measure its concentration and to assess whether the 24-hour collection has been adequate.

Measurement of serum creatinine concentration is another method used to estimate renal function, and it is the most common laboratory test employed for this purpose. Studies have shown an inverse relationship between serum creatinine and GFR or creatinine clearance (Figure 5-2): as serum creatinine increases, GFR proportionately decreases. In the figure note that the increase in serum creatinine from 1 to 2 mg/dL reduces creatinine clearance by 50%. However, although serum creatinine is easy to determine, a number of factors can interfere with its estimation and alter its concentration (Table 5-2).

Table 5-1. Methods for estimation of glomerular filtration rate

Substance or Agent	Source	Testing complexity	Clinical utility	Accuracy	Comment
Inulin	Exogenous	++++	+	++++	Cumbersome and time-consuming
Urea	Endogenous	+	++	++	Serum urea concentration varies with protein intake, liver function and volume status
Creatinine clearance	Endogenous	++	+++	++	Creatinine secretion increases with deterioration in renal function and muscle mass
Serum creatinine	Endogenous	+	++++	++	Same as above
Vitamin B_{12}	Exogenous	+++	+	+++	Vitamin B_{12} is bound to protein and only free vitamin clearance reflects GFR
RADIOISOTOPES					
^{125}I-Iothalamate	Exogenous	+++	++	+++	Reliable markers for GFR in both normal and diseased kidneys. Iothalamate is secreted and overestimates inulin clearance
$^{99m}T_c$-DTPA[a]	Exogenous	+++	++	+++	
^{51}Cr-EDTA[a]	Exogenous	+++	++	+++	

[a] DTPA = diethylenetriaminepentaacetic acid; EDTA = ethylenediaminetetraacetic acid.

How to Calculate Creatinine Clearance

The clinical laboratory gives you the following values on a male subject whose weight is 75 kg.

Serum creatinine: 1.2 mg/dL
Urine creatinine: 1728 mg/total volume
Total urine volume: 1440 ml/24 hours

To calculate the creatinine clearance, first use the clearance formula UV/P; second, convert urine creatinine into mg/dL and total urine volume into ml/min.

$$\text{Urine creatinine (mg/dL)} = \frac{\text{1728 mg/total volume}}{\text{1440 ml or 14.40 dL}} = \text{120 mg/dL}$$

$$\text{Urine volume (ml/min)} = \frac{\text{1440 ml}}{\text{1440 min/day}} = \text{1 ml/min}$$

$$\text{Creatinine clearance} = \frac{UV}{P} \text{ or } \frac{120 \times 1}{1.2} = \text{100 ml/min}$$

Now determine whether the 24-hour urine collection was adequate. Since the subject is male and weighs 75 kg, his urinary creatinine excretion per day should be between 1500 and 1875 mg. The laboratory value is 1728 mg/day. Therefore, the 24-hour urinary volume of 1440 ml represents an adequate collection.

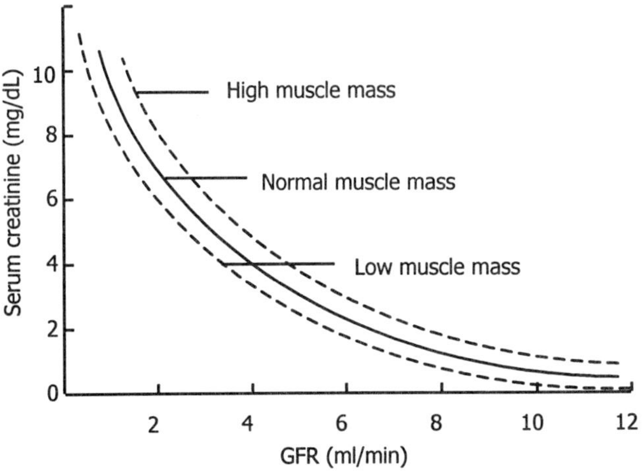

Figure 5-2. The relationship between serum creatinine concentration and GFR or creatinine clearance according to the muscle mass.

The determination of creatinine clearance has some limitations. First, creatinine is both filtered and secreted. Secretion of creatinine increases in patients with kidney disease (i.e., increasing serum creatinine concentration). Therefore, creatinine clearance overestimates GFR in a patient with deteriorating renal function. Second, creatinine production varies from day to day because of changes in protein intake and also varies with muscle mass or gender. Third, it is frequently difficult to obtain 24-hour urine collections; and fourth, in patients with severe proteinuria, creatinine secretion increases (as it does in patients with kidney disease), and therefore overestimates GFR.

Despite these limitations, determination of creatinine clearance is a convenient and practical approach to follow renal function in an outpatient or inpatient population.

Table 5-2. Factors that alter serum creatinine levels

Factor or Condition	Serum creatinine	Mechanism
Fasting	↑	Production of acetoacetate and acetone which interfere with the color reaction.
Protein meal (red meat)	↑	Conversion of creatine to creatinine.
Cephlosporins	↑	Increase in chromogens.
5-Flucytosine	↑	Increase in chromogens.
Trimethoprim	↑	Decrease in tubular secretion of creatinine.
Cimetidine	↑	Same as above
Triamterene	↑	Same as above
Spironolactone	↑	Same as above
Amiloride	↑	Same as above
Probenecid	↑	Same as above
Bilirubin	↓	Biliverdin increases blank.

↑ = increase; ↓ = decrease

How to Use an Alternative Method to Calculate Creatinine Clearance

Since estimation of creatinine clearance takes at least 24-36 hours, alternate methods have been introduced. One such method uses age, weight, and serum creatinine to calculate creatinine clearance by the following formula:

$$\underset{\text{(ml/min)}}{\text{Creatinine clearance}} = \frac{\text{(140-age in years) x (weight in kg)}}{\text{72 x serum creatinine (mg/dL)}}$$

where 72 is a constant.

The value obtained from this formula should be multiplied by 0.85 for creatinine clearance in females because of a relative smaller muscle mass compared to that in males.

ESTIMATION OF RENAL PLASMA FLOW (RPF): PAH CLEARANCE

RPF can be measured by direct methods such as renal vein cannulation or use of an electromagnetic flow meter on the renal artery. Since these methods are invasive, indirect methods have been devised. The method used to measure RPF is based on the Fick principle and uses techniques similar to those used in calculating inulin clearance (Figure 5-3). According to the Fick principle, the blood flow through any organ can be calculated if one knows: (1) the total amount of any substance removed by the organ during a single passage of blood through that organ, and (2) the concentration of that substance in the blood entering and leaving that organ. For the kidney, the RPF can be:

$$RPF = \frac{\text{Amount of substance in urine}}{(\text{Concentration in renal artery}) - (\text{Concentration in renal vein})}$$

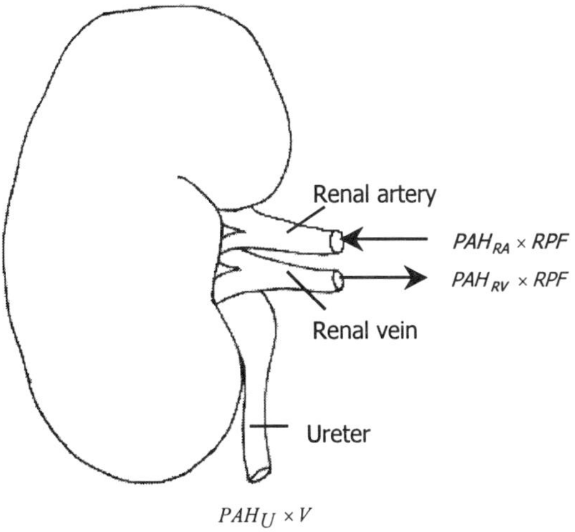

Figure 5-3. Measurement of renal plasma flow (RPF) by the Fick principle, which is equal to the amount of PAH entering the kidney (PAH_{RA} x RPF) and the amount leaving the kidney (PAH_{RV} x RPF + PAH_U x V). Solving for RPF: RPF = PAH_U x V/ PAH_{RA} - PAH_{RV}. PAH_{RA} = para-aminohippuric acid in renal artery; PAH_{RV} = para-aminohippuric acid in renal vein: PAH_U = para-aminohippuric acid in urine; V = urine flow rate.

Any substance that is present in the urine can be used for estimation of RPF provided that its concentration can be measured simultaneously in the renal artery and renal vein. This measurement could be avoided if that substance were removed completely from blood during one passage through the kidney, which would lead to zero concentration of that substance in the renal vein. For all practical purposes, the concentration of that substance in the peripheral vein is essentially equal to that in the renal artery. The above formula can then be simplified as:

$$RPF = \frac{\text{Concentration of substance in urine (UV)}}{\text{Plasma concentration of substance (P)}}$$

The substance that is used clinically to measure RPF is para-aminohippuric acid **(PAH)**. It is filtered and also secreted by the proximal tubule. In addition, PAH is neither metabolized nor removed from the circulation elsewhere. Therefore, the clearance of PAH approximates the RPF. Total extraction of PAH from renal circulation is not possible, because about 10% of it remains in the medulla and renal pelvis. The PAH clearance therefore underestimates RPF by about 10% in normal kidneys. This incomplete clearance is called the **effective RPF** or **ERPF**.

How to Calculate the Effective Renal Blood Flow (ERBF)

In order to convert ERPF into ERBF, the hematocrit (Hct) must be taken into account. Generally, the hematocrit represents 45%, and plasma 55%, of the blood. The rate of RBF can then be calculated as:

$$ERBF = \frac{ERPF}{1 - Hct}$$

The ERPF in men and women 20-40 years of age is approximately 650 and 600 ml/min/1.73m^2, respectively. Assuming a normal Hct of 45%, the ERBF is:

$$\text{Men: } \frac{650}{1-0.45} \text{ or } \frac{650}{0.55} = 1182\ \text{ml/min/1.73 m}^2$$

$$\text{Women: } \frac{600}{1-0.45} \text{ or } \frac{600}{0.55} = 1091\ \text{ml/min/1.73 m}^2$$

Remember that the above ERBF values represent only 90% of normal RBF values.

The determination of RPF with PAH clearance has some limitations. First, PAH extraction ratios vary from 0.81 to 1.00 among normal individuals. Second, PAH secretion is inhibited by drugs such as probenecid or endogenous substances such as lactate. These substances cause reduced extraction ratios. Third, PAH secretion is limited over a restricted plasma concentration. Higher (> 2 mg/ml) plasma concentrations saturate tubular secretory capacity, and thus impede secretion as well as clearance. Fourth, in kidney disease, the extraction of PAH decreases due to destruction of the tubular secretory system as well as accumulation of PAH in the medulla (due to high medullary blood flow).

The practical difficulties with the PAH clearance technique preclude its use as a routine test in clinical medicine. Therefore, two radioisotope scans - ^{131}I-orthoidohippurate or 99^{m} T$_{c}$- mercaptoacetyltriglycine (MAG$_3$) scans - are used for measurement of RPF. The clearance of these radioisotopes parallel that of PAH clearance. Unlike GFR testing (see Table 5-1), these are the only tests that are used routinely for RPF studies.

FILTRATION FRACTION (FF)

From the previous discussion, we understand that the normal RPF is between 600 and 650 ml/min. However, not all of this plasma is filtered at the glomerulus. The fraction of plasma that enters the Bowman's space is called the **filtration fraction** (FF). It is calculated as follows:

$$FF = \frac{GFR}{RPF} \times 100$$

For example, if GFR is 120 ml/min and RPF is 600 ml/min; then FF is:

$$\frac{120}{600} \times 100 = 20\%$$

This calculation reveals that only 20% of the plasma entering the glomerulus is filtered. The remaining 80% of the plasma leaves the glomerular capillaries via the efferent arteriole into the peritubular capillaries and subsequently into the systemic circulation. The FF may be a useful indicator in following renal function changes in certain physiologic and pathologic renal diseases. When an increase in FF occurs there is an increase in filtration of plasma at the glomerulus. As a result, the protein concentration in the plasma leaving the efferent arteriole is increased. Consequently, the oncotic pressure in the peritubular capillaries is increased more than usual. Because of this increase in oncotic pressure, reabsorption of solutes is increased in the proximal tubule. Table 5-3 summarizes changes in FF in various physiologic and pathologic conditions.

Table 5-3. Changes in filtration fraction (FF)

Condition	GFR	RPF	FF
Acute glomerulonephritis	↓↓	↓	↓↓
Exercise	↓↓	↓	↓↓
Congestive heart failure	N	↓	↑
Early pregnancy	↑	↑↑	↓
Late pregnancy	↑	↓	↑
Hypertension	NC or ↓	↓	↑
Early diabetes	↑	NC	↑
Constriction of afferent arteriole	↓	↓	NC
Constriction of efferent arteriole	↑	↓	↑
Ureteral obstruction	↓	NC	↓
Increase in K_f	↑	NC	↑

NC =no change; ↑ = mild increase; ↑↑ = moderate increase; ↓ = mild decrease; ↓↓ = moderate decrease; K_f = ultrafiltration coefficient.

MEASUREMENT OF REABSORPTION AND SECRETION

Clearance methods can be used not only for measurements of GFR and RPF, but also to identify and characterize tubular transport mechanisms; i.e., reabsorption or secretion of substances by the tubules. With certain exceptions, most substances are filtered and are either reabsorbed or secreted.

If a substance is filtered but its clearance is less than that of inulin, then the substance on a net basis is reabsorbed. Glucose is an example of a substance that is reabsorbed. On the other hand, if the clearance of a substance exceeds that of inulin, then the substance is secreted. PAH is an example of a secreted substance. If the clearance of a substance is equal to that of inulin, then the substance is only filtered. The best example is creatinine (assuming that only 5-10% of creatinine is secreted).

In order to calculate the reabsorption and secretion rates, one needs to know how much of a solute is filtered at the glomerulus and how much of this solute is excreted in the urine. The amount of solute filtered in the glomerulus per unit time is called the **filtered load**. The filtered load is the product of GFR and plasma concentration of the solute. Excretion rate is that amount of a solute excreted per unit time. The filtered load, excretion rate, reabsorption or secretion rates can be calculated using the following equations:

$$\text{Filtered load} = \text{GFR} \times [P]_s$$
$$\text{Excretion rate} = V \times [U]_s$$
$$\text{Reabsorption rate} = \text{Filtered load} - \text{Excretion rate}$$
$$\text{Secretion rate} = \text{Excretion rate} - \text{Filtered load}$$

where $[P]_s$ or $[U]_s$ are plasma and urinary concentration of solute, respectively. V is urine flow rate.

Net reabsorption of a solute has occurred if the filtered load exceeds that of the excretion rate, whereas the net secretion of a solute has occurred when filtered load is less than that of the secretion rate.

SUMMARY

1. Inulin is a fructose polymer that can be used to determine the glomerular filtration rate (GFR). In clinical practice, determination of GFR by inulin infusion is time-consuming. Therefore, creatinine clearance and serum creatinine concentration have become the standard procedures for approximate estimation of GFR. In order to determine accurate measurement of GFR, ^{125}I -iothalamate clearance technique is used.

2. Renal plasma flow (RPF) is measured by the Fick principle, using para-aminohippuric acid (PAH). However, PAH clearance has some limitations. Therefore, a radioisotope test is used for measurement of RPF.
3. The filtration fraction (FF) is the percentage of plasma that is filtered at the glomerulus, which is about 20%. Several physiologic and pathologic conditions influence the FF.

CLINICAL APPLICATIONS

Renal function is generally assessed by measuring the kidney's ability to remove the waste products of metabolism. Clinically, serum creatinine and blood urea nitrogen (BUN) concentrations reflect the degree of renal function. Therefore, periodic determinations of creatinine and BUN are essential to follow the severity of kidney disease. In addition, clinicians also determine creatinine clearance as a reflection of glomerular filtration rate (GFR) to assess kidney function (see Case 1). This rough estimation of GFR is also helpful in adjusting the dosage of medications that are excreted by the kidney. Unlike GFR, renal blood flow (RBF) is not routinely measured in clinical practice. Precise measurement of GFR as well as RBF requires clearance techniques.

STUDY QUESTIONS

Case 1

A 70-year-old woman was admitted for urinary tract infection. Her urine culture grew E. coli which is sensitive to gentamicin (an aminoglycoside antibiotic). The recommended dose is 80 mg intravenously every 8 hours. Her serum creatinine is 1.0 and she weighs 60 kg.

Question 1. Explain why you need to adjust the dose of gentamicin.

Answer: This is an elderly patient, whose creatinine clearance is decreased even though her serum creatinine is within normal limits. Routine estimation of creatinine clearance using the formula UV/P takes at least 36 hours. Therefore, creatinine clearance should be determined using the following formula:

$$\text{Creatinine clearance (ml/min)} = \frac{(140 - \text{age}) \times (\text{wt. in kg})}{72 \times \text{serum creatinine (mg/dL)}}$$

$$= \frac{(140 - 70) \times (60\ \text{kg})}{72 \times 1.0} \quad \text{or}$$

$$= \frac{70 \times 60}{72 \times 1.0} = 58.33 \text{ ml/min}$$

For females, multiply 58.33 by 0.85, which is 49.58. This patient's creatinine clearance is about 50 ml/min.

Since gentamicin is excreted by the kidney, its dose should be reduced in order to avoid gentamicin nephrotoxicity. One way to follow nephrotoxicity is frequent determination of serum creatinine levels.

Question 2. Would you adjust the dose in a 20-year-old patient with a serum creatinine of 1.0 mg/dL and body weight of 60 kg?

Answer: In this patient, the creatinine clearance is 85 ml/min (using the above formula). Therefore, a slight or no reduction in dosage is needed. This case illustrates the utility of calculating creatinine clearance in clinical management of a patient using the above formula without a 24-hour urine collection.

Case 2
From the data given in the table, calculate the creatinine, inulin, and PAH clearances.

Creatinine (mg/dL)		Inulin (mg/dL)		PAH (mg/dL)		Urine flow Rate
Plasma	Urine	Plasma	Urine	Plasma	Urine	(ml/min)
1.0	100	20	1800	2.0	1200	1.0
2.0	67	30	1000	3.0	1400	1.5
3.0	50	40	700	4.0	1400	2.0
4.0	40	50	500	5.0	1300	2.5
5.0	30	60	400	6.0	1200	3.0

Answer: To calculate the renal clearance of any of the above substances, use the clearance (C) formula:

$$C \text{ (ml/min)} = UV/P$$

where U is the urine concentration of the substance (e.g. creatinine), V is the urine flow rate and P is the plasma concentration of the substance.

By substituting the values into the formula, we obtain the following clearances for creatinine (C_{cr}), inulin (I_{cr}) and PAH (PAH_{cr}).

Creatinine		C_{cr}	Inulin		I_{cr}	PAH		PAH_{cr}	Urine
Plasma	Urine		Plasma	Urine		Plasma	Urine		flow
1.0	100	100	20	1800	90	2.0	1200	600	1.0
2.0	67	67	30	1000	50	3.0	1400	700	1.5
3.0	50	50	40	700	35	4.0	1400	700	2.0
4.0	40	40	50	500	25	5.0	1300	650	2.5
5.0	30	30	60	400	20	6.0	1200	600	3.0

Case 3

A 40-year-old man with AIDS and pneumocystis carinii pneumonia is treated with trimethoprim-sulfamethoxazole (Bactrim) and sent home. Two weeks later, the patient comes to your clinic for a follow-up visit. He weighs 60 kg and a routine serum chemistry shows creatinine of 2.4 mg/dL and BUN of 15 mg/dL. Two weeks before, his creatinine and BUN were 1.0 and 10 mg/dL, respectively. The calculated GFR from ^{125}I-iothalamate clearance is 80 ml/min.

Question 1. Explain the reason for his acute increase in creatinine and BUN.

Answer: Trimethoprim increases serum creatinine levels acutely by inhibiting the tubular secretion of creatinine. The GFR remains normal despite an increase in serum creatinine concentration. In this patient, this was verified by ^{125}I -iothalamate clearance technique.

SUGGESTED READING

1. Levinsky, N.G. and Lieberthal, W. Clearance techniques. In: Handbook of Physiology, section 8: Renal Physiology. E.E. Windhager (ed.). Oxford University Press, New York, 1992; pp. 227-247 (*An in-depth review of various clearance methods for estimation of GFR, RPF, and tubular function*).
2. Schuster, V.L. and Seldin, D.W. Renal clearance. In: The Kidney: Physiology and Pathophysiology, 2nd edition. D.W. Seldin and G. Giebisch (eds.). Raven Press, New York, 1992; pp. 943-978 (*A critical review , as above, of clearance techniques for estimation of GFR, RPF, and tubular function in normal and a variety of renal diseases*).

CHAPTER 6

BASIC PRINCIPLES OF TUBULAR TRANSPORT

Objectives

After reading this chapter, the student should be able to:

1. Differentiate transcellular from paracellular transport pathways.
2. Understand the functional categories of membrane transport proteins and the morphological polarization of epithelial cells.
3. Define the terms symport, cotransport, antiport, passive and active transport, simple diffusion, facilitated diffusion, and solvent drag.
4. Differentiate primary from secondary active transport.

In this chapter, we will discuss the basics of renal epithelial cell transport processes which include both reabsorption and secretion of solutes.

TRANSPORT ACROSS TUBULAR EPITHELIUM

The glomeruli filter about 180 L (GFR 125 ml/min x 1440 min/day = 180 L/day) of plasma per day. About 99% of this glomerular filtrate is reabsorbed throughout the nephron, and 1% is excreted. Both reabsorption and secretion of solutes occur by transepithelial transport. There are two general routes for transepithelial transport (Figure 6-1). One is the **transcellular** route in which substances (water, ions, and small molecules) pass through the apical and basolateral membranes of epithelial cells to enter the blood. The other is the **paracellular** route, which involves the movement of certain molecules through **tight junctions** also called **zonulae occludens**. Tight junctions are impermeable to macromolecules, such as proteins and polysaccharides. However, water and small ions penetrate with variable permeabilities. Some epithelial cells are characterized by tight junctions that are highly permeable to water and small ions. These so called **leaky**, or **low-resistance** epithelia, are largely located in the proximal convoluted tubules. Other epithelial cells, localized in collecting ducts, have tight junctions that are less permeable to water and solutes. These epithelial cells are called **tight**, or **high-resistance**, epithelia.

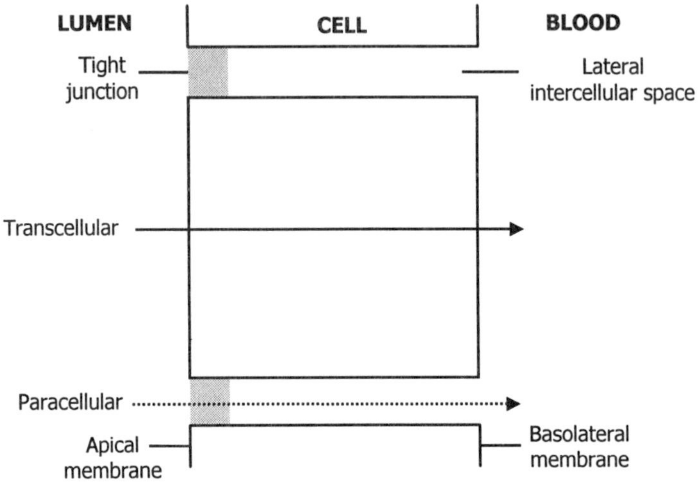

Figure 6-1. Illustration of transcellular and paracellular pathways of transport in an epithelial cell. Note that the solute must pass through the interstitium before it enters the blood.

The epithelial cells exhibit inherent morphological and chemical **polarization**, i.e., the properties of the apical and basolateral membranes are different despite similar membrane composition. This asymmetry in membrane properties of the two sides permits transcellular transport which is due to unequal distribution of enzymes in apical and basolateral membranes (Table 6-1).

Table 6-1. Distribution of some membrane-bound enzymes in the proximal nephron

Apical membrane	Basolateral membrane
Alkaline phosphatase	Na/K-ATPase
H-ATPase	Ca-ATPase
Mg-ATPase	Na/HCO_3 symporter
cAMP-dependent protein kinase	Cl/HCO_3 antiporter
Protein kinase C	
Phosphoprotein phosphatase	

The transcellular ion transport requires the interaction of an ion with membrane transport proteins, which fall into several functional categories: **pumps**, **channels**, **carriers**, **exchangers** (antiporters), and **cotransporters**. **Pumps** are transport proteins that use energy derived from the hydrolysis of ATP. The pumps that are important for renal function are Na/K-ATPase, Ca-ATPase, and H-ATPase (Table 6-2). A **channel** is a watery space or pore that runs through the bilayer of the cell membrane and allows the movement of ions to pass through it. The best studied channel is the **Na^+ channel**, which is located in the apical membrane, particularly, of the distal nephron and the collecting duct. **Carriers** are distinct from channels. After binding to a solute, a carrier protein undergoes a conformational change, and the solute is carried to the other side of the membrane. After releasing the solute, the carrier protein assumes its original conformation. The glucose transporter is an example. Unlike carriers, **exchangers** rarely undergo a conformational change without binding a molecule. The Cl/HCO_3 exchanger in the basolateral membrane of the proximal tubule is a good example of an exchanger. This type of transport in which substances are transported in opposite directions is called **countertransport** or **antiport**. **Cotransporters** translocate more than one solute in the same direction simultaneously. This type of transport is called **symport**. Examples include Na-glucose or Na-amino acid transport systems in the proximal tubule.

Table 6-2. Renal transport systems

Transport system	Tubule	Cell localization	Function
Pumps			
Na/K-ATPase	All segments of nephron	Basolateral	Pumps 3 Na^+ out and 2 K^+ into the cell
H-ATPase	Proximal Distal Cortical collecting	Apical Apical and basolateral	Pumps 3 H^+ into lumen for each ATP molecule hydrolyzed
Ca-ATPase	Medullary collecting Proximal Distal	Apical Basolateral	Pumps Ca^{2+} ions out of the cell
H/K-ATPase	Cortical Collecting	Apical	Pumps 1 H^+ into and 1 K^+ out of lumen
Channels			
Na	Probably all segments of nephron	Apical	Entry from the lumen into the cell
K	Proximal Thick ascending limb Cortical collecting	Apical	Secretion into the lumen
	Proximal Thick ascending limb Distal Cortical collecting	Basolateral	Secretion into peritubular capillaries
Cl	Proximal Thick ascending limb Cortical collecting	Basolateral	Secretion into peritubular capillaries

Cotransport (symport)			
Na/glucose	Proximal	Apical	Transports glucose into the cell
Na/amino acid	Proximal	Apical	Transports amino acids into the cell
Na/HPO_4	Proximal	Apical	Transports 2 Na^+ and 1 phosphate into the cell
K/Cl	Proximal Distal	Basolateral	Cl^- is reabsorbed with K^+ into peritubular capillaries
	Cortical collecting	Apical	Secretes K^+ and Cl^- into the lumen in the ratio of 1:1
Urea	Inner medullary collecting	Apical* and basolateral	Facilitated diffusion into the interstitium
Na/K/Cl	Thick ascending limb	Apical	Transports 1 Na^+, 1 K^+ and 2 Cl^- into the cell
Na/HCO_3	Proximal	Basolateral	Transports 2-3 HCO_3^- for each Na^+ out of the cell
Countertransport (Antiport)			
Na/H	Proximal	Apical	Secretes 1 H^+ into lumen for each Na^+ reabsorbed
Na/NH_4	Proximal	Apical	NH_4^+ replaces H^+ in Na/H antiporter
Cl/HCO_3	Proximal Cortical collecting	Apical	Cl^- is reabsorbed in exchange for HCO_3^- secretion into the lumen
	Proximal	Basolateral	Cl^- exits and HCO_3^- enters the cell
Na/Ca	Proximal	Basolateral	Ca^{2+} exits and Na^+ enters the cell

*The apical membrane carrier is the rate-limiting step in urea transport.

If the transport produces a change in charge by distribution across the membrane, the transport is said to be **electrogenic**. A good example of electrogenic transport system is Na/K-ATPase. This pump transports 3 Na^+ ions out of the cell and pumps 2 K^+ ions into the cell, thus producing a net gain of a charge. Conversely, the H/K-ATPase pumps one H^+ into and one K^+ out of the cell without creating any change in voltage. This transport is said to be **electroneutral**.

Table 6-2 summarizes the location and function of the most important transport systems in various segments of the nephron.

Table 6-3. Mechanisms of membrane transport

Passive	Active
Simple diffusion	Primary transport
Facilitated diffusion	Pumps
Carriers	Secondary transport
Channels	Cotransport
Solvent drag or bulk flow	Countertransport
	Endocytosis

Basic Mechanisms of Transport

Solutes are essentially transported by two mechanisms: **passive** (dissipative) transport and **active** (conservative) transport. Passive transport includes **simple diffusion**, **facilitated diffusion,** and **solvent drag**. (Table 6-3). These processes do not require an expenditure of metabolic or cellular energy. In contrast, active transport requires an expenditure of cellular energy. Active transport can be either **primary,** in which the energy is derived directly from the hydrolysis of ATP, or **secondary**, in which the energy is derived from ionic concentration gradients (usually Na^+) that have been established and maintained by the primary active transport system. Facilitated diffusion and active transport (primary or secondary) involve the mediation of carrier or transport proteins.

PASSIVE TRANSPORT

Simple Diffusion

Simple diffusion, which arises from random molecular motion, is defined as the passive movement of a solute from a higher to a lower concentration until equilibrium is established. In simple diffusion, movement of the solute is always "downhill" i.e., down a concentration (chemical) gradient. The driving force for diffusion of nonelectrolyte solutes is provided by this concentration gradient across the cell membrane. Small, highly lipid-soluble molecules diffuse much faster across the cell membrane than large, less lipid-soluble molecules. An example of simple diffusion is the passage of urea in the proximal tubule. In the case of charged electrolytes, the diffusion depends on the electrical charge on both sides of the cell membrane.

Facilitated Diffusion

As in simple diffusion, the movement of solute in facilitated diffusion is downhill, from a higher to lower concentration. However, the transport is *facilitated* by specific carrier proteins or channels residing in the cell membrane (Figure 6-2). The driving force for this diffusion is provided by the concentration gradient, and the carrier proteins merely augment the transport process. Ion channels are highly selective and this property is due to the charge lining the channel and size of the channel. A channel lined with negative charges allows only cations but not anions to pass through. Also, smaller charged ions pass through the channels much easier than the larger ions. D-glucose and neutral amino acids are transported by facilitated diffusion. Urea transport into the interstitium of the inner medullary collecting duct is also mediated by a carrier that does not involve any metabolic energy.

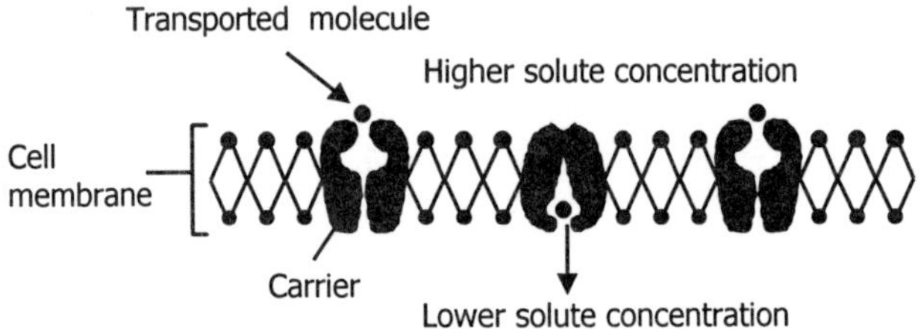

Figure 6-2. Simplified model of facilitated diffusion across the cell membrane. Note the conformational change in the carrier protein.

Unlike simple diffusion, facilitated diffusion exhibits certain carrier-mediated characteristics such as stereospecificity, saturation kinetics, and competition by similar compounds. Stereospecificity is expressed by the transportation of only D-isomers of sugars and the L-form of amino acids. Saturation limits the rate of transport of a solute and displays zero order reaction kinetics. For example, at a high solute concentration, all carrier proteins are occupied, and further increase in solute concentration does not increase the rate of transport. Structurally similar compounds can also compete for the same carrier site. For example, D-galactose can compete with D-glucose for the same carrier, and thus retard the transport of D-glucose. Most mechanisms of facilitated diffusion are either symporters or antiporters.

Solvent Drag

The osmotic flow of water (solvent) may drag certain solutes across the cell membrane through channels or paracellular pathways. This process does not require metabolic energy, and thus contributes substantially to net solute flow across the cell membrane. The coupling of the solute with solvent and their simultaneous movement is called **solvent drag**. Hyperkalemia due to hyperglycemia is an example of solvent drag. Because glucose, is an effective osmolyte, it pulls water from the intracellular to the extracellular (blood) compartment. This water carries K^+ with it, and thus causes hyperkalemia. The driving force for solvent drag is hydrostatic pressure.

ACTIVE TRANSPORT

Primary Active Transport

As defined above, primary active transport depends on the generation of energy from hydrolysis of ATP. In the kidney, about 95% of ATP generation occurs in mitochondria by oxidative phosphorylation. If ATP generation decreases the active transport of solutes across the epithelia also decreases. Generally, primary active transport is mediated by pumps (Figure 6-3). Pumps are transport proteins that use energy from the hydrolysis of ATP. The best studied active transport ATPases are: Na/K-ATPase, Ca-ATPase, and H-ATPase. Of these, the most abundant pump in the kidney is Na/K-ATPase. This enzyme which is present in the basolateral membrane, pumps 3 Na^+ ions out and 2 K^+ into the cell. It is inhibited by ouabain or digoxin. Na/K-ATPase has 2 subunits designated α and β, with molecular weights of 112 and 35 kilodaltons, respectively. Studies have shown that about 50% of Na^+ reabsorption in the kidney is mediated by this enzyme system. Besides being electrogenic, the Na/K-pump maintains cell volume and balance of many electrolytes and nonelectrolytes across the epithelia (see At a Glance Box 6-1).

Ca-ATPase is also located in the basolateral membrane. Intracellular Ca^{2+} is about 10,000 times less than the extracellular Ca^{2+}. This difference in Ca^{2+} concentration is due to a cell membrane Ca-ATPase which pumps Ca^{2+} out of the cell. Another Ca-ATPase exists in the sarcoplasmic reticulum of the cell. It pumps Ca^{2+} from cytoplasm into the sarcoplasmic reticulum for storage.

At a Glance Box 6-1
Cellular functions of the Na/K pump

Maintenance of transmembrane Na^+ and K^+ gradients
Regulation of cell volume
Generation and maintenance of resting membrane potential
Salt and H_2O transport
Maintenance of intracellular Ca^{2+} (via Na/Ca-exchange)
Maintenance of intracellular Mg^{2+} (via Na/Mg-exchange)
Regulation of intracellular pH (via Na/H-exchange)
Maintenance of Na/K/2Cl cotransport
Cotransport of sugars, amino acids, and vitamins

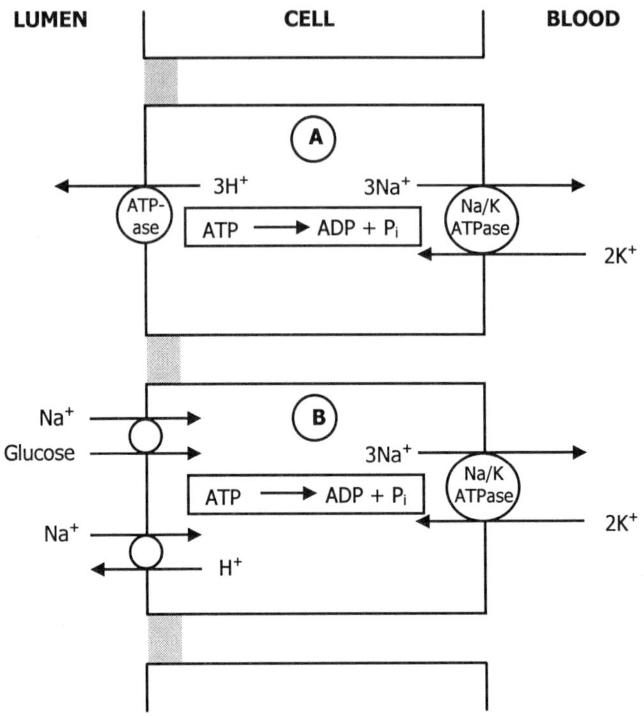

Figure 6-3. Primary (A) and secondary (B) active transport systems. Na/K-ATPase or Na/K pump is shown at the basolateral membrane which transports 3 Na^+ ions out and 2 K^+ ions into the cell, whereas H-ATPase transports 3 H^+ ions into the tubular lumen. In secondary active transport, Na^+ and glucose move in the same direction (symport) into the cell, whereas Na/H antiport transports Na^+ ion into the cell and H^+ ion out of the cell. Adenosine triphosphate (ATP) is hydrolyzed by Na/K-ATPase and/or H-ATPase into adenosine diphosphate (ADP) and inorganic phosphate (P_i) to generate energy. Arrows indicate the direction of transport of solutes.

H-ATPase has been demonstrated in the apical membrane of the proximal tubule and intercalated cells (Type A) from the cortical collecting and medullary collecting ducts. The H-ATPase has been reported to pump 3 H^+ for each ATP hydrolyzed from the cell into the tubular lumen. This pump is, therefore, electrogenic (Figure 6-3).

Secondary Active Transport

In secondary active transport, a molecule is transported from a lower to higher concentration gradient. Thus, this form of transport requires energy.

However, this energy is derived from the Na^+ concentration gradient created by the primary active transport mechanism; i.e., Na/K-ATPase. Na/K- pump transports 3 Na^+ ions out of the cell in exchange for 2 K^+ ions. As a result, the intracellular concentration of Na^+ is low (15-30 mEq/L) compared to the blood or luminal Na^+ concentration (140 mEq/L). This gradient provides the energy for Na^+ to move into the cell. Another molecule, such as glucose, amino acid, Cl^-, is coupled to Na^+ for transport into the cell. Thus, two sites in a carrier protein (one for Na^+ and another for other solute) are involved in secondary active transport, which can be either a symporter or an antiporter. Na^+-glucose transport is an example of symport, while the Na/H transport is an example of antiport. This antiport which involves the transport of 1 H^+ out of the cell and 1 Na^+ into the cell in the proximal tubule, is energized by the transmembrane Na^+ gradient (see Figure 6-3). Thus, the secondary active transport uses metabolic energy from ATP indirectly.

Endocytosis

In this process, a localized region of the cell membrane invaginates to form a pocket, which then pinches off into the cytoplasm as a vesicle. This form of transport requires energy, which is derived from hydrolysis of ATP. Many macromolecules and small proteins are reabsorbed in the proximal tubule by endocytosis.

SUMMARY

1. Transepithelial transport of solutes occurs by transcellular and paracellular pathways. The transcellular solute transport involves the interaction of a solute with membrane transport proteins.
2. The membrane transport proteins are classified into pumps, channels, carriers, exchangers, and cotransporters. Exchangers transport solutes in opposite direction, in which case the transport is called antiport or countertransport Cotransporters, on the other hand, transport solutes in the same direction.
3. Two mechanisms of solute transport have been described: passive and active. Passive transport is the movement of a solute down its electrochemical gradient and does not require metabolic energy. Active transport utilizes metabolic energy. Passive transport can occur either by simple diffusion or facilitated diffusion, the latter involves membrane proteins as carriers or channels. Another form of passive transport is called solvent drag, in which the solute is dragged with water movement. Active transport can be primary active transport in which case the energy is derived from the hydrolysis of ATP or secondary active transport in which case the energy is derived from the Na^+ concentration gradient

created by the primary active transport. Na/K, Ca, and H-ATPases are pumps involved in primary active transport, whereas countertransporters and cotransporters are membrane proteins involved in secondary active transport.

STUDY QUESTIONS

Case 1

A patient with congestive heart failure (CHF) is treated with digoxin (a drug that improves cardiac output). Two weeks later the patient improves his cardiac function as noticed by disappearance of shortness of breath and improvement in exercise tolerance.

Question 1. Explain this patient's intracellular and extracellular ionic concentration.

Answer: Digoxin inhibits the Na/K-ATPase activity. This enzyme maintains concentration gradients for both Na^+ and K^+ across the cell membrane by transporting 3 Na^+ ions out and 2 K^+ ions into the cell. As a result, the intracellular Na^+ concentration remains low and the intracellular K^+ concentration high. When Na/K-ATPase is inhibited by digoxin, opposite changes occur. Therefore, it is not uncommon to see a slight increase in serum K^+ concentration in patients with CHF who are on digoxin.

Question 2. How does the patient improve cardiac function?

Answer: The increase in intracellular Na^+ concentration decreases the force necessary to pump Ca^{2+} out of the cell via the Na/Ca exchanger. The result is an increase in intracellular Ca^{2+} concentration, which then increases the cardiac muscle contraction with improvement in cardiac output. Blood flow to the kidney is also increased.

Question 3. What would happen to renal transport mechanisms if ATP production were poisoned?

Answer: Primary active transport system would be inhibited and other transport systems dependent on energy are inhibited as well. This results in the excretion of all the filtered electrolytes and water in the urine, and thus regulation of electrolyte and fluid balance is impaired. This is not compatible with life.

Question 4. Discuss the similarities and differences between primary active and secondary active transport systems.

Answer: Both transport systems are carrier-mediated and demonstrate stereospecificity, saturation kinetics, and competition by similar compounds. Also, both use energy to transport solutes against an electrochemical gradient, i.e., solute is moved from an area of low concentration to an area of high concentration. This "uphill" movement of a solute requires energy.

The major difference between primary and secondary active transport systems is the source of energy used in these systems. Primary active transport derives its energy directly from hydrolysis of ATP by the Na/K-ATPase enzyme. In the secondary active transport, the energy is derived from the Na^+ concentration gradient generated by the primary active transport system i.e., Na/K-ATPase. In other words, secondary active transport uses energy from ATP indirectly.

SUGGESTED READING

1. Stokes, J.B. Principles of epithelial transport. In: Clinical Disorders of Fluid and Electrolyte Metabolism. 5th edition. R.G. Narins (ed.). McGraw-Hill, Inc. New York, 1994; pp. 21-44 (*A clearly written chapter summarizing the principles of membrane transport systems*).
2. Reeves, W.B. and Andreoli, T.E. General principles of renal tubular transport. In: Textbook of Nephrology. 3rd edition, S.G. Massry and R.J. Glassock (eds.). Williams and Wilkins, Baltimore, 1995; pp. 71-86 (*Another clearly written chapter reviewing basic transport processes and their regulation*).
3. Wingo, C.S. and Weiner, I.D. Ion transport by the renal tubule. In: Nephrology. R.L. Jamison and R. Wilkinson (eds.). Chapman & Hall, London, 1997; pp. 44-60 (*A recent review of solute transport in various segments of the nephron*).

CHAPTER 7

TUBULAR TRANSPORT ALONG THE NEPHRON

Objectives

After reading this chapter, the student should be able to:

1. Discuss the role of proximal tubule in solute and water reabsorption.
2. Describe the mechanisms by which NaCl, glucose, amino acids, and proteins are reabsorbed in the proximal tubule.
3. Describe the mechanisms involved in the secretion of organic anions and cations.
4. List several drugs and compounds that influence the transport of uric acid.
5. Describe the mechanism by which NaCl is transported across the thick ascending limb of Henle and distal tubule.
6. Discuss the functional differences between the principal and intercalated cells.
7. Discuss the effects of furosemide, amiloride, and aldosterone on NaCl and K^+ transport.

In Chapter 4, we have discussed how glomerular ultrafiltrate is formed. The protein-free ultrafiltrate is modified in composition as it passes through various segments of the nephron to form urine. This difference in composition is due to reabsorption of water and solute and secretion of certain specific solutes. Reabsorption facilitates conservation of essential substances and secretion involves elimination of specific organic anions and cations of both endogenous and exogenous origin. Both passive and active transport mechanisms (Chapter 6) are involved in reabsorption and secretion of solutes across the renal tubular epithelium. Let us see how various segments of the nephron participate in water and solute reabsorption and secretion.

The kidneys filter about 180 L of plasma daily. Most of this plasma must be reclaimed in order to maintain fluid and electrolyte homeostasis. Only 1 to 1.5 L of urine is formed per day. The proximal tubule is the major site of reclamation, whereas the other segments reclaim to a variable degree.

PROXIMAL TUBULE

The proximal tubule, as a whole, reabsorbs about 60% of the filtered solute and water (Table 7-1). It can be arbitrarily divided into two zones of reabsorption. Reabsorption of Na^+, glucose, amino acids, lactate, and HCO_3^- occurs primarily in the first half (early) of the proximal tubule, while the Cl^- is predominantly reabsorbed in the second half (late) of the proximal tubule. Reabsorption of Cl^- is coupled with Na^+ reabsorption. In addition, secretion of many organic anions and cations occurs in the second half of the proximal tubule.

Table 7-1. Solute and water reabsorption in the proximal tubule

Substance	% Filtered load reabsorbed
Sodium	60-70
Potassium	60-80
Bicarbonate	80-90
Chloride	35
Glucose	>95
Amino acids	>95
Low-molecular wt. proteins	>85
Calcium	60-70
Phosphate	80-90
Magnesium	30-40
Urea	50
Water	50-60

TUBULAR REABSORPTION

Sodium (Na^+)

The kidney filters approximately 25,200 mEq (GFR x serum Na^+ concentration: 180 L x 140 mEq/L= 25,200 mEq/day) of Na^+ daily. Of this amount, the proximal tubule reabsorbs 15,120-17,640 mEq (60-70%). Na^+ enters the cell by **passive** and **active** transport mechanisms. Passive entry of Na^+ into the proximal tubule occurs down its electrochemical gradient because the luminal Na^+ concentration is approximately 140 mEq/L compared to 15-35 mEq/L inside the cell. This gradient is maintained mostly by the action of Na/K- ATPase at the basolateral membrane. Na^+ also moves into the cell due to active Na^+-dependent cotransport of glucose and amino acids, lactate, or phosphate (Figure 7-1). This cotransport creates a negative potential difference of 4 mV in the tubule, which, in turn, is partly responsible for passive diffusion of Na^+ across the membrane. Another active mechanism of Na^+ entry is through the Na/H antiporter, which pumps Na^+ into and H^+ out of the cell. During this process, HCO_3^- is generated and reabsorbed (see Figure 7-1).

Na^+ extrusion from the cell into the peritubular capillaries is accomplished by the Na/K-ATPase. As mentioned in Chapter 6, this Na/K-ATPase transports 3 Na^+ ions out and 2 K^+ ions into the cell. In this way, the intracellular Na^+ concentration in the proximal tubule is maintained at approximately 15-35 mEq/L.

In summary, Na^+ reabsorption in the first half of the proximal tubule occurs actively by glucose, amino acids or phosphate cotransport and by Na/H antiport mechanisms. The active transport of Na^+ into the cell creates a negative potential difference, which causes Na^+ to enter by passive diffusion.

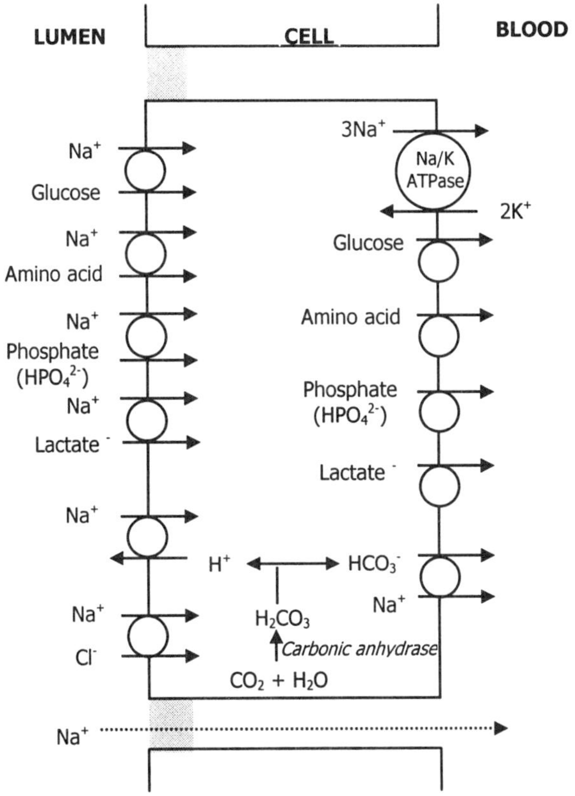

Figure 7-1. Cellular model for Na^+ entry into the first half (early part) of the proximal tubule. Note that many of these mechanisms are also present in the second half (later part) of the proximal tubule.

Chloride (Cl^-)

Cl^- reabsorption occurs primarily in the second half of the proximal tubule. As with Na^+, reabsorption of Cl^- occurs by both **active** and **passive** mechanisms and is linked to Na^+ reabsorption. Recent studies have shown that active NaCl entry could be mediated by three mechanisms: (1) direct Na^+ and Cl^- symport; (2) Na/H or Cl/HCO_3 antiport; and (3) Cl/formate or Cl/oxalate antiport (Figure 7-2). Although the tubular concentrations of either formate or oxalate are substantially low, they combine with the H^+ ion secreted by the Na/H antiporter to form formic acid or oxalic acid. These acids are converted into their bases inside the cell. These bases then return to the tubular lumen via Cl/formate or Cl/oxalate antiporters. Thus, a substantial amount of Cl^- is reabsorbed through these antiporters.

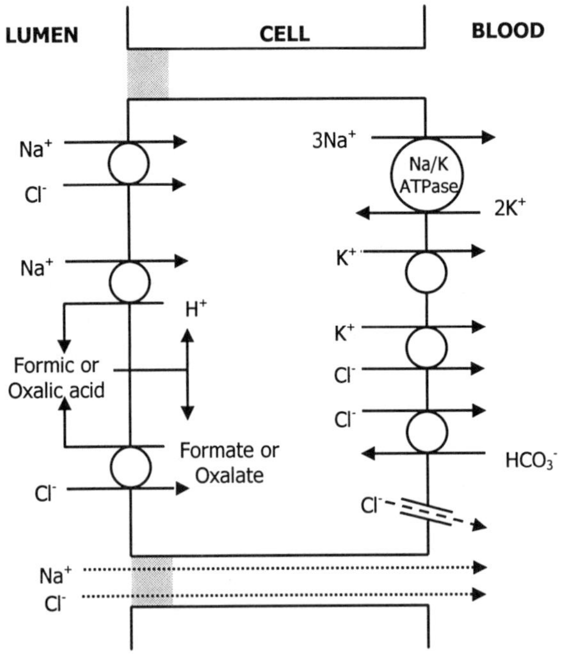

Figure 7-2. Cellular model for Na^+-coupled Cl^- entry into the second half (later part) of the proximal tubule. Note that many of these transport mechanisms are also present in the first half of the proximal tubule. Broken arrow at the basolateral membrane indicates Cl^- conductance channel.

Passive transport of Cl^- occurs via the tight junctions. Because of the high tubular Cl^- concentration, a gradient is established between the tubular lumen and intercellular space. This gradient drives Cl^- into the intercellular space and creates a positive voltage in the tubular lumen, thus providing a mechanism for passive Na^+ reabsorption. The mechanisms by which Cl^- exits from cell to the peritubular capillaries are poorly understood. Possible mechanisms include Cl^- conductance through the basolateral membrane, K/Cl symport, Na^+-dependent Cl/HCO_3, and Na^+-independent Cl/HCO_3 antiport (see Figure 7-2). Conductive Cl^- efflux across the basolateral membrane seems to play a minor role in Cl^- absorption.

Water (H_2O)

About 50% of filtered H_2O is reabsorbed in the proximal tubule. (H_2O reabsorption is about 65% in rats, 45% in dogs, and 30% in monkeys). H_2O reabsorption occurs passively by transcellular pathway. Evidence indicates that H_2O reabsorption occurs secondary to the reabsorption of NaCl. Three mechanisms have been proposed to explain H_2O movement from the lumen to the peritubular capillaries: (1) the sum of the transepithelial hydraulic and osmotic pressure differences; (2) luminal fluid hypotonicity; and (3) lateral intercellular hypertonicity. Although the transepithelial hydraulic-osmotic pressure difference is < 5 mm Hg, it is probably sufficient to allow H_2O to flow across the cell membrane in the renal epithelia. This transcellular mechanism seems likely in the late proximal tubule. In the early proximal tubule, the rate of solute reabsorption is faster than the rate of H_2O reabsorption, which generates luminal hypotonicity and facilitates H_2O movement. Once solutes are inside the cell, they are actively transported into the intercellular space. The Na/K-ATPase supplies the energy necessary for this transport. Cl^- also enters the intercellular space through tight junctions. These ions raise the osmolality of the intercellular space. Because of luminal hypotonicity as well as hypertonicity of the intercellular space, H_2O moves across the cell through transcellular route into the intercellular space (Figure 7-3). Since the intercellular space is restricted in size and H_2O and solute concentrations are high, the hydrostatic pressure increases. This increased hydrostatic pressure then drives fluid and solutes across the basement membrane into the interstitium and peritubular capillaries.

Rapid water transport across the proximal tubule is due to a water channel protein called aquaporin-1 (AQP-1). It is expressed in both the apical and basolateral membrane of the proximal tubule cell. It is estimated that the proximal tubule cell contains over 20 million copies of AQP-1.

H_2O reabsorption follows solute reabsorption throughout the proximal tubule. This reabsorption is isosmotic because the concentration of luminal Na^+ does not change due to concomitant reabsorption of H_2O. The osmolality of the proximal tubular fluid is similar to that of plasma (285 mOsm/kg H_2O). In isosmotic reabsorption, for each 285 mOsm reabsorption of solute, approximately 1 L of H_2O is reabsorbed.

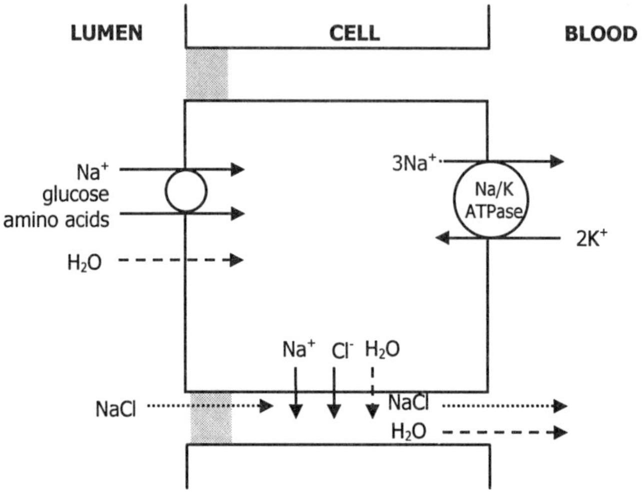

Figure 7-3. Transcellular transport of water in the proximal tubule. Note that water is also transported from intercellular space into peritubular capillaries (blood).

Potassium (K^+)

Approximately 60-80% of the filtered K^+ is reabsorbed in the proximal tubule. The remaining K^+ is reabsorbed in the thick ascending limb of Henle's loop. The K^+ that appears in the urine is secreted in the distal convoluted tubule and the cortical collecting duct. The renal handling of K^+ is discussed in Chapter 12.

Bicarbonate (HCO_3^-)

About 85% of the filtered HCO_3^- is reclaimed in the proximal tubule. Reabsorption of HCO_3^- occurs through the secretion of H^+ ions into the tubular lumen by the H-ATPase and Na/H antiporter. Details of HCO_3^- reabsorption are discussed with acid-base physiology in Chapter 11.

Calcium, Phosphate, and Magnesium

The cellular mechanisms involved in the reabsorption of these ions in nephron segments are presented in Chapters 13, 14, and 15, respectively.

D-glucose Transport

The reabsorption of glucose represents a potent transport mechanism in the proximal tubule. About 99.7% of the filtered glucose is reabsorbed in the proximal tubule, and less than 75 mg are excreted in the urine in a normal individual. Glucose is transported from the early and late proximal tubular lumen into the cell by a process called **secondary active transport** (Figure 7-1). In this process, glucose combines with specific carrier proteins or transporters present in the apical membrane. The glucose transporters of the early proximal tubule are called the SGLT-2 (sodium-glucose luminal transporter- 2), and that of the late proximal tubule is termed SGLT-1. In the early proximal tubule, glucose combines with Na^+ in a 1:1 stoichiometry, and in the late proximal tubule the stoichiometry is 2 Na^+: 1 glucose. Inside the cell glucose is released from the carrier protein and is partly metabolized. Some of the glucose is passively transported into the blood across the basolateral membrane by **facilitated** diffusion (i.e., without coupling to Na^+). The carriers that participate in facilitated diffusion belong to the GLUT family of glucose transport genes. Thus, glucose transport involves both secondary active transport in the apical membrane and facilitated diffusion in the basolateral membrane.

Glucose titration curve

A glucose titration curve explains the relationship between plasma glucose concentration and glucose reabsorption (Figure 7-4). This curve is obtained by intravenous infusion of glucose and measuring its rate of reabsorption as the plasma concentration is increased. Whenever renal glucose titration curve is discussed, one needs to know the meaning of 3 terms: **tubular transport maximum (Tm)**, **renal threshold**, and **splay**.

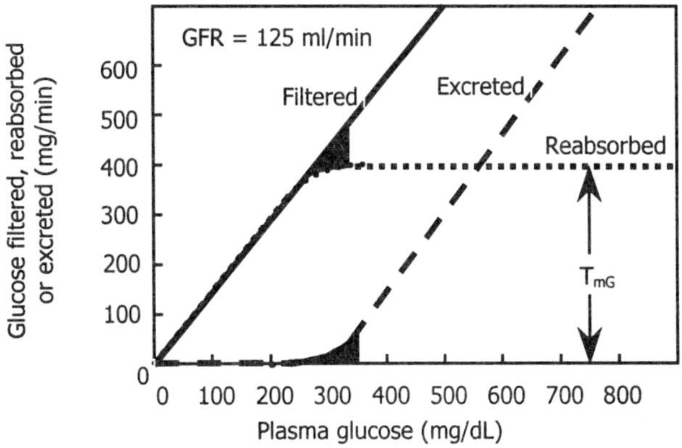

Figure 7-4. Glucose titration curve. Filtration, reabsorption, and excretion of glucose in normal man. Shaded area represents splay.

The normal fasting plasma glucose concentration is approximately 100 mg/dL. Assuming the plasma glucose of 100 mg/dL and the GFR of 125 ml/min, the filtered glucose load (plasma glucose in mg/ml x GFR) is 125 mg/min. All of this glucose is reabsorbed and practically no glucose appears in the urine. In other words, the clearance of glucose is zero.

The proximal tubule has the capacity to reabsorb filtered load of glucose up to 375 mg/min (plasma glucose: 3 mg/ml x GFR: 125 ml/min) in a normal subject. This is called Tm for glucose or Tm_G, i.e., 375 mg/min. Below this Tm_G, no glucose appears in the urine. At this Tm_G, all glucose transporters are saturated. Further increase in filtered load of glucose (i.e., above 375 mg/min) cannot be handled by the proximal tubule. As a result, glucose appears in the urine. In a healthy individual the filtered load of glucose is one-third of the Tm_G, (125 mg/min.) Theoretically, glucose should not appear in the urine until plasma glucose exceeds 300 mg/dL. However, glucose appears in the urine when the plasma glucose levels are approximately 180-200 mg/dL. This plasma concentration at which glucose first appears in the urine is called the renal threshold. Why does this happen? This happens because all nephrons do not have the same Tm_G, which is explained by nephron heterogeneity. Indeed, it has been shown that the nephron with a relatively short proximal tubule cannot handle all the filtered load of glucose and, therefore, will spill glucose into the urine at plasma glucose concentrations of 180-200 mg/dL. Also, the glomerulus of a nephron with large filtering surface area will spill glucose. This phenomenon of functional heterogeneity in individual nephrons is called splay. Another reason for splay is related to the saturation kinetics of the glucose transport proteins. These transport proteins need high luminal glucose concentrations to achieve full saturation. In the absence of high luminal glucose levels, the transport proteins are not fully saturated. As a result, some glucose leaks into the urine.

Amino Acids

The proximal tubule reabsorbs > 95% of the filtered amino acids. The transport mechanisms for amino acids are rather complex; however, for understanding purposes they are similar to those for glucose (Figure 7-1). Transport across the apical membrane occurs by an Na^+-dependent amino acid carrier complex. These amino acids exit largely at the basolateral membrane by another carrier-mediated transport mechanism, via an Na^+ -independent facilitated diffusion. However, Na^+ -amino acid cotransport mechanisms have also been demonstrated at the basolateral membrane of the late proximal tubule.

Evidence suggests that there are at least several different transport systems or carrier proteins, one for each class of amino acids. Thus, separate carrier proteins transport neutral amino acids (alanine, leucine, isoleucine, etc.); acidic amino acids (glutamic and aspartic acids); basic amino acids (arginine and lysine); and imino amino acids (proline and hydroxyproline). Note that each transport mechanism can carry more than one amino acid. This capacity creates competition for a specific carrier among structurally related amino acids within a group.

Besides Na^+, other inorganic ions such as K^+, Cl^-, and H^+ have been shown to participate in amino acid transport. For example, transport of glutamate across the apical membrane involves a cotransport with two Na^+ ions and a countertransport with a K^+ ion (not shown in Figure 7-1).

Similar to glucose, amino acids have a Tm, which is set very high. Because of high Tm all the filtered load of amino acids is reabsorbed and less than 1% is excreted in the urine.

Low- Molecular Weight Proteins (LMWP)

It is usually stated that the filtrate is virtually protein-free. The amount of protein that is present in the filtrate is negligible when compared to the plasma concentration of these proteins. For example, the filtrate contains about 200 mg/L of protein compared to about 70 g/L in plasma. Assuming a GFR of 180 L/day, the total filtered protein is 36 g/day (180 L/day x 200 mg/L = 36 g). The urinary excretion of protein in a healthy individual is less than 150 mg/day. This calculation suggests that most of the filtered protein is reabsorbed by the renal tubule.

LMWPs have a molecular weight less than 69,000 daltons and include such proteins as hormones (insulin, glucagon, parathyroid hormone, growth hormone, ADH, angiotensin II, etc.), enzymes (amylase, lysozyme, etc.), and small proteins (Bence-Jones proteins, β_2-microglobulin, myoglobin, etc.). Many of these LMWPs are filtered at the glomerulus. The major site where these proteins are reabsorbed is the proximal tubule. The kidney has four mechanisms of transport for these LMWPs. One is **endocytosis**. Proteins such as insulin or lysozyme enter the cell by endocytosis where they are hydrolyzed by lysosomal enzymes into their constituent amino acids. These amino acids are then transported across the basolateral membrane. The second mechanism involves the hydrolysis of filtered proteins into amino acids by brush border enzyme of the luminal membrane; the amino acids are then transported by specific amino acid carrier proteins. The third one is a carrier-mediated transport mechanism of small intact peptides, and the fourth mechanism is the peritubular uptake of peptides.

The filtration of albumin is limited. However, its concentration in the filtrate is 1-3 mg/L, i.e., 180 to 540 μg/day are filtered. Since the urinary excretion of protein is less than 150 mg/day, most of the albumin is reabsorbed by endocytosis.

Urea

Approximately 50% of the filtered urea is reabsorbed in the proximal tubule. The concentration of urea in the tubular lumen increases as a result of NaCl and water reabsorption. Urea then diffuses passively down its concentration gradient into the cell.

Organic Acids

Weak organic acids such as acetate, lactate, citrate, and oxalate are useful metabolic substrates, and therefore are completely absorbed by the proximal tubule (see Figure 7-1). The urine is usually devoid of these acids.

TUBULAR SECRETION

Secretion is the opposite of reabsorption. In secretion, the proximal tubule possesses active secretory pathways. The major function of these pathways is to eliminate toxic end products of metabolism. In addition, a number of exogenous drugs are also removed from circulation by secretion. Except for K^+, H^+, and NH_4^+, most of the secreted substances are either organic weak acids (anions)(Table 7-2) or organic bases (cations)(Table 7-3). Substances bound to proteins are not filtered. These substances are either excreted or transported to their site of action by means of secretion. For example, the diuretic furosemide is delivered to its site of action (thick ascending limb of Henle's loop) by this process.

Table 7-2. Examples of organic anions

Endogenous	Exogenous
Bile salts	Penicillins
Fatty acids	Cephalosporines
Hippurates	Chlorothiazide
Oxalate	Hydrochlorothiazide
Prostaglandins	Furosemide
Urate	Salicylate
Ketoacids	Probenecid
Cyclic AMP	Radiocontrast agents

Secretion of organic anions occurs in two steps: (1) transport from peritubular capillaries into the cell across the basolateral membrane; and (2) secretion from the cell into the tubular lumen across the apical membrane. The first step is a **secondary active transport** mechanism deriving energy from the gradient of Na^+ ions created by the Na/K ATPase. The second step does not require metabolic energy, but it involves a specific **carrier** molecule. Para-aminohippurate (PAH) is a prototype organic anion that has been used to explain the mechanism of organic anion secretion in the proximal tubule. PAH transport across the basolateral membrane depends on the Na^+-dicarboxylate (α-ketoglutarate, glutarate) symporter (Figure 7-5). This symporter transports dicarboxylates from peritubular capillaries into the cell. PAH entry into the cell is then coupled to the exit of dicarboxylate by a PAH-dicarboxylate antiport mechanism. PAH entry in the cell causes the concentration of PAH inside the cell to increase. As a result, PAH then moves into the tubular lumen across the apical membrane in exchange for another anion such as Cl^-, urate, or hydroxyl ions. Several endogenous and exogenous organic anions are thought to be secreted in a similar manner.

Table 7-3. Examples of organic cations

Endogenous	Exogenous
Creatinine	Cimetidine
Choline	Ranitidine
Dopamine	Quinidine
Histamine	Procainamide
Epinephrine	Atropine
Serotonin	Isoproterenol
Acetylcholine	Amiloride
	Tetraethyl-ammonium

Like glucose, organic anions demonstrate Tm limitation and competitive inhibition. For example, PAH or probenecid can compete with the secretory pathway for penicillin G, and thus inhibit its secretion. The plasma concentration of penicillin G will then increase.

Secretion of organic cations also occurs in two steps. First, organic cations enter the cell membrane by facilitated diffusion driven by the cell inside-negative membrane potential. Second, secretion into the tubular lumen occurs by proton-cation exchange. The proton gradient between the lumen and the cell is maintained by Na/H antiporter (Figure 7-6).

Similar to organic anions, organic cations demonstrate Tm and competitive inhibition. Cimetidine, a histamine H_2 blocker used to treat peptic ulcer disease, inhibits the secretion of creatinine, and thus elevates its plasma concentration without diminishing glomerular filtration rate (GFR).

A number of factors influence the renal excretion of organic anions and cations. These factors include renal plasma flow, GFR, binding to plasma protein, urine pH, and urine flow. When renal plasma flow and GFR are decreased (as in renal failure), some of the accumulated organic anions may diminish the excretion of other biologically important organic acids by competing for tubular secretion. Changes in protein binding can influence the secretion of organic anions. For example, the diuretic furosemide is extensively bound to serum proteins and is secreted into the renal tubule for its action in the thick ascending limb of Henle's loop. However, its secretion can be blocked by exogenous administration of probenecid, indomethacin, or aspirin. Furosemide action can also be decreased in hypoalbuminemic conditions. Because less binding of the drug to albumin occurs, the concentration of unbound (free) furosemide increases. Free furosemide diffuses into the interstitium, leaving very little for secretion. Infusion of furosemide with albumin may cause natriuresis in the hypoalbuminemic patient.

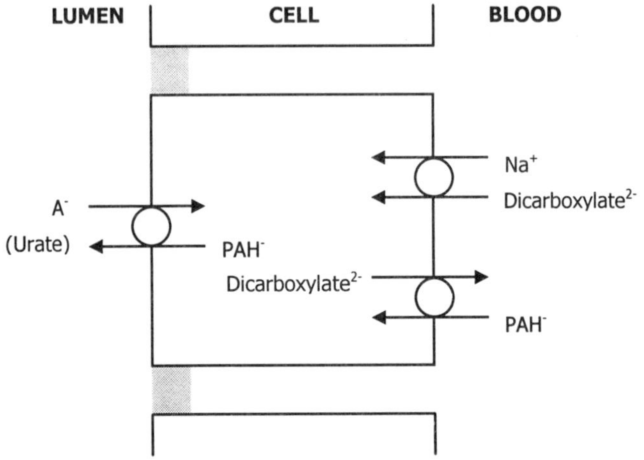

Figure 7-5. Cellular model for secretion of para-aminohippurate (PAH) and other organic anions in the proximal tubule. A^- = anion (Cl^-, urate, etc.).

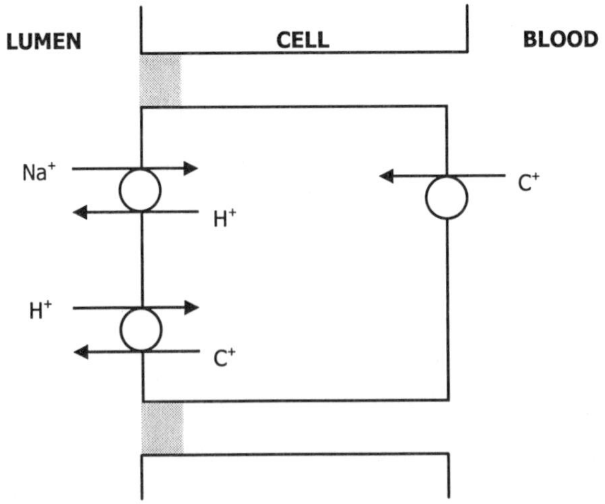

Figure 7-6. Cellular model for secretion of an organic cation (C^+) in the proximal tubule.

The influence of pH on the secretion of some organic anions can be demonstrated by renal handling of aspirin (acetyl-salicylic acid). Aspirin is metabolized to salicylic acid, which has a pK_a of 3.0. At blood pH of 7.4 or at alkaline urine pH, salicylic acid exists in the ionized form of salicylate. Conversely, at low pH, the concentration of salicylic acid increases, and it can diffuse into the cell membrane easily because of its nonpolar or unionized nature. The promotion of aspirin secretion in the form of salicylate at an alkaline pH is a protective mechanism. Alkalinization of urine pH with $NaHCO_3$ increases salicylate excretion in aspirin overdose. Phenobarbital excretion can also be augmented by increasing urine pH.

SECRETION AND TUBULAR REABSORPTION (Bi-directional Transport)

Several organic anions and cations undergo both reabsorption and secretion. A good example of a substance that undergoes this bi-directional transport is uric acid. Uric acid is the end-product of purine metabolism. It has a pK_a of 5.75. Therefore, at physiologic blood pH of 7.4 the uric acid exists as urate anion.

Most of the urate is free; only 10% is bound to plasma proteins. It is therefore freely filtered at the glomerulus. It then undergoes extensive reabsorption in the first half of the proximal tubule. Subsequently, the urate is secreted and is finally reabsorbed again in the second half of the proximal tubule. As a result, only 8 to 10% of the filtered urate is excreted in the urine. Tubular reabsorption of urate appears to occur by a secondary active transport process. Studies indicate that the apical membrane contains a carrier protein that exchanges intracellular anion (PAH, lactate, Cl^-, etc.) for urate in the tubular lumen. Urate may exit across the basolateral membrane by diffusion down its electrochemical gradient or by a carrier-mediated process. Tubular secretion of urate, although less understood, is thought to occur by a process of anion exchange. Once inside the cell, it enters the tubular lumen by another anion exchange mechanism, particularly the Cl/urate antiporter.

A number of drugs can inhibit the reabsorption and secretion of uric acid, resulting either in low or high serum uric acid concentration (Table 7-4).

THIN LIMBS OF HENLE'S LOOP

The fluid that leaves the proximal tubule and enters the thin descending limb (TDL) of Henle's loop is isosmotic (about 300 mOsm/kg H_2O) to plasma. The TDL is highly permeable to water and relatively less permeable to solutes (Na^+, Cl^-, K^+, and urea). Water therefore moves from the tubule into the surrounding interstitium. The TDL is abundant in AQP-1 water channel proteins. As a result, the concentration of the tubular fluid increases. In long-looped nephrons, the tubular fluid osmolality increases gradually from 300 to 1200 mOsm/kg H_2O at the tip of the papilla (see Chapter 9).

Table 7-4. Examples of some drugs that influence reabsorption or secretion of uric acid

Reabsorption		Secretion	
Increase	Decrease	Increase	Decrease
HCTZ	Probenecid	Glycine	Aspirin (low dose)
Furosemide	Sulfinpyrazone		Pyrazinamide
Acetazolamide	Aspirin (high dose)		Ethambutol
Amiloride	Radiocontrast agents		Nicotinic acid
Chronic lead ingestion	Ascorbic acid (high dose)		Ethanol
			Lactate

The transport characteristics of the thin ascending limb (TAL) of Henle's loop are different than those of the TDL. The TAL is impermeable to water, moderately permeable to urea, and highly permeable to NaCl. Urea diffuses into and NaCl diffuses out of the tubular lumen. Since water does not diffuse out, the tubular fluid is diluted and the osmolality decreases. The decreased osmolality of the tubular fluid creates a large osmolality difference between the tubular lumen and the surrounding medullary interstitium, which has a high osmolality.

THICK ASCENDING LIMB OF HENLE'S LOOP (TALH)

About 30% of the filtered NaCl is reabsorbed in the thick ascending limb of the Henle's loop (TALH). The TALH is virtually impermeable to water but highly permeable to NaCl. This combination of virtually low permeability to water and high reabsorptive rates of NaCl makes the tubular fluid more dilute with a low NaCl concentration. Because the tubular fluid is diluted in the TALH, it is often referred to as the **diluting segment**. The osmolality of the tubular fluid at the end of the TALH is about half (150 mOsm/kg H_2O) that of plasma. Both TAL and TALH lack aquaporins.

The reabsorption of NaCl at the apical membrane occurs by a secondary active transport process. The principal transporter, called the Na/K/2Cl cotransporter, transports $1Na^+$, $1K^+$ and $2Cl^-$ into the cell (Figure 7-7). This cotransporter is principally located in the medullary TALH. Because of Cl^- movement, the tubular lumen has a positive potential difference as opposed to the negative potential difference in the proximal tubule. Also, the K^+ that enters the cells diffuses back into the tubular lumen through a K^+ channel. The net effect is the movement of $2Cl^-$ with $1Na^+$.

The exit of Cl^- at the basolateral membrane is accomplished by two mechanisms. One involves the exit through conductive Cl^- channel, this movement is facilitated by the negative intracellular voltage. The second mechanism involves coupling of Cl^- with K^+ and their exit as K/Cl cotransport (see Figure 7-7).

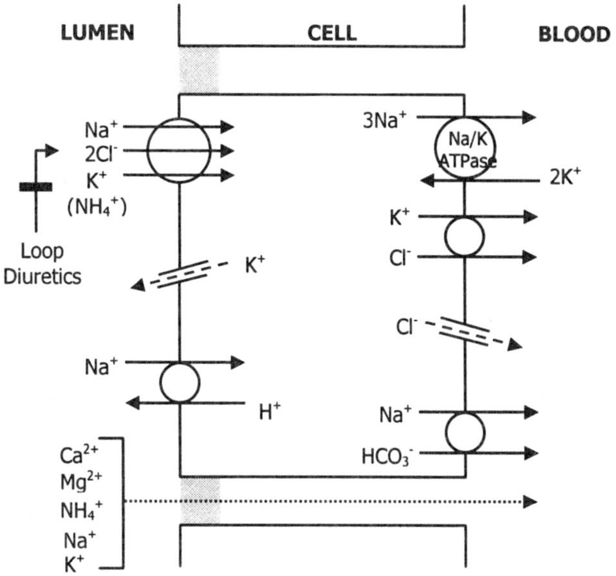

Figure 7-7. Cellular model for Na/K/2Cl cotransport and for the transport of other cations in the thick ascending limb of Henle's loop. Broken arrows indicate diffusion of respective ions through specific conductance channels. Thick broken arrow represents inhibition of Na/K/2Cl cotransporter by loop diuretics.

To summarize, the transport processes in TALH actively reabsorb NaCl. As a result of this reabsorption the concentration of NaCl in the tubular lumen is low, while the interstitial concentration of NaCl is high. Since water remains in the tubular lumen, the osmolality of the fluid in the tubular lumen is extremely low, while that of medullary interstitium is extremely high. Thus, the TALH maintains medullary hypertonicity. This medullary hypertonicity can be dissipated or lowered by inhibiting NaCl reabsorption. So-called loop diuretics, such as furosemide and bumetamide, inhibit the Na/K/2Cl cotransporter (see Figure 7-7). As a result, NaCl absorption is inhibited and medullary tonicity is reduced.

In addition to NaCl, many cations such as Ca^{2+}, Mg^{2+} and NH_4^+ are reabsorbed in the TALH. This reabsorption occurs mainly through the tight junctions and intercellular pathways (see Figure 7-7). The driving force for this paracellular pathway seems to be the positive transepithelial potential difference created by $2Cl^-$ and $1Na^+$ transport and also by backleak of K^+ into the tubular lumen. NH_4^+ can replace K^+ and enter the cell through Na/K/2Cl cotransporter. Mg^{2+} is also transported transcellularly.

Some evidence suggests that a Na/H antiporter is located in the apical membrane of the TALH. This mechanism provides for HCO_3^- generation as well as another route for Na^+ reabsorption.

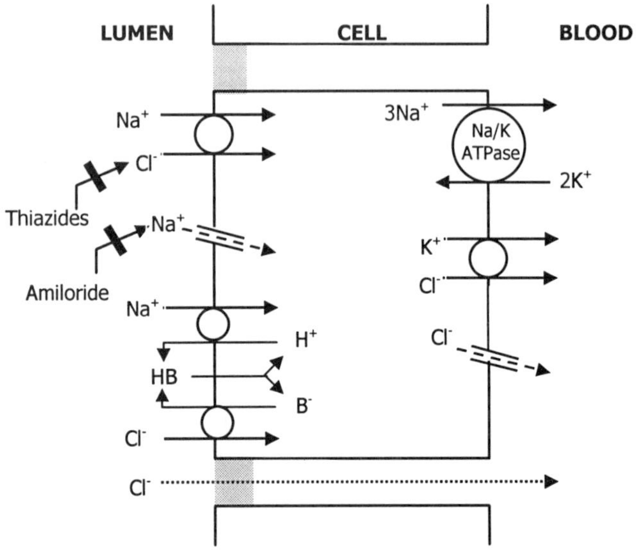

Figure 7-8. Cellular model for NaCl reabsorption in the distal convoluted tubule cell. Note the thiazide-sensitive Na/Cl cotransporter and amiloride-inhibitable Na^+ channel. Broken arrows indicate transport through specific conductance channels. Similar mechanisms exist for NaCl transport in the connecting tubule cell. B^- = base; HB = neutral acid.

DISTAL TUBULE

For an understanding of transport mechanisms, the distal convoluted tubule (DCT) and the connecting tubule (CNT) will be discussed together as the distal tubule. The DCT represents that segment of the nephron beyond the macula densa. Both DCT and CNT reabsorb approximately 10% of the filtered load of NaCl. Na^+ is actively transported and the highest Na/K-ATPase activity is present in the basolateral membrane. Na^+ transport across the apical membrane occurs by three mechanisms. First, Na^+ enters the cell by Na^+ conductance channel. This Na^+ reabsorption creates a negative potential difference in the lumen. This difference drives some Cl^- across the paracellular pathway. Na^+ transport through the Na^+ channel is inhibited by amiloride (Figure 7-8). Second, NaCl reabsorption occurs by a Na/Cl cotransporter, which is inhibited by thiazide diuretics. Third, NaCl transport involves parallel Na/H antiport and Cl/base exchange with recycling of H^+ and base. The base exchanged with Cl^-

appears to be formate or oxalate. Cl^- leaves the cell by K/Cl cotransport and by Cl^- conductance channel. The DCT is impermeable to water. The mechanisms for NaCl transport in CNT seem to be similar to those in the DCT.

COLLECTING DUCT

The collecting duct is divided into the cortical collecting duct (CCD), the outer medullary collecting duct (OMCD), and the inner medullary collecting duct (IMCD). These segments of the collecting duct help regulate the urinary excretion of Na^+, K^+, H^+, water, and urea. Compared to other parts of the nephron, the collecting duct, as a whole, reabsorbs only 2 to 3% of the filtered Na^+.

As discussed in Chapter 2, the collecting duct consists of two major types of cells: principal and **intercalated** cells. The intercalated cells are further divided into Type A or Type B cells. Principal and intercalated cells are morphologically and functionally different. Principal cells are primarily involved in Na^+ reabsorption and K^+ secretion. Type A intercalated cells are responsible for H^+ secretion and Type B cells for HCO_3^- secretion.

In the principal cell, Na^+ enters and K^+ leaves the cell across the apical membrane through conductive channels (Figure 7-9). The Na^+ channel is inhibited by amiloride. K^+ secretion into the lumen is inhibited by barium but not by amiloride. However, amiloride decreases K^+ secretion indirectly. Cl^- reabsorption occurs mainly by the paracellular pathway which is due to the large lumen-negative voltage generated by transcellular Na^+ transport. Transcellular Cl^- transport mechanism has also been described via an apical Cl/HCO_3 exchanger. The exit of Cl^- across the basolateral membrane occurs through Cl^- conductive channels.

Type A intercalated cells are involved in H^+ secretion and reabsorption of HCO_3^- (Figure 7-10), whereas Type B intercalated cells are responsible for HCO_3^- secretion via an apical Cl/Cl or Cl/HCO_3 exchanger (Figure 7-11). Both types of intercalated cells lack Na/K-ATPase. The energy for active Cl^- reabsorption from tubular lumen is derived from the H/ATPase located in the basolateral membrane of the Type B intercalated cell (Figure 7-11). The CCD is impermeable to water.

Aldosterone increases Na^+ reabsorption and K^+ secretion in the principal cell of the CCD. Also, aldosterone increases basolateral Na/K-ATPase activity. Aldosterone seems to activate quiescent Na^+ channels rather than synthesize or insert new Na^+ channels into the apical membrane. Enhanced K^+ secretion into the tubular lumen is due to enhanced basolateral K^+ influx via stimulated Na/K-ATPase by aldosterone.

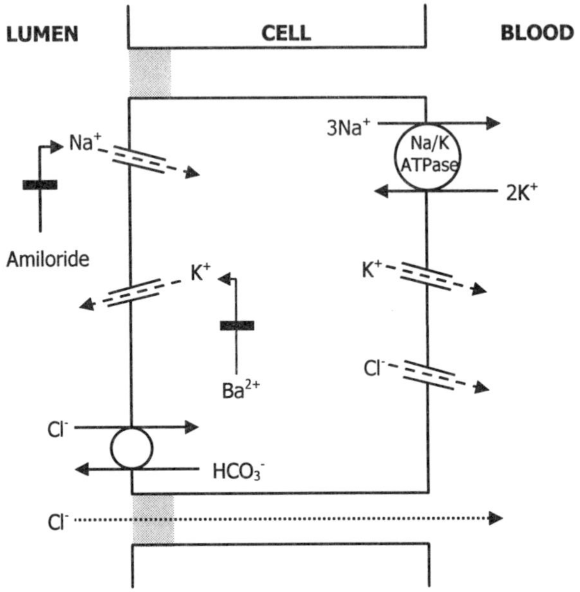

Figure 7-9. Cellular model for NaCl transport in the principal cell of the cortical collecting duct. Note that an amiloride-inhibitable Na^+ channel, a barium (Ba^{2+}) inhibitable K^+ channel and a Cl/HCO_3 exchanger are present in the apical membrane of the cell. Broken arrows indicate transport through specific conductive channels.

Antidiuretic hormone (ADH) also promotes Na^+ reabsorption by the principal cell by insertion of additional Na^+ channels into the apical membrane via cAMP. Atrial natriuretic peptide, bradykinin, increased intracellular Ca^{2+}, and prostaglandin E_2 have been shown to inhibit Na^+ reabsorption in the CCD.

The major function of the OMCD intercalated cell is H^+ ion secretion, and its transport is driven by H-ATPase in the luminal membrane (see Figure 7-10). This proton secretion into the lumen requires recycling of Cl^-. Entry of Cl^- from the blood across the basolateral membrane is linked to HCO_3^- exit through the Cl/HCO_3 exchanger (see Figure 7-10). Na^+ transport is decreased in the OMCD. This decrease, in combination with H^+ ion secretion, makes the lumen potential positive.

The cells of the IMCD function like principal cells in the CCD. These cells reabsorb Na^+ through conductive channels. Na^+ entry and K^+ secretion into the lumen are stimulated by aldosterone. The transport of Na^+ creates a negative potential in the lumen, which promotes Cl^- reabsorption via the paracellular pathway. Water permeability is low and ADH increases water reabsorption.

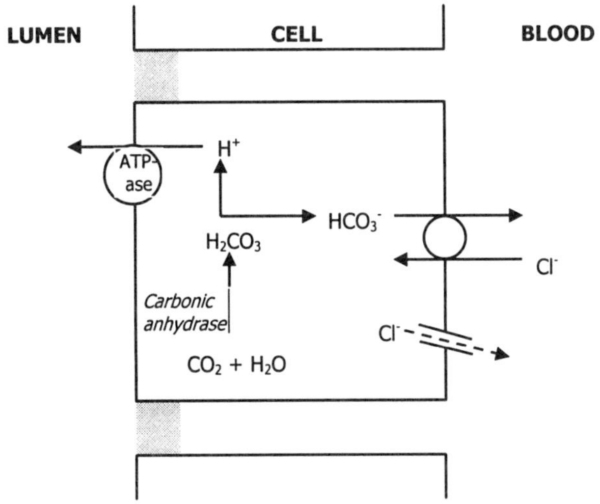

Figure 7-10. Cellular model for H^+ ion secretion and HCO_3^- reabsorption in Type A intercalated cell of cortical collecting duct. H^+ and HCO_3^- ions are generated from hydrolysis of carbonic acid (H_2CO_3). Broken arrow indicates Cl^- conductance channel.

The transport of urea in the collecting duct is passive. Both CCD and OMCD are less permeable to urea than the terminal ICMD near the papilla. The high permeability in the terminal IMCD is due to a carrier-mediated facilitated diffusion in both apical and basolateral membranes. ADH increases urea permeability in the terminal IMCD. The urea that is transported into the interstitium from IMCD is used for recycling through the thin limbs of Henle's loop (Chapter 9).

SUMMARY

1. The kidneys filter about 180 L of plasma daily. Most of the ultrafiltrate is reclaimed by various segments of the nephron. Only 1 to 1.5 L of urine is excreted daily. Several organic anions and cations of endogenous and exogenous origin are eliminated by secretion.
2. The proximal tubule, as a whole, reabsorbs 60% of the glomerular filtrate. Na^+ reabsorption in the proximal tubule occurs by both active and passive transport mechanisms, and is coupled to Cl^- , K^+, glucose, amino acids, lactate, and phosphate. Water transport occurs secondary to NaCl reabsorption. Reabsorption of ultrafiltrate in the proximal tubule is isosmotic. Uric acid is both reabsorbed and secreted, and, therefore undergoes bi-directional transport.

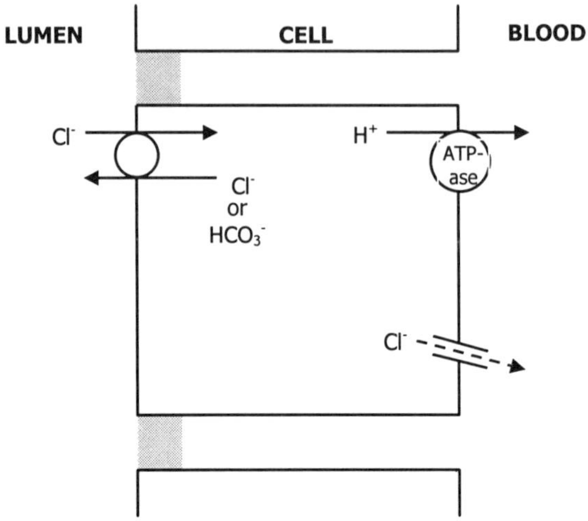

Figure 7-11. Cellular model for HCO_3^- secretion and Cl^- reabsorption in Type B intercalated cell of the cortical collecting duct. Broken arrow indicates Cl^- conductance channel.

3. The thin descending limb of Henle's loop is more permeable to water than NaCl, K^+, and urea, causing high tubular fluid osmolality. Conversely, the thin ascending limb is impermeable to water and permeable to NaCl and urea. This causes hypotonicity of tubular fluid.
4. About 30% of filtered NaCl is reabsorbed in the thick ascending limb of Henle's loop (TALH). The major transporter of NaCl is called the Na/K/2Cl cotransporter. This cotransporter is responsible for maintaining medullary hypertonicity. The Na/K/2Cl cotransporter is inhibited by loop diuretics such as furosemide. The TALH is impermeable to water. Because of NaCl absorption and impermeability of water, the tubular fluid is diluted, and the TALH is called the diluting segment.
5. The distal tubule reabsorbs about 10% of the filtered NaCl via an NaCl cotransporter and Na^+ channel. Thiazide diuretics inhibit NaCl cotransporter, and K^+-sparing diuretic such as amiloride inhibits Na^+ channel.
6. The cortical collecting duct contains two types of cells: principal and intercalated cells. The intercalated cells are of two types: Type A and Type B cells. The principal cell is primarily involved in Na^+ reabsorption and K^+ secretion. Aldosterone acts on these principal cells and promotes Na^+ reabsorption and K^+ secretion. Type A intercalated cells are responsible for H^+ ion secretion via H-ATPase and Type B cells for HCO_3^- secretion. Thus, the intercalated cells are involved in acid-base regulation.
7. Urea transport occurs by passive diffusion in the proximal tubule, loop of Henle, cortical collecting duct, outer medullary and inner medullary collecting ducts. However, in the terminal inner medullary collecting duct

near the papilla, urea transport occurs by a carrier-mediated facilitated diffusion which is stimulated by antidiuretic hormone.

CLINICAL APPLICATIONS

Several proximal tubular defects have been described in both children and adults. **Fanconi syndrome** is caused by defective reabsorption of amino acids, glucose, urate, phosphate, K^+ and HCO_3^- and results in excess urinary excretions of these solutes. Aminoaciduria may arise from genetic deficiencies of the specific carrier proteins in the proximal tubule. **Hartnup** disease is the result of increased urinary excretion of neutral amino acids (alanine, serine, leucine, isoleucine, etc.). It is characterized by cerebellar ataxia, mental retardation, short stature, and skin rash. Treatment with oral **nicotinamide** has been found to be effective in some patients. **Cystinuria** is another disorder characterized by excessive urinary loss of cystine, ornithine, arginine and lysine. Patients with this disease develop **cystine stones**. **Renal glucosuria** is a condition in which glucose appears in the urine in the presence of normal plasma glucose levels. This condition is usually benign and is probably a consequence of a genetic defect in the SGLT- 2 glucose transporter. Some patients may develop an isolated defect in the proximal tubule. Examples are cystinuria, renal glucosuria, or renal hypophosphatemia. In these isolated conditions, renal tubular reabsorption of other substances is normal. Proximal renal tubule HCO_3^- wasting results in **proximal renal tubular acidosis**.

A number of drugs can inhibit the reabsorption and secretion of urate, resulting either in low or high serum uric acid concentration (Table 7-4). A similar effect can be seen in volume expansion or volume depleted conditions. Conditions such as normal pregnancy, inappropriate secretion of antidiuretic hormone, and AIDS are characterized by low serum uric acid concentrations. Rhabdomyolysis (muscle necrosis) , tumor lysis syndrome (destruction of tumor cells by anticancer drugs), and preeclampsia (hypertension, edema, and proteinuria during pregnancy) are characterized by high serum uric acid concentration. Disorders of uric acid metabolism result in gout, uric acid kidney stones, and acute renal failure in human subjects.

The genes encoding for the Na/K/2Cl cotransporter, Na/Cl cotransporter, and Na^+ channel have recently been cloned. Mutations in each one of these genes have been shown to cause important clinical syndromes. For example, **Bartter's syndrome** is caused by a mutation in the Na/K/2Cl cotransporter. This syndrome is characterized by hypokalemia (low serum K^+ concentration), hypomagnesemia (low serum Mg^{2+} concentration), metabolic alkalosis, high plasma renin and aldosterone levels, and a normal blood pressure. Mutations in Na/Cl cotranspoter causes **Gitelman's syndrome**, which is characterized by hypokalemia, hypomagnesemia, metabolic alkalosis, and reduced urinary excretion of Ca^{2+} (hypocalciuria). The Na^+ channel is formed by the assembly of three subunits: α,β,γ. Mutations in the β- and γ-subunits of the channel causes a syndrome called the **Liddle's syndrome**. Patients with this syndrome have an overactivity of Na^+ channel, resulting in excessive Na^+ reabsorption with concomitant K^+ wasting and hypokalemia. These patients also demonstrate metabolic alkalosis, low plasma renin and aldosterone levels, but have hypertension.

STUDY QUESTIONS

Case 1

A 30-year-old man has a plasma glucose level of 100 mg/dL and a GFR of 125 ml/min.

Question 1. What is the filtered load of glucose?

Answer: The filtered load of glucose is 125 mg/min and can be calculated from the following formula:

Plasma concentration of glucose (mg/ml) x GFR (ml/min)
or
(1 x 125 = 125 mg/min)

Question 2. Does the subject have glucose in the urine?

Answer: Since Tm for glucose is 375 mg/min, all of the filtered load in this subject is reabsorbed and no glucose appears in the urine.

Question 3. If the above subject is infused with glucose intravenously and his GFR is maintained at 125 ml/min, at what plasma glucose concentration will this subject excrete glucose?

Answer: This subject will start spilling glucose in the urine when the plasma glucose concentration reaches at or above 3 mg/mL, because this subject reached Tm for glucose (i.e., 3 mg/mL x GFR:125 = 375 mg/mL) and any excess glucose that is filtered is excreted in the urine. However, not all nephrons have a Tm_G of 375 mg/min. Some demonstrate splay, and therefore spill glucose if plasma concentration exceeds 2 mg/mL or 200 mg/dL.

Case 2

A 30-year-old man was admitted for fever and left lower lobe pneumonia. Blood cultures were positive for pneumococcus. The patient was treated with penicillin G.

Question 1. If probenecid is simultaneously administered, what would the serum concentration of penicillin be?

Answer: Penicillin is an exogenous anion. Similarly, probenecid is also an exogenous anion. Both are secreted by the proximal tubule and demonstrate Tm and competitive inhibition. Probenecid, competitively inhibits the secretion of penicillin, and thus raises its serum concentration.

Case 3

A 10-year-old boy was admitted for aspirin overdose. In the emergency room, he was started on intravenous $NaHCO_3$ drip.

Question 1. Explain how alkalinization of urine improves his clinical condition.

Answer: Aspirin is metabolized to salicylic acid which has a pK_a of 3.0. At alkaline urine pH, (>6.5), salicylic acid exists as salicylate and is ionized. It, therefore, does not diffuse into the cell. Thus, alkaline urine pH promotes aspirin excretion in the form of salicylate, and improves his clinical condition of aspirin overdose.

Case 4

A 40-year-old patient with pulmonary tuberculosis was treated with isoniazid, rifampin, and pyrazinamide. At the start of anti-tuberculous medications, his serum electrolytes were normal. Following 4 weeks of treatment, his uric acid level was significantly elevated.

Question 1. Explain why serum uric acid level is elevated.

Answer: Pyrazinamide inhibits the secretion of uric acid and elevates its concentration. Isoniazid and rifampin do not have any effect on uric acid levels.

SUGGESTED READING

1. Berry, C.A., Ives, H.E., and Rector, F.C., Jr. Renal transport of glucose, amino acids, sodium, chloride, and water. In: The Kidney. 5th edition. B.M. Brenner (ed.). W.B. Saunders Company, Philadelphia, 1996; pp.334-370 (*A detailed discussion of organic solute and water reabsorption in the proximal tubule, and NaCl reabsorption in various segments of the nephron*).
2. Dantzler, W.H., Wright, S.H. and Lote, C.J. Organic solute transport. In: Nephrology. R.L. Jamison and R. Wilkinson(eds.). Chapman & Hall, London, 1997; pp. 61-70 (*A brief summary of glucose, amino acid, urate, and, organic anion and cation transport in the nephron*).
3. Reeves, W.B. and Andreoli, T.E. Tubular sodium transport. In: Diseases of the Kidney, 6th edition. R.W. Schrier and C.W. Gottschalk (eds.). Little, Brown and Company, Boston, 1997; pp. 127-162 (*A detailed review of NaCl transport and its regulation along the length of the nephron*).

CHAPTER 8

REGULATION AND DISORDERS OF EXTRACELLULAR FLUID VOLUME

Objectives

After reading this chapter, the student should be able to:

1. Describe the afferent mechanisms that perceive volume changes in the body.
2. Explain how glomerular filtration rate, peritubular Starling forces, medullary blood flow, arterial pressure, sympathetic tone, and hormones regulate NaCl balance.
3. Discuss the concept of glomerulo-tubular balance.
4. Discuss the conditions associated with Na^+ excess.
5. Define the effective circulating volume and distinguish it from extracellular fluid volume.
6. Discuss the causes of Na^+ loss.
7. Discuss the clinical manifestations of extracellular fluid volume contraction.

REGULATION OF EXTRACELLULAR FLUID VOLUME

In Chapter 7, we discussed how NaCl and water are handled by various segments of the nephron. Since Na^+ is the major extracellular solute, the total amount of this electrolyte determines extracellular fluid (ECF) volume. Therefore, retention or excretion of Na^+ by the kidneys is critical for the regulation of ECF volume. This regulation of NaCl is precise in normal individuals. However, in some patients, Na^+ is retained causing ECF volume expansion. In other patients, Na^+ is lost and the ECF volume is low. This chapter discusses the various factors that regulate NaCl and water transport by the kidneys and thus the regulation of ECF volume.

Na^+ concentration in the plasma is determined by the amount of Na^+ that is ingested and excreted. The estimated Na^+ intake is between 100 and 350 mEq/day, which is equal to approximately 6 to 21 g of salt. Na^+ is ingested as NaCl. Following ingestion, NaCl is rapidly absorbed from the intestine. Na^+ then enters the blood and equilibrates with its surrounding interstitium (see

Chapter 1). Excretion of Na^+ by the kidneys lags behind this equilibration. As a result, water moves from the intracellular compartment into the extracellular compartment and increases its volume. This transient increase in extracellular volume stimulates the kidneys to excrete appropriate amounts of NaCl and water to maintain Na^+ balance and body weight. At a steady state, Na^+ intake equals Na^+ excretion.

How does the kidney respond to changes in Na^+ intake? Two important regulatory mechanisms are operative (see At a Glance box 8-1). First, afferent mechanisms sense changes in Na^+ intake and ECF volume. Second, once afferent mechanisms have perceived these changes, efferent mechanisms transmit signals to the kidneys for appropriate response. The afferent mechanisms that sense ECF volume changes include a number of pressure receptors, such as baroreceptors and mechanoreceptors located in the cardiopulmonary, hepatic, renal, and central nervous systems. Since pressure and volume are directly related, these receptors are also called **volume regulatory receptors**, and thus respond to stretch caused by changes in ECF volume. The coordination of afferent and efferent mechanisms that maintain Na^+ and fluid balance is described as follows. The afferent mechanisms sense the ECF volume and convey the information to an integrative control center in the central nervous system (CNS) via an afferent neural pathway. The efferent mechanisms, through their neurohumoral pathways, influence the kidneys to produce appropriate change in the ECF volume. Depending on the volume status, the CNS integrative control center is either inhibited or stimulated.

AFFERENT (SENSING) MECHANISMS

Low-pressure volume receptors

Low-pressure volume receptors, located in the cardiac atria, pulmonary veins, and vena cava, have been implicated as ECF volume sensors. When ECF volume is depleted, low-pressure volume receptors sense this ECF volume depletion and reduce their tonic inhibition of the integrative center in the CNS. As a result, peripheral sympathetic discharge is increased with subsequent Na^+ retention by the kidney. Conversely, volume expansion causes an opposite sequence of events.

Experimental evidence also implicates the inferior vena cava as a volume sensor. Constriction of the thoracic inferior vena cava in dogs causes a decrease in Na^+ excretion. This decrease in Na^+ excretion is attributed to a reduction in intrathoracic blood volume associated with renal retention of Na^+. On the other hand, immersing humans in a water bath to the neck causes an increase in intrathoracic volume and results in natriuresis (excretion of Na^+). Stretching or distention of the left atrium also causes enhanced Na^+ excretion. When atria are distended by volume, a reflex response is initiated and is carried via the vagus nerve to the integrative control center in the CNS. Stimulation of this area, in turn, causes a decrease in the sympathetic activity of the kidney.

At a Glance Box 8-1
Afferent and efferent mechanisms involved in renal Na^+ excretion

Afferent
Intrathoracic low-pressure (venous) receptors
- Cardiac atria
- Pulmonary veins

High-pressure (arterial) volume receptors
- Carotid sinus
- Aortic arch

Hepatic volume receptors
Intrarenal volume receptors
- Juxtaglomerular apparatus
- Arterial perfusion pressure receptors
- Interstitial pressure receptors

Central nervous system receptors

Efferent
Glomerular filtration rate
Physical factors
Peritubular capillary Starling forces
Tubular luminal composition
Medullary blood flow
Renal nerves
Humoral factors
Renin-angiotensin-aldosterone system
Prostaglandins
Kallikrein-kinin-system
Atrial natriuretic peptide
Digitalis-like factor
Nitric oxide

As a result, Na^+ excretion is enhanced. Supine posture increases atrial distention or pressure and thus promotes Na^+ excretion. Standing or hemorrhage decreases atrial distention, which causes a decrease in Na^+ excretion.

High-pressure volume receptors

Volume sensing receptors are also present in the aortic arch and the carotid sinus. Stimulation of these receptors by volume expansion results in enhanced Na^+ excretion, as seen in atrial distention. The baroreceptors of the carotid sinus and aortic arch also respond to blood pressure changes. An increase in arterial pressure stimulates these receptors and diminishes peripheral sympathetic activity, causing urinary Na^+ excretion to increase. A decrease in arterial pressure reduces stimulation of these receptors, causing urinary Na^+ excretion to decrease.

Hepatic volume receptors

The presence of hepatic volume sensing receptors is suggested by experiments in which saline is infused into the portal vein of cats. This infusion causes Na^+ excretion. An identical infusion into the systemic vein causes less natriuresis. Infusion of sucrose into the portal vein does not induce Na^+ excretion, suggesting the presence of a Na^+- sensing mechanism in the liver.

Intrarenal volume receptors

Studies have shown that the juxtaglomerular apparatus (JGA) of the kidney responds to reduced renal pressure by stimulating renin release, which in turn causes increased aldosterone secretion and Na^+ retention. This Na^+ retention occurs in the absence of any changes in glomerular filtration rate, which suggests the presence of baroreceptors in the JGA. An increase in renal interstitial hydrostatic pressure has also been shown to cause an increase in Na^+ excretion. Increases in interstitial pressures can be produced by such maneuvers as expansion of intravascular volume, constriction of renal veins and, an increase in arterial pressure.

CNS volume receptors

The CNS may contain a volume sensor that regulates urinary Na^+ excretion. Infusion of saline into the carotid artery produces greater Na^+ output than does infusion into a systemic vein. The mechanism for this Na^+ diuresis is unknown.

EFFERENT (RESPONSE) MECHANISMS

The efferent mechanisms mediate the final regulation of Na^+ and water balance. These are discussed briefly in the following sections.

Glomerular Filtration Rate (GFR)

In general, a relatively constant GFR is maintained by autoregulation through tubuloglomerular feedback mechanisms. However, minor, transient changes in GFR do occur. Following a high protein meal and high salt intake, the GFR increases substantially. This increase in GFR increases the filtered load of Na^+ (GFR x plasma Na^+ concentration), which causes natriuresis and diuresis to maintain Na^+ as well as fluid balance. Conversely, in situations of water deprivation and decreased salt intake, hypovolemia ensues. As a result, the GFR is decreased and the filtered load of Na^+ also decreases, which leads to Na^+ and water retention. These alterations in Na^+ and fluid excretion in association with changes in GFR are regulated by the tubular reabsorption of a constant fraction of the filtered load of salt and water. For example, if GFR is increased, the rate of proximal tubular reabsorption of salt and water also increases, so that the fraction of the filtered load that is reabsorbed remains constant. This relationship between the GFR and the renal tubules is called **glomerulo-tubular balance** (G-T balance). If this relationship did not exist, then minor increases in GFR would lead to massive urinary losses of salt and water, and thus a loss of Na^+ and water balance. The G-T balance, therefore, minimizes major alterations in salt and water excretion. It is important to note that the G-T balance is different from tubuloglomerular feedback mechanism. The G-T balance can be illustrated by the following example. Let us assume that under steady state conditions the GFR is 100 ml/min, of which 70% or 70 ml is reabsorbed in the proximal tubule and the remaining 30% or 30 ml is delivered to the loop of Henle and other parts of the nephron. If the GFR is increased by 20%, i.e., 120 ml/min, and the proximal tubule reabsorbs only a constant volume (i.e., 70 ml) rather than a constant fraction (i.e., 70%), the delivery to the loop is 50 ml and the tubules cannot handle the excess load. If, on the other hand, the G-T balance were operative, the proximal tubule would reabsorb a constant fraction (i.e., 70%) which would be 84 ml, and only 36 ml would be delivered to the loop of Henle. Thus, the G-T balance prevents changes in the loop delivery rate of the filtrate independent of fluctuations in the GFR.

The maintenance of G-T balance is particularly important in conditions in which changes in GFR occur, such as chronic volume expansion, pregnancy, and renal failure. A dissociation between GFR and tubular reabsorption is seen in some patients with chronic renal failure. In these patients, the GFR and the filtered load of Na^+ are decreased. Yet these patients maintain normal Na^+ excretion by decreasing tubular Na^+ reabsorption by the surviving nephrons.

Peritubular Starling Forces

How is G-T balance maintained? Two physical factors seem to play an important role: peritubular Starling forces and the tubular composition of the fluid. Reabsorption of solutes and fluid from the interstitium into peritubular capillaries is regulated by the Starling forces. Starling forces that favor movement from the interstitium into peritubular capillaries are the capillary oncotic pressure (π_{cap}) and the hydrostatic pressure in the interstitium (P_{is}). The opposing forces are the capillary hydrostatic pressure (P_{cap}) and the oncotic pressure in the interstitium (π_{is}). Albumin concentration provides the oncotic pressure. Accordingly, if the albumin concentration is elevated, the oncotic pressure is also elevated. The serum concentration of albumin in the peritubular capillaries is increased because of the protein-free ultrafiltrate that is formed at the glomerulus. This increased serum albumin concentration favors reabsorption of Na^+ and water into the blood in the proximal tubule and Henle's loop. In the distal tubule and the collecting duct, the permeability of water is low compared to that in the proximal tubule. Therefore, Starling forces do not operate for water reabsorption in these distal segments of the nephron.

It then follows that any condition that increases P_{cap} or decreases π_{cap} inhibits peritubular reabsorption. For example, dilatation of the efferent arteriole increases P_{cap}, which opposes solute and water reabsorption. Conversely, constriction of the efferent arteriole decreases P_{cap} and increases π_{cap}. Thus, reabsorption is promoted.

Clinically, dilatation of the efferent arteriole can be achieved by inhibiting AII production with angiotensin converting enzyme (ACE)-inhibitors such as captopril or enalapril. Inhibition of AII production results in a decrease in GFR and π_{cap}, but it increases P_{cap}. As a result, Na^+ absorption is decreased.

The other physical factor that maintains G-T balance is the composition of fluid in the tubular lumen, particularly in the proximal tubule. Increased filtration at the glomerulus results in increased concentrations of glucose and amino acids in the proximal tubular lumen. Since Na^+ reabsorption is linked to the reabsorption of these molecules, it is apparent that Na^+ reabsorption depends on the tubular concentration of substances such as glucose and amino acids.

Medullary Blood Flow

Studies have shown that alterations in the medullary blood flow may influence Na^+ transport in the loop of Henle. Increase in medullary blood flow, such as occurs in volume expansion, results in a decrease in the medullary concentration of solute and water. This decrease in the medullary concentration of solute and water in turn, causes a decrease in water reabsorption from the descending limb of Henle's loop. As a result, delivery of NaCl to the thick ascending limb of Henle's loop increases and its reabsorption decreases, causing excess NaCl and water excretion.

Arterial Pressure

Acute elevations in arterial pressure have been shown to promote NaCl and water excretion. This increase in salt and water excretion occurs independently of GFR and renal plasma flow, and the mechanisms remain unclear.

Renal Nerves

As discussed in Chapter 2, the kidney is innervated by sympathetic nerves. Evidence indicates that stimulation of renal nerves promotes Na^+ reabsorption and thus decreases its excretion. Conversely, renal denervation decreases tubular Na^+ reabsorption and promotes Na^+ excretion.

Volume expansion caused by infusion of NaCl stimulates intrathoracic volume receptors, which in turn decrease the sympathetic nerve activity to the kidney. Decreases in Na^+ intake cause the intravascular volume to decrease, which enhances renal sympathetic nerve activity. This system is one of the important regulatory mechanisms for Na^+ conservation in states of ECF volume contraction.

Hormonal Factors

Table 8-1 summarizes the effects of various hormones on NaCl and water transport by the renal tubules. Most of the hormones except aldosterone exert their effects within minutes. The action of aldosterone cannot be observed for at least an hour. Therefore, it seems unlikely that aldosterone plays a significant role in the rapid regulation of NaCl excretion.

Figures 8-1 and 8-2 summarize the afferent and efferent mechanisms that control Na^+ excretion in a normal individual on a low and high salt intake. Physiologic adaptations to low salt intake are depicted in Figure 8-1. First, a decrease in salt intake causes a decrease in ECF volume, which lowers perfusion pressure to the kidneys. As a result, the filtered load of Na^+ at the glomerulus is decreased. Second, decreased perfusion pressure triggers the release of renin, which in turn causes the formation of angiotensin II (AII). AII causes renal vasoconstriction as well as aldosterone release: the latter stimulates renal tubular reabsorption of Na^+. Third, ECF volume contraction activates afferent volume receptors, which increase sympathetic tone and decrease ANP release. Increase in sympathetic tone causes renal vasoconstriction, which results in a decrease in peritubular hydrostatic pressure and an increase in filtration fraction. The combination of the two processes stimulates Na^+ reabsorption by the kidney. Finally, ECF volume contraction increases the serum protein concentration and contributes to an increase in oncotic pressure in peritubular capillaries. These factors favor Na^+ reabsorption by the kidney.

Table 8-1. Actions of hormones on NaCl and water transport by various segments of the nephron

Nephron segment	Hormone	Effect on transport of	
		NaCl	Water
Proximal tubule	Angiotensin II	↑ absorption	↑ absorption
	Glucocorticoids	↑ absorption	↑ absorption
	Atrial natriuretic peptide (ANP)	↓ absorption	↓ absorption
	Parathyroid	↑ absorption	↑ absorption
Thick ascending limb	Aldosterone	↑ absorption	UK
	ADH	↑ absorption	UK
Cortical collecting duct	ADH	↑ absorption	↑ absorption
	Aldosterone	↑ absorption	UK
	Bradykinin	↓ absorption	UK
	Digitalis-like factor	↓ absorption	UK
	PGE_2	↓ absorption	UK
Outer medullary collecting duct	ADH	UK	↑ absorption
Inner medullary collecting duct	ADH	UK	↑ absorption
	Aldosterone	↑ absorption	UK
	ANP	↓ absorption	↓ absorption

UK = unknown; ADH = antidiuretic hormone; ↑ = increase; ↓ = decrease.

As Na^+ intake increases, the output of Na^+ also increases. However, Na^+ excretion initially lags behind intake, resulting in a transient increase in plasma Na^+ concentration (abbreviated as $[Na^+]$) and ECF volume. The afferent mechanisms sense the excess ECF volume and convey the message to the efferent mechanisms, which inhibit Na^+-retaining mechanisms (renin-angiotensin-aldosterone and renal nerve activity) and activate Na^+-losing mechanisms (ANP and digitalis-like factor). Alterations in physical factors also occur to inhibit Na^+ reabsorption. As a result of these changes, urinary excretion of Na^+ is promoted (see Figure 8-2).

DISORDERS OF ECF VOLUME

So far we have discussed how ECF volume is regulated by afferent and efferent mechanisms in a normal individual. Derangement in any one of these mechanisms can cause either in ECF volume expansion or contraction. Conditions such as congestive heart failure, cirrhosis of the liver, and nephrotic syndrome (see At a Glance box 8-2) are characterized by ECF volume expansion and edema. These clinical conditions are associated with salt and water retention despite excess ECF volume. These patients are in positive Na^+ balance because their Na^+ excretion is less than Na^+ intake. The conditions of volume expansion, particularly cardiac and liver failure, are associated with increased expression of aquaporin-2 water channel. Conversely, a decrease in

ECF volume is associated with a decrease in salt and water content, which is called volume contraction or depletion. A volume contracted patient is in a negative Na^+ balance because Na^+ intake is less than Na^+ excretion.

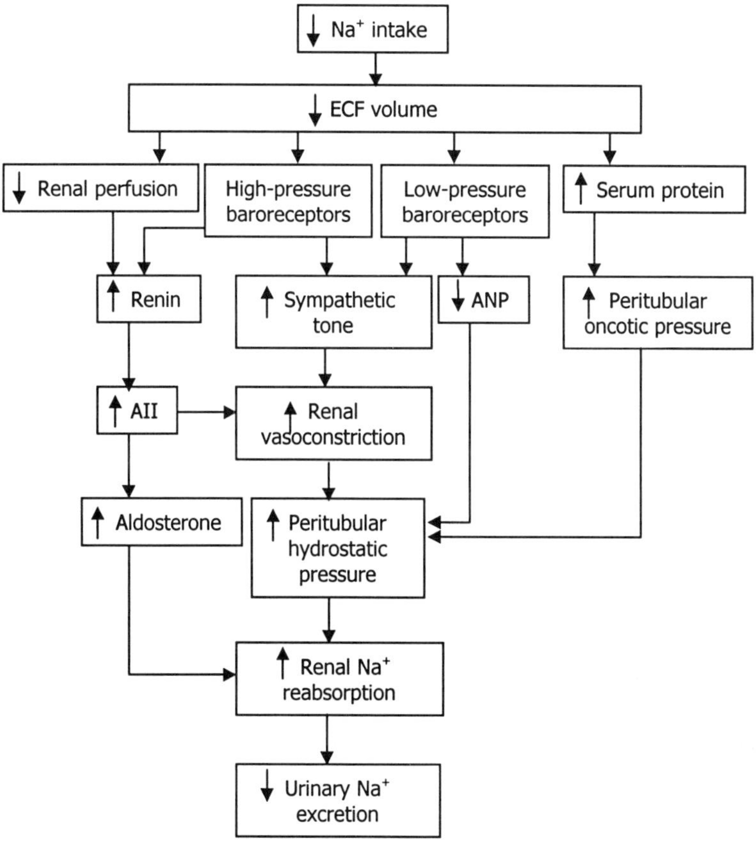

Figure 8-1. Renal response to decreased Na^+ intake. ECF = extracellular fluid volume; AII = angiotensin II; ANP = atrial natriuretic peptide.

At a Glance Box 8-2
Conditions associated with ECF volume expansion

Congestive heart failure
Cirrhosis of the liver
Nephrotic syndrome

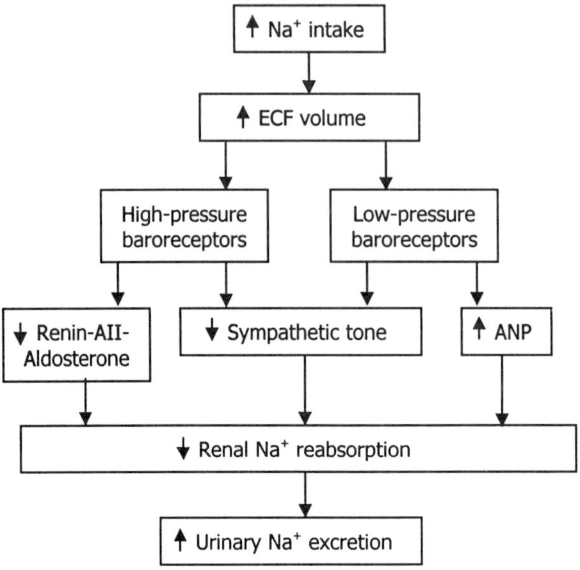

Figure 8-2. Renal response to increased Na^+ intake. ECF = extracellular fluid volume; AII = angiotensin II; ANP = atrial natriuretic peptide (Many of the steps shown in Fig. 8-1 are omitted for simplicity).

Let us see how the patients with expanded ECF volume retain Na^+. To gain insight into the mechanism of Na^+ retention, one should understand the concept of effective circulating volume and distinguish it from ECF volume.

CONCEPT OF EFFECTIVE CIRCULATING VOLUME (ECV)

A fundamental characteristic of expanded ECF volume conditions, as stated above, is avid retention of Na^+ and edema. Therefore, it is essential to understand the concept of ECV in these conditions. ECV is not a measurable quantity. It refers to a component of the ECF volume that is perfusing the tissues. Therefore, the ECF volume and ECV are not identical. For example, congestive heart failure is a condition of ECF volume expansion. The expected increase in Na^+ excretion to this volume expansion does not occur. Instead, the excretion of Na^+ decreases. The kidney thus behaves as if it were responding to a low-volume state. This decrease in Na^+ excretion is explained by the concept of ECV. In congestive heart failure, ECV is decreased. This decrease in ECV activates salt-retaining mechanisms through stimulation of high-pressure baroreceptors, as seen in states of low salt intake. As a result, Na^+ is retained despite an increase in ECF volume. Although no adequate experimental evidence supports the concept of ECV, it is generally believed that ECV reflects "underfilling" of the arterial vascular system in congestive heart failure and severe liver disease.

In a healthy individual, normal ECV is determined by a balance between cardiac output and peripheral vascular resistance. As a result, both venous return and cardiac output are maintained in the normal range. When either cardiac output or peripheral vascular resistance is decreased, the ECV is decreased.

ECF VOLUME EXCESS STATES

Two mechanisms are operative in ECF volume excess states. First, alterations in Starling forces across the capillary occur that favor movement of fluid from intravascular (blood) to the interstitial compartment to cause edema. Second, Na^+ retention is promoted by the kidney to maintain ECF volume expansion.

Congestive Heart Failure (CHF)

Congestive heart failure is a condition in which cardiac output is decreased due to heart disease. It is characterized by ECF volume expansion and edema. Na^+ is retained due to decreased ECV, which activates salt-retaining mechanisms, namely, renin-angiotensin-aldosterone and the sympathetic nervous system. The release of ADH is also increased, which stimulates water reabsorption by the kidney. The net result is formation of edema (Figure 8-3). The effect of atrial natriuretic peptide (ANP) on Na^+ excretion is attenuated. The major site for Na^+ reabsorption in CHF is the proximal tubule.

Treatment of CHF includes improvement of cardiac output with fluid and salt restriction and vasodilator drug therapy. Vasodilator therapy increases venous return, thereby improving cardiac output. Edema and excess total body Na^+ content can also be treated with diuretics (Chapter 16).

Cirrhosis of the Liver

ECF volume expansion, edema, ascites, and Na^+ retention are the most common clinical findings in patients with severe liver disease. The initiating process for these clinical manifestations is hepatic cell death. Pathologically, the liver in cirrhosis is characterized by fibrosis and nodular regeneration. Liver function tests (aminotransferases, bilirubin, alkaline phosphatase) are abnormal. Na^+ and water retention precedes the formation of ascites in patients with liver disease. This is explained by the peripheral arterial vasodilation hypothesis. According to this hypothesis, arterial vasodilation in the splanchnic circulation occurs early in cirrhosis with a decrease in ECV and activation of neurohumoral vasoconstrictors and ADH release (Figure 8-4). As a result, Na^+ reabsorption is increased in the proximal and distal tubules. Water reabsorption is promoted by ADH. Although the mediators of the splanchnic vasodilation are unknown, substances such as nitric oxide and endotoxin have been implicated.

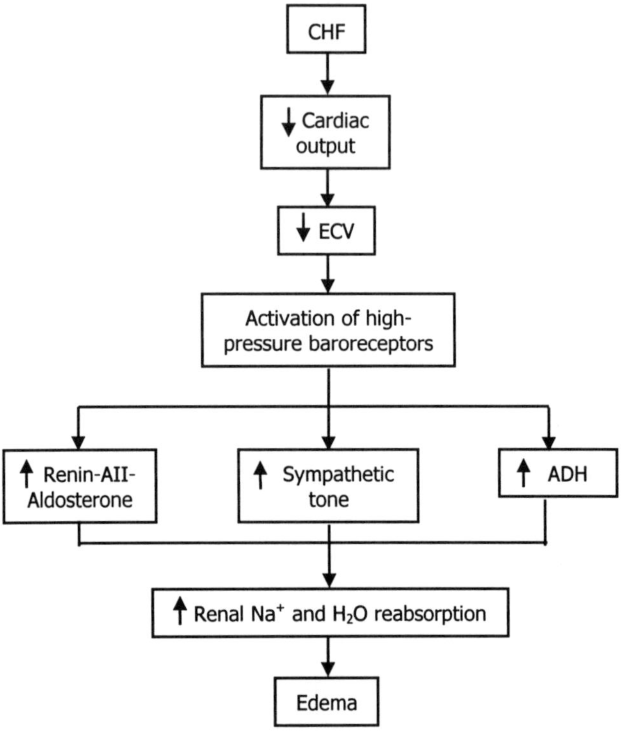

Figure 8-3. Mechanisms for the initiation of renal Na^+ and water retention in congestive heart failure (CHF). ECV = effective circulating volume.

Diuretics, Na^+, and water restriction have become the mainstay of therapy in cirrhotic patients. Paracentesis (removal of ascites from the peritoneal cavity) offers symptomatic relief in those patients with severe ascites and respiratory difficulty.

Nephrotic Syndrome

Unlike patients with CHF and cirrhosis, patients with nephrotic syndrome have some underlying renal disease. Also, ECV is not decreased in all patients with nephrotic syndrome. This syndrome is characterized by proteinuria in excess of 3.5 g/day, hypoalbuminemia, hyperlipidemia, edema, and lipiduria. The mechanism for salt and water retention is not clear. The traditional ("underfill") theory implies that loss of protein in the urine causes hypoalbuminemia and decreased plasma oncotic pressure. These factors favor fluid movement into the interstitium, resulting in intravascular hypovolemia and activation of salt-retaining mechanisms (Figure 8-5). Two lines of evidence, however, argue against this traditional theory. First, not all patients with congenital deficiency of albumin (analbuminemia) develop edema. Second, some patients with nephrotic syndrome have either normal or increased intravascular volume despite hypoalbuminemia. This evidence suggests that mechanisms other than hypoalbuminemia and decreased intravascular volume play a role in the renal retention of Na^+ in nephrotic syndrome.

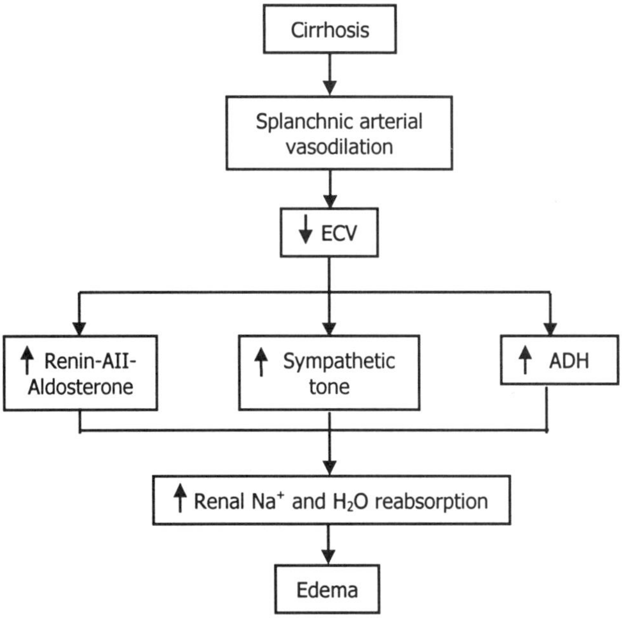

Figure 8-4. Mechanisms for the initiation of renal Na^+ and water retention in cirrhosis of the liver. ECV = effective circulating volume.

Experimental evidence also suggests that Na^+ and water retention occur in the kidney due to an intrarenal cause independent of salt-retaining mechanisms. As a result, the plasma volume is expanded, and this overfilled plasma volume leaks into the interstitium to cause edema. This is called the "overfill" hypothesis (Figure 8-6). Hypoalbuminemia and decreased oncotic pressure may enhance edema formation. The major site for Na^+ reabsorption in patients with nephrotic syndrome is the collecting duct.

Treatment of nephrotic syndrome includes: (1) elimination of the underlying cause, if possible; (2) water and Na^+ restriction, if necessary; (3)

control of hypertension; (4) low protein diet; and (5) ACE-inhibitors. Dietary restriction of protein to less than 1 g/kg/day and small doses of ACE-inhibitors have been particularly shown to reduce proteinuria in patients with nephrotic syndrome. Judicious use of diuretics to reduce edema is also of benefit in some patients. In addition to this conservative management, the use of corticosteroids and other immunosuppressive agents (e.g., cyclophosphamide, chlorambucil, etc.) has been shown to be beneficial in some patients.

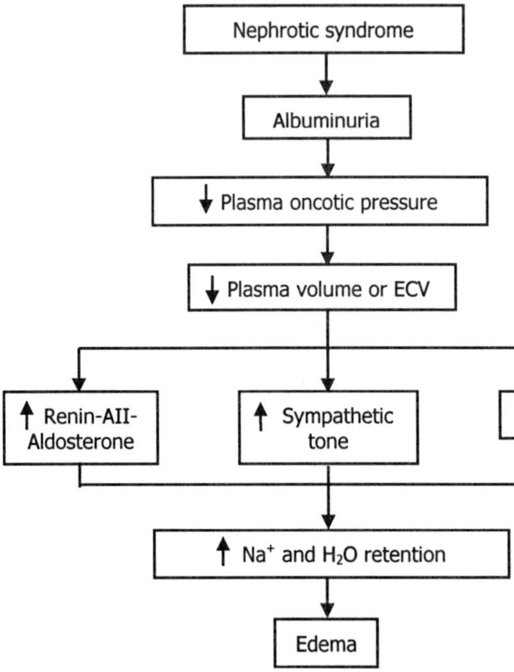

Figure 8-5. The traditional ("underfill") hypothesis for Na^+ and water retention in nephrotic syndrome. ECV = effective circulating volume.

Clinical evaluation of patients with expanded ECF volume includes medical history, physical examination, and appropriate laboratory data (electrolytes, albumin, lipids, liver function tests, and a urinalysis for lipiduria and fatty casts in patients with nephrotic syndrome). Expected physical findings in these patients are summarized in Table 8-2.

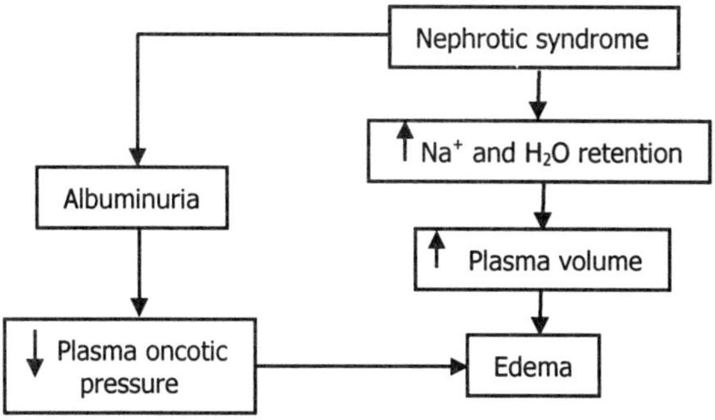

Figure 8-6. Mechanisms of "overfill" hypothesis for edema formation in nephrotic syndrome.

ECF VOLUME DEFICIT STATES

As previously stated, the maintenance of ECF volume is dependent on the concentration of Na^+ in the body. A high plasma [Na^+] in the body causes an expansion of ECF volume and a low plasma [Na^+] causes a reduction in ECF volume. It is rather difficult to induce volume contraction in humans with normal renal function, because the kidney can retain all of the filtered Na^+ and excrete Na^+-free urine in response to activation of salt-retaining mechanisms. For this reason, reduced Na^+ intake does not produce volume contraction in humans with normal renal function. However, ECF volume contraction occurs in patients who are unable to conserve Na^+ when salt intake is reduced. The signs and symptoms of volume contraction depend on the rapidity of Na^+ loss. Sudden loss of Na^+ causes a marked reduction in blood pressure and cardiac output, whereas slow and sustained loss results in a slight decrease in blood pressure. In contrast to patients with ECF volume excess, patients with volume contraction have decreased ECV and body weight.

Table 8-2. Physical findings in patients with ECF volume expansion

Findings	CHF	Liver failure	Nephrotic syndrome
Blood pressure	↑	N	N
Jugular venous pressure	↑	N	N
Crackles (lungs)	+	+/-	-
Plural effusion	+/-	+/-	+/-
Hepatojugular reflex	+	-	-
Ascites	-	+	-
Pitting edema	+	+	+

N = normal; ↑ = increase; + = present; - = absent; +/- = present or absent depending upon the severity of the disease.

Na^+ loss occurs through renal as well as extrarenal routes, and the causes are shown in the At a Glance Box 8-3.

At a Glance Box 8-3
Extrarenal and renal causes of Na^+ loss

Extrarenal causes
1. Gastrointestinal losses
   - Vomiting
   - Diarrhea
   - Nasogastric suction
   - Fistulas
   - Bleeding
2. Transcellular losses
   - Acute pancreatitis
   - Ileus
   - Peritonitis
   - Small bowel obstruction
   - Pleural effusions
3. Skin losses
   - Excessive sweating
   - Burns
   - Inflammatory skin diseases
   - Cystic fibrosis

Renal causes
1. Na^+ loss by the normal kidney
   - Diuretics
   - Adrenal insufficiency
   - Decreased renin production
2. Na^+ loss by the abnormal kidney
   - Chronic renal failure
   - Diuretic phase of ARF
   - Post-obstructive diuresis
   - Renal transplantation
   - Salt-losing nephropathy
   - Tubulo-interstitial diseases

Clinically, volume contraction results from loss of Na^+ and water as well as other electrolytes. It is customary to classify volume contraction into **hypotonic, isotonic**, and **hypertonic** volume contraction. Hypotonic volume contraction occurs as a result of electrolyte (salt) loss in excess of water loss. This excess electrolyte loss causes a decrease in plasma osmolality, which shifts water from the ECF to the ICF compartment to maintain osmotic equilibrium (see Chapter 1). Isotonic volume contraction is due to the loss of salt and water in proportionate amounts; i.e., 154 mEq for each liter of water. As a result, the plasma osmolality does not change, and therefore, no shift in water between ECF and ICF compartments occurs. However, the loss of isotonic fluid is entirely from the ECF, resulting in the contraction of the ECF compartment. Diarrhea is a cause of isotonic contraction. In hypertonic contraction, water is lost in excess of salt. As a result, the plasma osmolality increases, which causes a shift of water from ICF to ECF compartment. Decreased intake of water, excess sweating or urinary loss of water and salt due to an increase in serum glucose levels generally cause hypertonic contraction.

Diagnosis of ECF volume contraction can be made by obtaining appropriate medical history, physical signs and symptoms, and laboratory findings (see At a Glance Box 8-4).

The goals of therapy in a volume contracted patient are two-fold: (1) to improve perfusion pressure to vital organs such as the brain, kidney, and liver; and (2) to improve physical symptoms of the patient.

Mild to moderate degrees of volume contraction (dry mucous membranes) can be treated with oral administration of water (2-4 liters/day) and liberal dietary intake of salt (100-200 mEq of Na^+). Severe volume contraction with orthostatic blood pressure and pulse changes requires intravenous fluid administration. The recommended solution is normal or isotonic (0.9%) saline sufficient to raise blood pressure. Other solutions such as albumin, dextrans, or blood can be given depending on the cause and severity of volume contraction.

At a Glance Box 8-4

Clinical and laboratory diagnostic features of ECF volume contraction

History
Dietary history of Na^+ and water intake
GI losses: vomiting, diarrhea, bleeding
History of renal disease
History of medications
History of symptoms: thirst, weakness, lethargy, dizziness
Physical signs
↓ Skin turgor
Dry mucous membranes
↓ Sweating
Orthostatic or postural blood pressure (fall in systolic BP>15 mm Hg on standing) and pulse changes (>15 beats/min)
Weight loss
↓ Jugular venous pressure
↓ Intraocular pressure
Laboratory findings
↑ Serum creatinine
↑ Blood urea nitrogen (BUN)
↑ Hematocrit
↑ Serum uric acid
↓ Urine volume
↑ Urine osmolality and specific gravity
↓ Urinary [Na^+]

SUMMARY

1. The maintenance of extracellular fluid (ECF) volume requires that the kidneys' excrete urinary Na^+ to match dietary Na^+ intake. Two mechanisms are involved in the final regulation of Na^+ balance and ECF volume. Afferent mechanisms sense changes in Na^+ intake and ECF volume and efferent mechanisms respond to these changes to maintain ECF volume in the normal range.
2. Spontaneous changes in GFR due to high or low salt intake are perceived

by the proximal tubule which modulates Na^+ and water reabsorption appropriately by a phenomenon called glomerulo-tubular balance. Autoregulation also prevents changes in GFR.

3. When GFR is low, as in low Na^+ intake, Na^+ excretion is low. Conversely, when GFR is increased by volume expansion, the excretion of Na^+ is increased. Thus, Na^+ balance is maintained under normal physiologic conditions.
4. Derangements in either afferent or efferent mechanisms cause changes in ECF volume. Expanded ECF volume conditions such as congestive heart failure, cirrhosis of the liver, and nephrotic syndrome are characterized by retention of Na^+ and water. In congestive heart failure and cirrhosis of the liver, retention of Na^+ and water is due to decreased effective circulating volume (ECV). ECV represents a portion of the intravascular (blood) volume that is determined by cardiac output and peripheral vascular resistance. A decrease in either one of these factors causes a decrease in ECV, which is a potent stimulator of Na^+ and water reabsorption. Patients with ECF volume expansion present with leg edema.
5. ECF volume contraction is caused by decreased Na^+ intake or loss of Na^+ from the body through extrarenal and renal routes. Patients with severe volume contraction present with hypotension and dizziness. Infusion of isotonic (0.9%) saline improves both blood pressure and dizziness.

STUDY QUESTIONS

Case 1

A 70-year-old man was brought to the emergency room for lethargy and dizziness. He was taking a diuretic (hydrochlorothiazide) for hypertension. His blood pressure was 120/80, pulse 110 (lying) 100/60, pulse 120 (sitting). He was afebrile. His laboratory data were:

Na^+ = 134 mEq/L	Creatinine = 1.5 mg/dL
K^+ = 3.1 mEq/L	Glucose = 140 mg/dL
Cl^- = 88 mEq/L	Hemoglobin = 14%
HCO_3^- = 28 mEq/L	Hematocrit = 50%
BUN = 40 mg/dL	Urinary Na^+ = 10 mEq/L

Question 1. Explain the reason for this patient's dizziness and lethargy.

Answer: The patient has orthostatic blood pressure and pulse changes, which are due to intravascular volume contraction probably caused by the diuretic. Increases in BUN and creatinine, a BUN/creatinine ratio of >20, hemoconcentration (high hematocrit), and low urinary [Na^+] also indicate volume contraction. When the blood pressure in an elderly hypertensive patient decreases to these levels, the blood flow to the brain and other vital organs is decreased. Both dizziness and lethargy are related to relative hypotension.

Question 2. How would you treat this patient?

Answer: Because this patient is symptomatic, rapid correction of volume contraction is essential. The initial choice of solution is normal (0.9%) saline. During the first hour, the patient should receive at least 1 L of normal saline intravenously. Since normal saline remains in the extracellular compartment, it increases blood pressure and also improves perfusion to the kidney and brain. As a result, the glomerular filtration rate (GFR) is increased and the patient's lethargy should improve. Since K^+ is excreted with improvement in GFR, K^+ supplementation is necessary. Subsequent administration of intravenous solutions depends on the serum chemistry.

Case 2

A 60-year-old female with a past medical history of congestive heart failure (CHF) and hypertension was admitted for shortness of breath and weight gain of 10 lbs in the last 2 months. Chest x-ray showed pulmonary edema. She has 4 mm pitting edema in her lower extremities. She is taking digoxin and captopril (an ACE-inhibitor), and noncompliant to diet.

Question 1. Explain the reason for her weight gain.

Answer: Dietary noncompliance results in high Na^+ intake. Upon questioning she was taking ibuprofen (Motrin) for leg pain. Both excess Na^+ intake and ibuprofen lead to fluid retention and eventually leg and pulmonary edema. The combination of digoxin and captopril improves cardiac output in a patient with CHF, if adherent to diet.

Question 2. Describe this patient's effective circulating volume (ECV) and urinary Na^+ excretion.

Answer: The ECV in patients with CHF is generally decreased, although the extracellular fluid volume is increased. Because of low ECV, the proximal tubule reabsorbs most of the filtered load of Na^+, and thus the urinary $[Na^+]$ is usually < 10 mEq/L.

Case 3

A 50-year-old female with cirrhosis of the liver is admitted for management of tense ascites. On physical examination, she has crackles in lungs and pitting edema in her lower extremities. Heart examination reveals an S_3 gallop. Her serum [Na^+] is 128 mEq/L.

Question 1. Does this patient have a Na^+ or water problem or both?

Answer: This patient has both Na^+ and water problems. Based on physical examination, she has an excess total body [Na^+]. In addition to cirrhosis, she has congestive heart failure (CHF). Both cirrhosis and CHF are characterized by decreased effective circulating volume. As a result, the patient will retain both Na^+ and water.

Question 2. How would you treat this patient?

Answer: Since her major problem is Na^+ and water retention, restriction of both will help the patient lose water. Since the patient has crackles, she would benefit from a loop diuretic such as furosemide. Bed rest is advisable to improve cardiac output and GFR. Her ascites and CHF should improve. If her ascites does not improve despite the above treatment modality, removal of ascites (paracentesis) is recommended.

Question 3. Distinguish glomerulo-tubular (G-T) balance from tubuloglomerular feedback (TGF).

Answer: G-T balance refers to the relationship between GFR and mostly proximal tubular Na^+ and water reabsorption in the control of Na^+ excretion. When the GFR and filtered load of Na^+ increase, both Na^+ and water reabsorption proportionally increase. This increase in Na^+ and water reabsorption prevents excess loss of Na^+ and water in the urine. The converse is true when the GFR and filtered load of Na^+ decrease. If G-T balance did not exist, small changes in GFR or tubular Na^+ reabsorption would result in massive changes in Na^+ excretion, leading to impaired Na^+ balance.

TGF is a mechanism by which the GFR and renal plasma flow are autoregulated (Chapter 4). When GFR is increased, the delivery of tubular fluid containing Na^+ and Cl^- is increased to the macula densa of the juxtaglomerular apparatus (JGA). Signals are then sent to increase afferent arteriolar resistance and decrease glomerular hydrostatic pressure, which returns the elevated GFR to normal. In contrast, when GFR is decreased and the delivery of Na^+ and Cl^- to the macula densa is decreased, the JGA responses lead to an increase in GFR. In this way, changes in GFR are attenuated by the TGF mechanism.

SUGGESTED READING

1. Bakris, G.L. and Stein, J.H. Sodium metabolism and maintenance of extracellular fluid volume. In: Fluid, Electrolyte, and Acid-Base Disorders. 2nd edition. A.I. Arieff and R.A. Defronzo (eds.). Churchill Livingstone, New York, 1995; pp. 29-49 (*This chapter provides a summary of hormonal regulation of sodium metabolism*).
2. Briggs, J.P., Singh, I., Sawaya, B.E. and Schnermann, J. Disorders of salt balance. In: Fluids and Electrolytes. 3rd edition. J.P. Kokko and R.L. Tannen (eds.). W.B.Saunders Company, Philadelphia, 1996; pp. 3-62 (*A detailed review of normal and abnormal regulation of salt balance*).
3. Miller, J.A., Tobe, S.W. and Skorecki, K.L. Control of extracellular fluid volume and the pathophysiology of edema formation. In: The Kidney. 5th edition. B.M. Brenner (ed.). W.B. Saunders Company, Philadelphia, 1996: pp. 817-872 (*Another detailed review of sodium balance in normal and abnormal conditions. This and the above reviews are complementary to each other*).
4. Abraham, W.T. and Schrier, R.W. Cardiac failure, liver disease, and the nephrotic syndrome. In: Diseases of the Kidney. 6th edition. R.W. Schrier and C.W. Gottschalk (eds.). Little, Brown and Company, Boston, pp. 2353-2392 (*This chapter describes various pathophysiologic mechanisms responsible for edematous states in heart failure, liver failure, and nephrotic syndrome*).

CHAPTER 9

URINARY CONCENTRATION AND DILUTION

Objectives

After reading this chapter, the student should be able to:

1. List the basic components necessary for urinary concentration and dilution.
2. Understand the mechanisms involved in countercurrent multiplication and countercurrent exchange.
3. Discuss the mechanisms of urea recycling and the process of urinary dilution.
4. Understand the concepts of free-water and negative free-water clearances.
5. List factors or conditions that impair the kidneys' ability to concentrate or dilute urine.

In the previous two chapters, we have discussed how the kidneys form an ultrafiltrate and then selectively reabsorb and secrete substances from this filtered fluid. In this chapter, we explore yet another crucial renal function, the maintenance of water balance. By regulating the excretion of water, the kidneys prevent life-threatening deviations both in body fluid volume and osmolality. For example, when water intake is excessive, the kidneys excrete a hypotonic (dilute) urine so that the normal body fluid osmolality is maintained. When water intake is inadequate, a hypertonic (concentrated) urine is formed by tubular reabsorption of water. In this way, deviations in body fluid osmolalities are avoided. The kidney can concentrate urine with an osmolality of up to 1200 mOsm/kg H_2O; conversely it can dilute urine to as low as 50 mOsm/kg H_2O. In order to either concentrate or dilute urine, the following basic components are necessary:

1) Intactness of the structure and function of the nephron segments that are primarily located in the renal medulla, together with an intact blood supply;
2) Countercurrent flow of fluid and blood;
3) Maintenance of medullary interstitial hypertonicity;
4) Appropriate secretion of the antidiuretic hormone (ADH);
5) A source of energy;

6) Rate of adequate fluid delivery to the medullary collecting ducts; and
7) Adequate protein and salt intake

The structural components necessary for urine concentration and dilution are the descending thin limb of Henle's loop, thin and thick ascending limbs of Henle, and the collecting duct. The vasa recta, which arise from the efferent arteriole, supply the blood to these nephron segments. The countercurrent flow of tubular fluid and of blood is provided by the loop of Henle and vasa recta, respectively. Medullary hypertonicity, as we have seen in Chapter 7, is maintained by the active reabsorption of NaCl by the thick ascending limb of Henle's loop and also by water abstraction by the vasa recta. This active transport of NaCl provides the energy source.[1] ADH promotes water reabsorption by the collecting tubule. In conditions of water excess, ADH secretion is inhibited. Inhibition of ADH results in water diuresis and a hypotonic urine. Conversely, inadequate water intake stimulates ADH excretion, which in turn, promotes water reabsorption. Antidiuresis results and hypertonic urine is formed.

Let us see how these basic components function in the processes of urine concentration and dilution.

CONCENTRATION OF URINE

Two processes are involved in urinary concentration: **countercurrent multiplication** and **countercurrent exchange**. The concept of countercurrent multiplication, originally evolved from industrial processes that separate and concentrate useful products, was pioneered by Kuhn (a Swiss engineer) and his colleagues to explain the corticopapillary osmotic gradient in the renal medulla. According to these investigators, the loop of Henle functions as a countercurrent multiplier (or augmenter) in which small transverse osmotic differences between the ascending and descending limbs are augmented by countercurrent flow. This augmentation causes a large axial (vertical) difference in osmotic gradient from cortex to papilla. For example, the osmolality of the cortex is approximately 300 mOsm/kg H_2O. This osmolality gradually increases from the cortex to the outer medulla, inner medulla, and then to the papilla where the osmolality is 1200 mOsm/kg H_2O. How this progressive increase in osmolality occurs by countercurrent multiplication is illustrated in Figure 9-1 and summarized as follows:

1 Urea, which is generated from protein intake, is also necessary to maintain medullary interstitial hypertonicity. The need for NaCl intake is quite obvious.

Countercurrent Multiplication

1. *Fluid that enters the descending limb of Henle's loop from the proximal tubule is isosmotic to plasma (for convenience let us use 300 mOsm/kg H_2O instead of 285 mOsm/kg H_2O).*
2. *The descending limb is more permeable to water than it is to NaCl and urea. As a result, water moves into the interstitium. Some NaCl and urea probably move into the lumen of the descending limb. Because there is less water and more NaCl in the lumen the concentration of the tubular fluid is increased. At the hairpin turn of the loop, the osmolality of the tubular fluid can reach as high as 1200 mOsm/kg H_2O.*
3. *The thin ascending limb of Henle's loop is impermeable to water but permeable to NaCl and urea. NaCl moves passively out of the lumen into the medullary interstitium, causing dilution of the tubular fluid. The tubular fluid becomes even more diluted as it moves up into the thick ascending limb of Henle's loop.*
4. *The primary driving force for hypertonic (concentrated) urine formation is the active reabsorption of NaCl by the thick ascending limb of Henle's loop. As a result of this reabsorption, the concentration of NaCl in the medullary interstitium increases. This medullary hypertonicity causes water to move out of the descending limb of Henle's loop. Since the thick ascending limb is impermeable to water, the tubular fluid becomes extremely dilute and its osmolality approaches 100 mOsm/kg H_2O.*
5. *The fluid that enters the cortical collecting duct is hypoosmotic to its surrounding interstitium. Water needs to move out of the lumen in order for the urine to become concentrated. In the presence of ADH, water is reabsorbed and the process of urine concentration begins at this point (ADH promotes water reabsorption in the cortical and medullary collecting duct. For details see Chapter 10). As shown in Figure 9-1, the osmolality of the fluid becomes 300 mOsm/kg H_2O in the cortical collecting duct, which is similar to the interstitial osmolality. Although the osmolalities are similar, the composition of the tubular and interstitial fluids is different. Much of the interstitial fluid osmolality is due to NaCl, whereas the tubular fluid osmolality is due to urea; nonreabsorbed solutes, such as creatinine; and to a lesser extent, NaCl.*
6. *As the fluid moves down the medullary collecting duct, water, and NaCl are reabsorbed leaving urea in the lumen as the major solute. At this point, the increased osmolality in the tubular fluid is*

primarily due to urea and other nonreabsorbable solutes. However, the inner medullary collecting duct is permeable to urea, and as a result, urea is transported into the interstitium by a carrier-mediated mechanism. This urea permeability is further enhanced by ADH. Finally, the urea concentration reaches an equilibration with the interstitium. This equilibrium will tend to diminish further accumulation of urea in the urine. At this point, the urinary osmolality of 1200 mOsm/kg H_2O is composed of 600 mOsm/kg H_2O of urea; the remaining fraction comprises nonreabsorbable solutes plus electrolytes such as Na^+, Cl^-, and K^+.

When we look at the osmolalities of tubular fluid and interstitium in Figure 9-1, we can see a transverse difference of 200 mOsm/kg H_2O between the ascending limb of Henle's loop and the interstitium. However, osmolality gradually increases (vertical or axial increase) at the outer medulla to the papilla in the descending limb of Henle's loop. This increase is called countercurrent multiplication, and it is due to the maintenance of medullary interstitial hypertonicity.

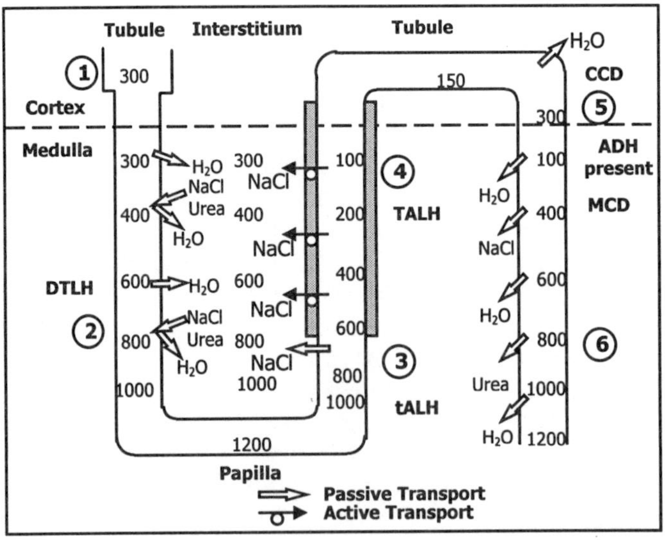

Figure 9-1. Mechanism of countercurrent multiplication to form a concentrated urine in the presence of ADH. Numbers refer to a process described in the text. DTLH = descending thin limb of Henle's loop; tALH = thin ascending limb of Henle's loop; TALH = thick ascending limb of Henle's loop; CCD = cortical collecting duct; MCD = medullary collecting duct.

How is this medullary hypertonicity maintained? Three mechanisms are responsible: (1) active NaCl reabsorption by the thick ascending limb of Henle's loop; (2) medullary blood supply by the vasa recta which acts as a countercurrent exchange; and (3) recycling of urea.

Countercurrent Exchange: the Vasa Recta

The vasa recta are the blood vessels that supply the medulla. These blood vessels, which have a hairpin configuration similar to the loop of Henle, carry about 10% of the total renal blood flow. The vasa recta serve two major functions: (1) they supply oxygen and nutrients to the medullary tubules; and (2) they remove water that is reabsorbed from the collecting duct and thus function as **countercurrent exchangers**. The latter function is important in the maintenance of medullary interstitial hypertonicity; otherwise, the accumulated water, if not removed, would dissipate the hypertonicity. Furthermore, the excess solute that enters the medullary interstitium is also removed by the vasa recta. The countercurrent exchange system is illustrated in Figure 9-2, and can be summarized as follows:

1. ***The vasa recta are highly permeable to solute and water. Blood entering the descending vasa recta has the same osmolality as the plasma (for convenience 300 mOsm/kg H_2O). As it flows through the medulla, blood loses water into the interstitium and gains solute. Both are passive movements. This exchange results in an increase in blood osmolality, as in the descending limb of Henle's loop. At the hairpin bend of the capillary, the osmolality reaches 1200 mOsm/kg H_2O, which is similar to the interstitial osmolality.***
2. ***As the blood flows through the ascending vasa recta, water is added and the solute diffuses back into the interstitium. The result is dilution of the blood and maintenance of medullary hypertonicity. The blood leaves the vasa recta with a slightly higher osmolality than the blood that entered the vasa recta. If it were not for this countercurrent flow in the ascending vasa recta, the blood would have left the vasa recta with an osmolality of 1200 mOsm/kg H_2O. The net result of this countercurrent exchange is to remove water that is added to the interstitium, and thereby aid in the maintenance of medullary hypertonicity.***

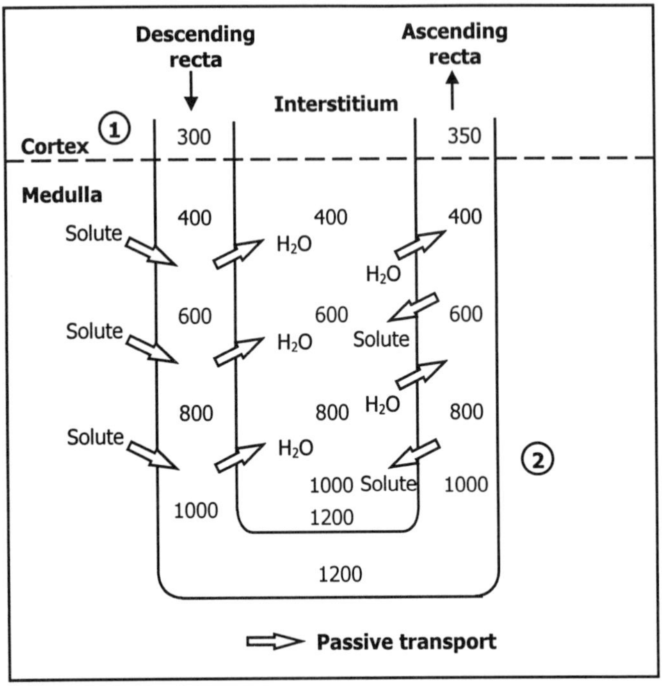

Figure 9-2. Mechanism of countercurrent exchange by the vasa recta. Note that the vasa recta protect the medullary hypertonicity rather than creating a gradient as shown in Fig. 9-1. Numbers refer to a process described in the text.

Recycling of Urea

The discussion so far implicates only NaCl as the major constituent of the renal medullary interstitium. Studies have indicated that urea constitutes about 50% of the solute content of the medulla and pelvis. That urea plays an important role in urinary concentration is evidenced by experiments conducted on animals fed a low-protein diet. These animals had a lower medullary urea content ratio than animals fed a normal diet, and also failed to concentrate their urine as much as their normal counterparts. In addition, the concentrating ability of the animals on low-protein diet returned to normal when they were given urea. Thus, urea concentration must be maintained in the medullary interstitium for hypertonicity.

In order to understand how urea is recycled, it is necessary to know how the tubule handles urea. Urea is filtered at the glomerulus. About 50% of urea is reabsorbed by the proximal tubule. Since water is also reabsorbed, the concentration of urea in the tubular fluid increases as it enters the descending limb of Henle's loop. As the tubular fluid reaches the papilla, the concentration of urea increases even further. This increase occurs due to the withdrawal of water, as well as addition of urea to the tubular fluid (the thin ascending limb is permeable to urea; therefore, some urea from the interstitium moves into the tubule). No urea exchange occurs in the thick ascending limb because the epithelium is impermeable to urea. As fluid enters the cortical collecting and outer medullary ducts, urea concentration increases markedly due to water reabsorption in the presence of ADH. Both of these segments have low permeabilities for urea. In contrast, the inner medullary collecting duct has a high permeability to urea, which is further enhanced by ADH. At this point, the tubular fluid contains a high concentration of urea, which is transported into the interstitium by a carrier-mediated mechanism, where it contributes to the medullary tonicity. Some of this interstitial urea reenters the thin ascending limb (and to a lesser extent, the descending limb) to recirculate in the tubules. The transport of urea into the interstitium from the inner medullary collecting duct and its reentry into the descending and thin ascending limbs of Henle's loop is called **urea recycling**.

The importance of urea recycling in the concentration of urine is summarized as follows: accumulation of urea in the medullary interstitium raises tonicity in the presence of NaCl. This medullary hypertonicity promotes water reabsorption from the descending limb and increases tubular fluid solute (both NaCl and urea) concentration and thus its osmolality. In this way, urea recycling participates in countercurrent multiplication. Another important role of urea recycling is water conservation. At a steady state, an individual must excrete solute that amounts to about 600 mOsm/kg H_2O. If the urine concentration is 1200 mOsm/kg H_2O, the minimum obligatory water excretion to account for this osmolality is 500 ml/day (600 mOsm/kg H_2O /0.5 L = 1200 mOsm/kg H_2O). If the entire collecting duct were impermeable to urea, the maximal osmolality one could achieve in the medullary interstitium would be only 600 mOsm/kg H_2O, which would primarily be due to electrolytes other than urea. In order to eliminate the obligatory solute load of 600 mOsm/kg H_2O, an individual would have to excrete 1000 ml water due to the tubules decreased concentrating ability. Thus, urea contributes to preservation of water excretion by contributing to medullary hypertonicity.

DILUTION OF URINE

As we stated earlier, the kidneys excrete dilute urine when water intake is excessive in order to maintain normal body fluid osmolality. From the previous discussion, it is clear that the osmolality of tubular fluid is about 150 mOsm/kg H_2O only in the cortical thick ascending limb of Henle's loop. Thus, the principal site of urinary dilution is the cortical thick ascending limb. Also, Figure 9-1 demonstrates that urine is concentrated to 1200 mOsm/kg H_2O in the presence of ADH. What would happen if ADH were absent or minimal? Since ADH promotes reabsorption of water in the cortical collecting and medullary collecting ducts, its absence would lead to dilution of tubular fluid (step 5 in Figure 9-3), and urine osmolality would be as low as 50 mOsm/kg H_2O (step 6 in Figure 9-3). This suggests that urinary dilution also occurs beyond the thick ascending limb in the absence of ADH.

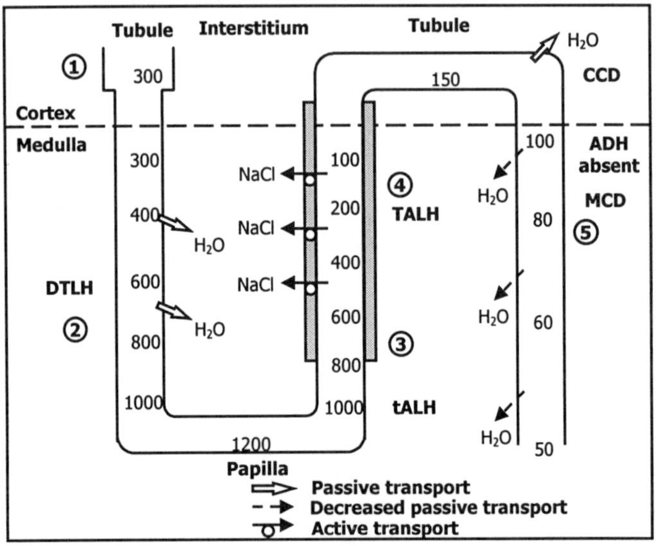

Figure 9-3. Mechanism of urinary dilution. Note that only thick ascending limb and collecting duct are involved in the process of urinary dilution. Numbers refer to a process described in the text for Fig. 9-1. DTLH = descending thin limb of Henle's loop; tALH = thin ascending limb of Henle's loop; TALH = thick ascending limb of Henle's loop; MCT = medullary collecting duct.

Studies have shown that water leaks into the interstitium from the inner medullary collecting duct in the absence of ADH. In fact, more water diffuses out of the medullary collecting ducts in water diuresis than in antidiuresis. If this is true, why is the urine not concentrated? Two explanations have been offered. First, the excess water that is reabsorbed increases blood flow to the vasa recta, and therefore increases solute loss from the medullary interstitium. Second, the reabsorption of NaCl in the medullary collecting duct is higher than water reabsorption. This high rate of NaCl reabsorption leaves the tubular fluid hypoosmotic, and therefore the urine is not concentrated.

In the absence of ADH, urea diffusion from the terminal inner medullary collecting duct also decreases. This results in a decrease in medullary hypertonicity. Urea excretion, therefore, increases in water diuresis.

ORGANIC OSMOLYTES

Water intake and water deprivation cause changes both in urine and inner medullary osmolality. During sleep, the inner medullary osmolality rises to produce concentrated urine because of water deprivation. Following water intake, for example during breakfast, both urine and inner medullary osmolalities decrease substantially. These rapid changes in osmolality may cause osmotic damage to the medullary cells. However, this does not happen because the inner medullary cells accumulate osmoprotective substances called **organic osmolytes**. These osmolytes are sorbitol, inositol, glycerylphosphoryl-choline, betaine, and taurine. During periods of water deprivation, the organic osmolytes accumulate in the cell to maintain hypertonicity. When water is ingested, the inner medullary cells release osmolytes into the urine to reduce the intracellular osmolality. Thus, the organic osmolytes prevent drastic intracellular osmolality changes in the inner medullary cells.

MEASUREMENT OF URINARY CONCENTRATION AND DILUTION

The ability of the kidney either to concentrate or dilute the urine can be quantitated by measuring the urinary osmolality. Under appropriate conditions, the kidney can dilute urine as low as 50 mOsm/kg H_2O or can concentrate urine up to 1200 mOsm/kg H_2O, as described previously. In a dilute urine, more water is excreted than solutes, i.e., the renal tubules reabsorbed less and excreted more water. Conversely, in a concentrated urine, more solute-free water is reabsorbed. To quantitate the amount of water excretion or reabsorption, the concepts of **free-water** and **osmolar clearance** were introduced. According to these concepts, the urine consists of two portions: one portion contains all the solute that is isosmotic to plasma, this portion is called the osmolar clearance (C_{osm}) and the other portion contains solute-free water and is called the free-water clearance (C_{H_2O}). Thus, we have the following equation:

$$V = C_{osm} + C_{H_2O} \quad (1)$$

where V is the total urine volume.

C_{osm} is defined by the standard clearance formula as:

$$C_{osm} = (U_{osm} \times V)/P_{osm} \quad (2)$$

where V is the urine volume in ml/min; U_{osm} and P_{osm} refer to urinary and plasma osmolalities, respectively.

C_{H_2O} is not defined by the clearance formula. Instead, it is defined as the difference between the urine volume and the osmolar clearance. Therefore, C_{H_2O} is:

$$C_{H_2O} = V - C_{osm} \qquad (3)$$

How To Calculate C_{H_2O} and C_{osm}

The following example illustrates the significance of C_{H_2O} and C_{osm} in a dilute urine.

A volunteer was infused via a central vein with 10 L of D5W (5% dextrose in water), and the following values were obtained:

P_{osm} = 280 mOsm/kg H_2O
U_{osm} = 50 mOsm/kg H_2O
Urine flow rate = 6 ml/min

$$C_{H_2O} = V - C_{osm}$$
$$= 6 - (50 \times 6/280) \text{ or } 300/280 = 1.07$$
$$= 6 - 1.07 = 4.93 \qquad (4)$$

Of the 6 ml of dilute urine, 4.93 ml accounts for free water (C_{H_2O}) and 1.07 ml represents isosmotic solution containing all the solute (C_{osm}).

In the above example, the urine was diluted because more water was added or the tubules reabsorbed less water. The opposite phenomenon occurs in an individual with concentrated urine, which is due to water reabsorption. This solute-free reabsorption of water is called **negative free-water clearance** (abbreviated as T^cH_2O). The abbreviation T^cH_2O stands for the difference between the osmolar clearance and the urine flow rate. Thus,

$$T^cH_2O = C_{osm} - V.$$

How To Calculate T^cH_2O

A volunteer was asked not to drink fluids for 12 hours. He lost 2% of his body weight. The following values were obtained.

P_{osm} = 290 mOsm/kg H_2O
U_{osm} = 870 mOsm/kg H_2O
Urine flow rate = 0.5 ml/min

$$C_{osm} = \frac{870 \times 0.5}{290} = 1.5 \qquad (5)$$

$$T^cH_2O = C_{osm} - V \text{ or } 1.5 - 0.5 = 1 \text{ ml}$$

This result indicates that 1.0 ml of water was reabsorbed per min. Another way of stating this is that T^cH_2O is equal to 1 ml/min.

SUMMARY

1. The kidneys prevent life-threatening deviations in body fluid volume and osmolality by regulating water excretion. During periods of water deprivation, the kidneys reabsorb water and excrete a concentrated urine. When water intake is excessive, the kidneys generate a dilute urine.
2. Urine is concentrated because of the combined function of the loop of Henle, which progressively generates a high osmolality in the medulla by a process called countercurrent multiplication and the action of ADH on the collecting duct to augment water permeability by regulating aquaporin-2 water channel protein.
3. The medullary hypertonicity created by countercurrent multiplication is maintained by the vasa recta, the blood vessels that supply the medulla, by a process called countercurrent exchange. Also, urea, which constitutes about 50% of the solute in the medullary interstitium, plays an important role in the maintenance of hypertonicity.
4. Dilute urine is formed when ADH levels are low or absent. Medullary hypotonicity, which may be due to excessive water intake, low-protein intake causing low urea production or inhibition of NaCl reabsorption in the thick ascending limb of Henle's loop by loop diuretics, also results in dilute urine. Organic osmolytes such as sorbitol, inositol, etc., protect cells of the medullary interstitium from osmotic damage caused by hypertonicity or hypotonicity.
5. The kidneys' ability to dilute or concentrate the urine is quantitated by measuring the amount of solute-free water (C_{H_2O}) that is excreted or reabsorbed (T^cH_2O) by the collecting duct.

CLINICAL APPLICATIONS

Several conditions can impair the concentrating ability of the kidney. First, the absence of ADH or drugs that can counteract the effects of ADH can impair urine concentration. Patients with **central diabetes insipidus** (CDI) or **nephrogenic diabetes insipidus** (NDI) are unable to concentrate their urine (see Chapter 10). Patients with CDI have absent or low ADH; those with NDI have high ADH levels, but their collecting tubules are resistant to ADH. Drugs such as **ibuprofen**, which inhibit prostaglandin synthesis, enhance the effects of ADH by relieving the antagonizing effects of prostaglandin E_1 on ADH action. Second, any drug that inhibits Na/K/2Cl cotransport at the thick ascending limb will impair the kidney's urine concentrating ability. Loop diuretics, such as **furosemide** or **bumetanide**, impair this cotransporter, and thus create medullary hypotonicity. Third, an increase in medullary circulation will wash out hypertonicity and impair urine concentration. For example, an increase in GFR increases the volume of the tubular fluid perfusing the medulla, which decreases medullary hypertonicity and thus impairs urine concentration. Compulsive water drinkers, who consume > 4L/day, can wash out their medullary hypertonicity. Fourth, any structural damage to the medulla may dissipate medullary hypertonicity. Diseases such as **glomerulonephritis, hydronephrosis,** or **sickle cell disease** can cause medullary damage. Fifth, **chronic renal failure** limits the concentrating ability of the surviving nephrons. In chronic renal failure, the delivery of solutes and water to the functioning nephrons increases, which overwhelms their handling capacity. As a result, the medullary hypertonicity decreases. Finally, individuals with severe **malnutrition** are unable to concentrate their urine due to poor salt and protein intake. A decrease in salt and protein intake would result in medullary hypotonicity because the osmoles in the interstitium are mostly contributed by salt and urea. Maximum concentrating ability also decreases with **aging**. This defect in the elderly is due to diminished medullary tonicity caused by decreased transport of NaCl in the thick ascending limb of Henle's loop.

Regardless of the cause, individuals with defective concentrating ability have **polyuria** (frequent urination) and **polydipsia** (frequent drinking) of varying degree. Frequent urination at night (**nocturia**) may be an early clue to a defect in concentrating ability.

An impairment in urinary dilution may be caused by both renal and nonrenal mechanisms. Chronic renal disease generally causes dilution of urine, but not to the minimal urine osmolality of 50 mOsm/kg H_2O due to the relatively large volume of fluid perfusing a small number of functioning nephrons. Consequently, **osmotic diuresis** occurs in a patient with chronic renal disease. Osmotic diuresis also occurs in individuals with diabetes. Excess levels of ADH can also impair urine dilution. This condition occurs in a patient with **syndrome of inappropriate secretion of ADH** (SIADH). Patients with SIADH cannot lower their urine osmolality below 100 m0sm/kg H_2O. Similarly, patients with **congestive heart failure** and **cirrhosis** of the liver (see Chapter 8) are unable to dilute the urine maximally. It should be noted that concentration and dilution mechanisms are closely interrelated and, therefore, share certain common causes such as chronic renal failure.

Unlike loop diuretics, thiazide diuretics impair diluting ability of the kidney. Thiazide diuretics act in the cortical distal tubule and inhibit NaCl reabsorption. They also disturb water transport. By inhibiting NaCl reabsorption, thiazides induce mild volume depletion, which promotes salt and water reabsorption in the proximal tubule. This leads to less delivery of filtrate to the distal tubule, so less C_{H_2O} is cleared. Also, volume depletion caused by thiazides stimulates ADH secretion, which in turn, promotes water reabsorption. These changes lead to less water in the urine, thus causing impairment in urinary dilution.

Aging, in addition to decreasing concentrating ability, also diminishes the diluting ability. The causes are multifactorial: (1) decrease in GFR; (2) diminished solute transport in the thick ascending limb of Henle's loop;and (3) inadequate suppression of ADH release.

STUDY QUESTIONS

Case 1

A 22-year-old female with a history of schizophrenia was admitted for altered mental status. The only medical history she gave was that she takes a "bunch" of medications and drinks a lot of water. The following values were obtained:

Plasma osmolality: 270 mOsm/kg H_2O
Urine osmolality: 150 mOsm/kg H_2O

Following an overnight fast, her urine osmolality remained at 450 mOsm/kg H_2O but her urine volume was 4 liters.

Question 1. Explain why this patient was unable to concentrate her urine to the maximum.

Answer: This patient was a compulsive water drinker. Because of her excess water intake, she washed out her medullary hypertonicity. Therefore, she was unable to concentrate her urine even though she fasted for 12 hours.

Case 2

A 60-year-old man with congestive heart failure was taking digoxin and furosemide (loop diuretic). He was admitted because of increasing shortness of breath. His urinary osmolality was 1100 mOsm/kg H_2O. His doctor repeatedly tells him that he was not taking furosemide regularly and for this reason he is accumulating water in his lungs, which is causing shortness of breath.

Question 1. Is the patient taking furosemide? If not, why?

Answer: Based on urine osmolality, the patient is able to concentrate his urine properly. This suggests that the patient maintains his medullary hypertonicity. Furosemide interferes with the absorption of NaCl by the thick ascending limb and thereby dissipating the medullary hypertonicity. This results in failure to concentrate urine.

The urine osmolality in this patient is 1100 mOsm/kg H_2O. Therefore, the patient was not taking furosemide. If he were taking furosemide, his urine osmolality would be 300-400 mOsm/kg H_2O.

Case 3

A patient has the following values:

Plasma osmolality = 280 mOsm/kg H_2O

Urine osmolality = 140 mOsm/kg H_2O
Urine volume = 10 L/day

Question 1. Calculate the free-water clearance (C_{H_2O}) in this patient.

Answer:

$V = C_{osm} + C_{H_2O}$

$$C_{osm} = \frac{\text{Urine osmolality x Urine volume}}{\text{Plasma osmolality}}$$

$$= \frac{140 \times 10}{280} = 5\ L$$

$C_{H_2O} = V - C_{osm}$

$= 10 - 5 = 5\ L$

The free-water clearance is 5 L/day.

Question 1. Calculate the negative free-water clearance (T^cH_2O) using the following values:

P_{osm} = 300 mOsm/kg H_2O
U_{osm} = 1200 mOsm/kg H_2O
Total urine volume = 2 L/day

Answer:

$T^cH_2O = C_{osm} - V$

$$C_{osm} = \frac{(1200 \times 2)}{300} = 8\ L$$

The negative free-water clearance is 8 - 2 = 6 L/day

Question 2. Match the following osmolality values with the nephron segments in the presence of ADH.

Tubule	mOsm/kg H_2O
A = Proximal tubule	100
B = Inner medullary descending thin limb	300
C = Hairpin loop	1200
D = Thin ascending limb	1000
E = Thick ascending limb	1000
F = Cortical collecting duct	300
G = Inner medullary collecting duct	1000

Answer:

A = 300 B = 1000 C = 1200 D = 1000
E = 100 F = 300 G = 1000

Question 3. Compare and contrast the countercurrent multiplication with countercurrent exchange.

Answer: Both these processes are dependent on the hairpin configuration of the descending and ascending loops of Henle. Countercurrent multiplication requires active transport of NaCl at the thick ascending limb of Henle into the medullary interstitium to maintain hypertonicity. It alone can maintain osmotic concentration gradient from the cortex to the papilla. In contrast, countercurrent exchange is a passive process and occurs in the vasa recta. Solutes and water diffuse in both directions across the vasa recta. Countercurrent exchange does not establish an osmotic concentration gradient, however, it maintains hypertonicity in the medullary interstitium by removing water that is reabsorbed from the collecting duct.

SUGGESTED READING

1. Roy, D.R., Layton, H.E. and Jamison, R.L. Countercurrent mechanism and its regulation. In: The Kidney: Physiology and Pathophysiology. 2nd edition. D.W. Seldin and G. Giebisch (eds.). Raven Press, New York, 1992; pp. 1649-1692 (*An in-depth review of urine concentration and dilution*).
2. Knepper, M.S. and Rector, F.C., Jr. Urinary concentration and dilution. In: The Kidney. 5th edition. B.M. Brenner (ed.). W.B. Saunders Company, Philadelphia, 1996; pp. 532-570 (*Another detailed review of mechanisms and regulation of urinary concentration and dilution*).
3. Jamison, R.L. The urinary concentrating mechanism. In: Nephrology. R.L. Jamison and R. Wilkinson (eds.). Chapman & Hall, London, 1997; pp. 71-86 (*This recent review provides information on aquaporins and osmolytes that are involved in maintaining urinary concentration and dilution*).

CHAPTER 10

REGULATION OF PLASMA OSMOLALITY AND DISORDERS OF WATER BALANCE

Objectives

After reading this chapter, the student should be able to:

1. Discuss the factors that control thirst.
2. Discuss the synthesis, structure, and mechanism of action of ADH.
3. Describe the osmotic and nonosmotic factors that control ADH release.
4. Discuss the disorders of water balance.

In Chapter 8, we discussed that Na^+ balance is maintained by its intake and excretion. In this chapter, we will discuss how plasma osmolality and water balances are maintained. Like Na^+ balance, water balance is determined by the amount of water that is ingested and excreted. In a normal individual, the major source of water intake is oral fluids. Water is also derived from other sources such as solid foods and intermediary metabolism. Intravenous fluids form the principal source of water intake in hospitalized patients. Also, dialysis patients may gain water during treatments.

Water is excreted principally by the kidney as urine. Other sources of water loss include the skin, respiratory, and gastrointestinal tracts. The water loss from organs other than the kidney is called **insensible loss**, which amounts to approximately 10 ml/kg/day. Fever increases insensible loss of water. At a steady state, water intake equals water loss.

If water intake and loss are not equal, the plasma osmolality is altered. However, in a healthy individual, plasma osmolality is controlled within fairly narrow limits (± 1-2%) by the hypothalamic-pituitary-antidiuretic hormone (ADH) system. Normal plasma osmolality varies from 280 to 295 mOsm/kg H_2O. If plasma osmolality increases by 1-2%, the subject feels thirsty; the circulating ADH levels increase, and the subject drinks fluids. This fluid is retained in the body by the action of ADH in the collecting duct, and the osmolality returns to normal. Opposite changes occur if plasma osmolality is decreased. Although the major influencing factor in maintaining normal plasma osmolality is the sensation of thirst, it is the combined effect of thirst, ADH, and the renal response to ADH that regulate plasma osmolality and water balance. **Osmoregulation** is the term generally used to refer to the regulation of body fluid osmolality.

CONTROL OF THIRST

Thirst is essential to the maintenance of normal body fluid osmolality. It is defined as a desire for water. Abnormal thirst may be physiological or pathological. The main regulator of thirst is the effective osmolality of body fluids. For example, an increase in plasma osmolality (hypertonicity) stimulates thirst by causing thirst osmoreceptor cells, which are located in the anterolateral hypothalamus near the third ventricle to shrink. These thirst receptors are partially distinct from those osmoreceptors that mediate the release of ADH. The threshold for thirst, that is, the level of plasma osmolality at which a subject develops an urge to drink water, varies from individual to individual. Water deprivation and infusion of hypertonic saline, or hyperglycemia raise plasma osmolality and thus stimulate thirst. Hypovolemia also stimulates thirst. The mechanism appears to be an increase in angiotensin II. In contrast, an increase in plasma osmolality due to urea or alcohol does not stimulate thirst because the thirst osmoreceptors do not shrink. These substances, called ineffective osmolytes, penetrate the cell plasma membrane easily, and thus unable to maintain any osmotic gradient. Therefore, the thirst osmoreceptors do not shrink.

Abnormal thirst may increase water intake, which lowers the plasma $[Na^+]$ and causes severe symptomatic (neurologic) **hyponatremia**. Abnormal thirst occurs in patients with schizophrenia and other related disorders. Lack of thirst may occur in newborns and in some elderly individuals. Decreased water intake causes an increase in plasma $[Na^+]$ and thus results in severe **hypernatremia**.

STRUCTURE AND SYNTHESIS OF ADH

ADH is a nonapeptide; that is, it contains 9 amino acids. Because arginine is located at position 8, ADH is also called arginine vasopressin (AVP). The terms AVP and ADH are synonymous. Cysteine is located at both the first and sixth positions; these two amino acids form a disulfide bridge (Figure 10-1). Removal of this disulfide bridge destroys the biologic activity of ADH. Substitution of lysine for arginine at position 8 yields lysine vasopressin, which is found in pigs. Oxytocin is another hormone that shares chemical similarity with ADH. It has isoleucine at position 3 and leucine at position 8. Oxytocin is a potent vasoconstrictor of the smooth muscles of the uterus and mammary glands and has less than 1% of the antidiuretic activity of ADH.

ADH is synthesized by the supraoptic and paraventricular nuclei of the hypothalamus. It is initially synthesized as a prohormone called **propressophysin**, which has a molecular weight of 20,000 daltons. This prohormone is composed of three components: ADH, neurophysin, and glycopeptide. The prohormone is packaged in secretory vesicles within the cell bodies of the hypothalamic nuclei. The secretory vesicles containing the prohormone are transported to the posterior pituitary gland through the hypothalamic neurohypophyseal tract. During this transport, the prohormone is cleaved to form ADH and its carrier, neurophysin. The fate of glycopeptide is unknown.

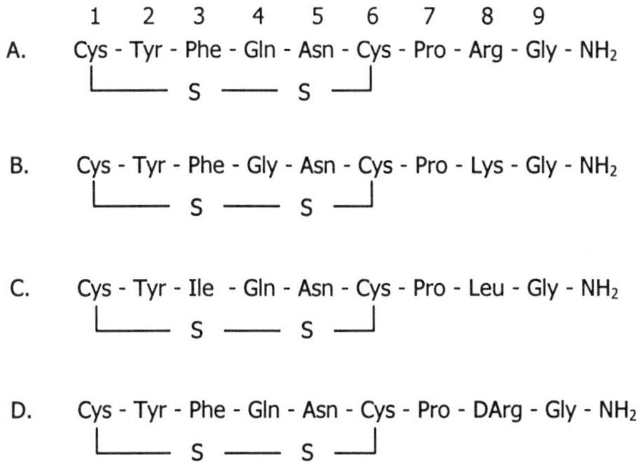

Figure 10-1. Structures of arginine vasopressin (A), lysine vasopressin (B), oxytocin (C) and desmopressin (D).

ADH is released from the posterior pituitary gland in response to a stimulus by calcium-dependent exocytosis. The half-life of ADH is 10-25 minutes as it is degraded by the liver and kidney. In plasma, it is cleared by a specific enzyme called **vasopressinase**.

CONTROL OF ADH RELEASE

The major physiologic stimulus for ADH release is plasma osmolality. An increase in plasma osmolality stimulates ADH release, while a decrease inhibits ADH release. It has been shown that when plasma osmolality is less than 280 mOsm/kg H_2O, the plasma levels of ADH are undetectable. Conversely, when plasma osmolality is greater than 295 mOsm/kg H_2O, the plasma levels of ADH are greatly increased. ADH release is controlled by the osmoreceptors located in the wall of the third ventricle. When these osmoreceptors sense either an increase or a decrease in plasma osmolality, they send impulses to the supraoptic and paraventricular nuclei for an appropriate response. This sequence suggests that the locations of osmoreceptor cells and supraoptic and paraventricular nuclei are different.

An increase in plasma osmolality of 1-2% causes shrinkage of osmoreceptor cells which causes ADH to be synthesized and released into the circulation. A decrease in osmolality causes swelling of osmoreceptor cells and eventual inhibition of ADH release. Since plasma osmolality is largely contributed by the concentration of Na^+, it is conceivable that the sensitivity of osmoreceptors depends on plasma [Na^+]. Indeed, it has been shown that infusion of hypertonic saline stimulates more ADH release than infusion of other solutes such as urea or glucose.

Besides osmotic stimulus, several other nonosmotic factors have been shown to influence ADH release. These factors are summarized in Table 10-1. Of these, hemodynamic changes such as volume contraction and hypotension play an important role in ADH release. These hemodynamic changes are mediated by the receptors located in the atria, aortic arch, and carotid sinus (Chapter 8). Figure 10-2 summarizes the integrative action of hypothalamic centers for thirst, ADH, and renal response to ADH in maintaining normal plasma osmolality in conditions of hypo-and hyperosmolality.

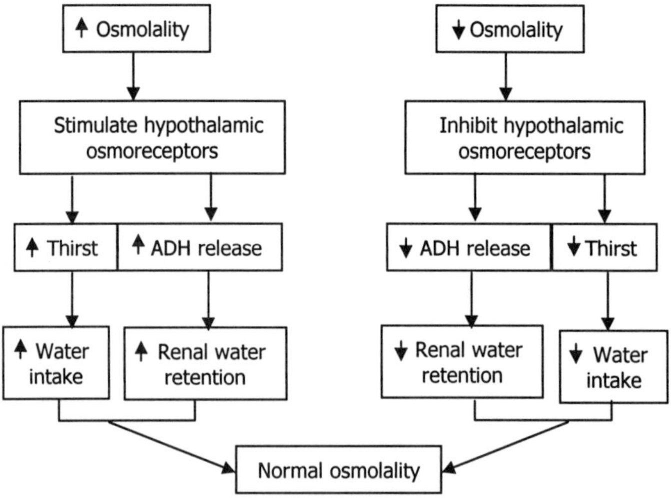

Figure 10-2. Mechanisms that maintain normal plasma osmolality in conditions of hypo- and hyperosmolality.

Table 10-1. Factors (partial list) that influence ADH release

Stimuli	Response
Osmotic	
Increase in plasma osmolality	↑
Decrease in plasma osmolality	↓
Nonosmotic	
Decrease in volume or blood pressure	↑
Increase in volume or blood pressure	↓
Nausea	↑
Pain	↑
Physical stress	↑
Hypoglycemia	↑
Low PO_2 and high PCO_2	↑
α-adrenergic agents	↓
β-adrenergic agents	↑
Cholinergic and dopaminergic agents	↑
Angiotensin II	↑
Narcotics	↑
Antimetabolites	↑
Oral hypoglycemics, particularly chlorpropamide	↑
Ethanol	↓
Phenytoin	↓
Prostaglandins (PGE_2)	↓
Atrial natriuretic peptide	↓

↑ = increase; ↓ = decrease

MECHANISM AND ACTIONS OF ADH

Mechanism

The main actions of ADH are on the kidney. However, as the name vasopression implies, ADH has pressor effects on the blood vessels. ADH exerts its effects through membrane receptors. To date, four different ADH receptors have been identified. V_1 receptors are present on the vascular smooth muscle, liver, and glomerular mesangial cells. Binding of ADH to these receptors increases the concentration of cytosolic Ca^{2+} through the inositol triphosphate pathway. V_2 receptors are present on the epithelial cells of the medullary thick ascending limb and the collecting duct. V_3 receptors are present in the kidney, pituitary, heart, spleen in the rat, whereas in humans it is restricted to the pituitary. The V_4 receptor (called vasopressin-activated calcium mobilizing receptor) is present in the kidney, heart, brain, and skeletal muscle.

The V_2 receptor is the major receptor that is responsible for water reabsorption in the collecting duct. Binding of ADH to this V_2 receptor in the collecting duct promotes water reabsorption from the tubular lumen by the following mechanism (Figure 10-3). ADH binds to the V_2 receptor located in the basolateral membrane. The V_2 receptor is coupled with a G-stimulatory protein. Activation of G-protein stimulates adenylate cyclase, which converts ATP into cAMP. This cAMP activates protein kinase A, which in turn stimulates intracellular vesicles-containing aquaporin-2 (AQP-2) water channels (see Chapter 2). These AQP-2 water channels are subsequently translocated to the apical membrane by exocytosis of intracellular vesicles for transport of water. This process of translocation is called **shuttle** hypothesis. Once ADH levels are low, water permeability is decreased with a shift of AQP-2 water channels back into the intracellular vesicles. Water exit at the basolateral membrane is facilitated by AQP-3 and AQP-4 water channels.

A number of factors block ADH-stimulated water reabsorption. Among these, prostaglandins E_2, atrial natriuretic peptide, hypercalcemia, hypokalemia, lithium, and demeclocycline (a tetracycline) are particularly important because of their clinical implications. These factors seem to affect some of the intracellular steps, as shown in Figure 10-3.

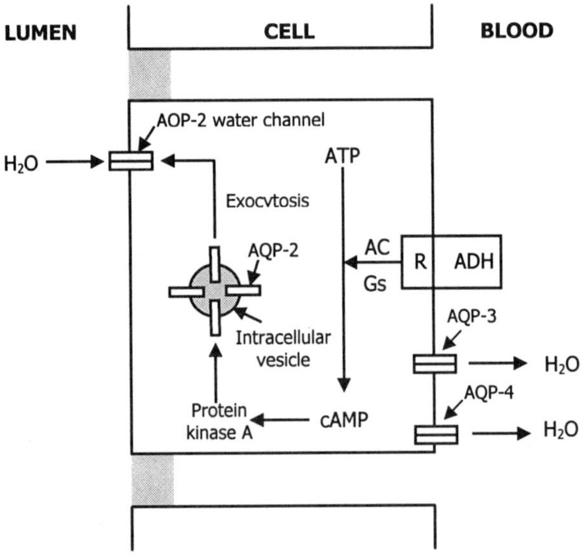

Figure 10-3. Mechanism of action of ADH on the epithelial cell of the collecting duct. R= V_2 receptor; AC = adenylate cyclase; Gs = G-stimulatory protein; AQP-2,3 and 4 = aquaporin-2,3 and 4 water channels.

Actions

As discussed in previous chapters, ADH has the following actions on the principal cells of the kidney:

(1) It increases water permeability in the cortical and medullary collecting ducts, and plays an important role in urinary concentration and dilution

(Chapter 9);

(2) It increases urea transport in the terminal inner medullary collecting duct, and thus participates in urea recycling in the process of urinary concentration; and

(3) It increases NaCl reabsorption in the medullary thick limb of Henle's loop.

DISORDERS OF WATER BALANCE

The disorders of water balance can be divided into two major groups for convenience of understanding: conditions associated with ADH secretion or resistance to ADH action and conditions associated with changes in plasma osmolality (hypo- or hyperosmolality).

Deficient ADH Secretion

The primary condition associated with deficient ADH secretion or synthesis is **central diabetes insipidus (CDI)**. The most common cause is damage or loss of the neurosecretory neurons in the hypothalamus or in the posterior pituitary gland. A number of pathologic processes, as listed in Table 10-2, can cause CDI. Clinically, patients present with abrupt onset of polyuria (frequent urination exceeding 3 L/day), nocturnal urination (nocturia), and polydipsia (frequent water drinking). These patients are able to maintain reasonable fluid balance and plasma osmolality provided that their thirst mechanism is intact. If their thirst mechanism is impaired, patients develop severe dehydration (volume contraction) and hypernatremia. Because of absent or low ADH, patients with CDI have low urine osmolality.

Treatment includes exogenous ADH administration. The most common drug is desmopressin, a synthetic analogue of ADH. Available as a nasal spray, it is administered in a dose of 10-20 μg once or twice daily. In some patients with CDI, a subnormal amount of ADH is present, and its action on the collecting duct can be augmented by an oral hypoglycemic agent, chlorpropamide (Diabenese). Patients on this drug should be monitored for hypoglycemia and hyponatremia.

Psychogenic polydipsia refers to a condition where patients drink too much water because of an underlying psychiatric disorder. These patients, called compulsive water drinkers, develop functional deficiency of ADH. Polyuria in these patients depends on their water intake. Because of excessive fluid intake, their ADH secretion is inhibited. As a result, they excrete dilute urine. There is no specific treatment for these patients.

Table 10-2. Causes, symptoms and treatment of ADH-deficiency syndromes

	Central DI	Psychogenic Polydipsia	Gestational DI
Causes	**Primary** Idiopathic (50%) Familial (autosomal dominant) **Secondary** Trauma to pituitary Skull fractures Hypophysectomy **Primary pituitary tumors** Craniopharyngiomas Adenomas Lymphomas **Secondary pituitary tumors** Metastatic lung or breast cancers **Infiltrative diseases** Sarcoidosis Histiocytosis X Wegener's granulomatosis **Infarction** Seehan's syndrome Sickle cell disease Stroke **Infections** Tuberculosis (TB) Meningitis (viral or bacterial)	Schizophrenia Neurosis (?)	Pregnancy
Symptoms	Polyuria	Polyuria	Polyuria
Treatment	Desmopression	No satisfactory treatment	Desmopressin

Gestational DI occurs in pregnant women. These patients have low levels of ADH because it is degraded by plasma vasopressinase, which is secreted in large quantities during gestation. Gestational DI has been successfully treated by desmopressin, which is resistant to vasopressinase action.

Resistance to ADH Action

The only condition associated with resistance to ADH action is called **nephrogenic DI**. Patients with this disorder have normal ADH secretion. However, the collecting duct is resistant to ADH action. The disease can be either inherited or acquired (see At a Glance Box 10-1). Inherited nephrogenic DI may be due to mutations in AQP-2 gene or V_2 receptor. Down-regulation of AQP-2 expression has been demonstrated in some forms of acquired nephrogenic DI (for example, lithium, hypercalcemia). Also, urinary excretion of AQP-2 in patients with nephrogenic DI is greatly reduced. Patients with nephrogenic DI present with modest polyuria (3-5 L/day). In congenital nephrogenic DI, males are affected more than females. Untreated cases present with dehydration, impaired growth, and mental retardation. Patients with congenital nephrogenic DI respond to a thiazide diuretic because it causes volume depletion and decreases urine output. In patients with acquired nephrogenic DI, treatment of the underlying cause greatly prevents polyuria.

At a Glance Box 10-1
Causes of nephrogenic diabetes insipidus

Hereditary-Congenital	**Acquired**
X-linked recessive	Chronic renal failure
Polycystic disease	Analgesic nephropathy
Medullary cystic disease	Obstructive uropathy
Sickel cell disease or trait	Sarcoidosis
Fanconi syndrome	Amyloidosis
	Multiple myeloma
	Urinary tract infection
	Hypercalcemia
	Hypokalemia
	Protein malnutrition
	Drugs (lithium, demeclocycline, loop diuretics, PGE_2)

CHANGES IN PLASMA OSMOLALITY

Clinically, disorders of water balance can be divided into those with hypoosmolality and those with hyperosmolality. Since plasma osmolality is largely determined by plasma [Na^+] (Chapter 1), a true decrease in plasma [Na^+] due to water excess results in hypoosmolality (<280 mOsm/kg H_2O). This condition is called hyponatremia. Conversely, an increase in plasma [Na^+] due to water loss causes hyperosmolality (>295 mOsm/kg H_2O), and the clinical condition is called hypernatremia. It is, therefore, evident that water content relative to [Na^+] can alter the plasma osmolality.

Hyponatremia

Hyponatremia is defined as a plasma [Na^+] < 135 mEq/L. As stated, it is a condition of water excess. In a normal individual, hyponatremia does not develop unless water intake is greater than renal excretion. Hyponatremia may also be caused by a defect in renal water excretion in the presence of normal water intake or loss of Na^+ either from the kidney, gastrointestinal tract, or skin. In each of these cases, water retention in excess of solute concentration results in hyponatremia.

Occasionally plasma [Na^+] is artifactually low in patients with severe hyperlipidemia or hyperproteinemia. Reduction in [Na^+] is due to displacement of plasma water by excess lipid or protein, but the plasma osmolality is normal. This condition is called **pseudohyponatremia**. These patients are asymptomatic and require no treatment. Severe hyperglycemia also lowers plasma [Na^+], which is attributed to water movement from intracellular to extracellular compartment. Plasma [Na^+] decreases by 1.6 mEq/L for each 100 mg/dL glucose above normal plasma glucose level (i.e., 100 mg/dL). Because of hyperglycemia, the plasma osmolality is high, and the condition is called **hypertonic hyponatremia**. True hyponatremia (i.e., **hypotonic hyponatremia**) can be divided into 3 categories depending upon their volume status (see At a Glance Box 10-2).

At a Glance Box 10-2
Causes of hyponatremia

HYPOVOLEMIC HYPONATREMIA
Extrarenal
- Diarrhea
- Vomiting

Renal
- Diuretics
- Mineralocorticoid deficiency
- Salt-losing nephropathy

HYPERVOLEMIC HYPONATREMIA
Extrarenal
- CHF
- Liver cirrhosis

Renal
- Nephrotic syndrome
- Acute renal failure
- Chronic renal failure

NORMOVOLEMIC HYPONATREMIA
- Primary polydipsia
- Hypothyroidism
- Glucocorticoid deficiency
- Drugs with ADH action
- Pain and stress
- SIADH

Discussion of the various causes of hyponatremia is beyond the scope of this book. However, one important cause of hyponatremia explains why it leads to hypoosmolality. This condition is called **syndrome of inappropriate**

secretion of ADH (SIADH). Patients with SIADH have high circulating levels of ADH despite mild volume expansion. The syndrome is caused by excess hypothalamic (cerebral disease) or nonhypothalamic (pulmonary disease or tumors) production of ADH. In addition, certain drugs may potentiate the action of endogenous ADH (see Table 10-1). The net result is retention of water in excess of Na^+. Thus, water excretion is impaired, causing hyponatremia and hypoosmolality.

Hyponatremia due to SIADH may be symptomatic or asymptomatic. Symptoms include nausea, lethargy, disorientation, and agitation. If untreated, patients may eventually develop seizures. Treatment of hyponatremia depends on symptomology and the rapidity with which it develops. Asymptomatic individuals should be treated with fluid restriction. If the patient is symptomatic and plasma [Na^+] is 110 mEq/L, then hypertonic saline (3% NaCl) is the treatment of choice until plasma [Na^+] reaches 120 mEq/L with an increment of 0.5 mEq/L/hour. Subsequent correction of plasma Na^+ concentration to 135 mEq/L should be attempted in 36-48 hours.

Hypernatremia

Hypernatremia is defined as a plasma [Na^+] > 145 mEq/L. It can be caused by either loss of water or gain of Na^+. Hypernatremia may develop when water is lost without replacement or without Na^+ loss as in CDI or a defect in thirst mechanism (primary hypodipsia). Rapid infusion of hypertonic saline without adequate water replacement may also cause hypernatremia due to gain of Na^+ (see At a Glance Box 10-3).

Patients with hypernatremia present with symptoms related to the central nervous system including lethargy, headache, disorientation, and confusion. These symptoms are due to movement of water out of the brain cells caused by hyperosmolality.

The goals of treatment are restoration of normal osmolality and volume. As in hyponatremia, treatment of hypernatremia depends on the speed with which the condition develops and symptoms. Patients tolerate chronic hypernatremia rather well. However, acute symptomatic hypernatremia should be treated with normal (0.9%) saline. The reduction in plasma [Na^+] should not be more than 0.6 mEq/L. Water deficit should be calculated from the plasma [Na^+] and body weight. Once symptoms disappear, patients can be given dextrose (5%) solution intravenously or pure water by mouth.

At a Glance Box 10-3
Causes of hypernatremia

Hypovolemic hypernatremia (water loss in excess of Na^+)
- Diarrhea
- Vomiting
- Burns
- Excessive sweating

Hypervolemic hypernatremia (gain of more Na^+ than water)
- Hypertonic saline
- $NaHCO_3$ administration
- Mineralocorticoid excess

Euvolemic hypernatremia (pure water loss)
- Excessive perspiration or sweating
- Central DI
- Nephrogenic DI
- Hypodipsia
- Essential hypernatremia

SUMMARY

1. In a healthy individual, plasma osmolality is maintained between 280 mOsm/kg H_2O and 295 mOsm/kg H_2O by the combined effects of thirst, ADH, and the kidney. Water intake and loss greatly influence plasma osmolality. ADH is synthesized by the supraoptic and paraventricular nuclei of the hypothalamus. The major physiologic stimulus for ADH release is plasma osmolality. In addition, nonosmotic factors such as volume contraction and hypotension stimulate ADH release. ADH acts on the collecting duct by binding to the V_2 receptor at the basolateral membrane of the epithelial cell, and subsequent intracellular changes translocate aquaporin-2 water channels to the apical membrane for water transport.
2. Disorders of water balance can result either from low or normal ADH levels. Central diabetes insipidus (CDI) is characterized by low or absent ADH levels. Patients with psychogenic polydipsia have also low levels of ADH because of compulsive water drinking. On the other hand, nephrogenic DI is characterized by normal levels of ADH but the collecting duct is resistant to the action of ADH. Gestational DI develops during pregnancy. All of these conditions with DI present with polyuria and polydipsia. Treatment depends on the nature of the disease condition.
3. When water intake and loss are not equal, changes in plasma osmolality occur. Water excess lowers plasma $[Na^+]$ as well as plasma osmolality, and the condition is called hyponatremia (plasma $[Na^+]$ <135 mEq/L). Conversely, water deficit increases plasma $[Na^+]$ and plasma osmolality, resulting in hypernatremia (plasma $[Na^+]$ >145 mEq/L). Treatment of both

hypo-and hypernatremia depends on symptoms and the rapidity of their development.

STUDY QUESTIONS

Case 1

A 25-year-old man was admitted to the hospital following an automobile accident involving skull fracture. After appropriate surgery, the patient was transferred to the recovery room. Two days later, the patient developed seizures, which were controlled by appropriate medications. His serum [Na^+] was 115 mEq/L and urine osmolality was 450 mOsm/kg H_2O. The nurses' record shows that he received 4 L of 5% dextrose in water per day for 2 days. He also received pain medications. His urine output was 1500 ml/day.

Question 1. Why did the patient develop symptomatic hyponatremia?

Answer: The patient had undergone head surgery. He may have sustained trauma to his posterior pituitary. He was under stress and also received pain medications. All of these procedures may have caused excessive release of ADH. Since his intake of fluids was more than his output (urine + insensible loss), he retained excess water in the presence of ADH. Consequently, the patient's serum [Na^+] was diluted to a symptomatic hyponatremia.

Question 2. How would you treat this patient's hyponatremia? Is water restriction sufficient to raise his serum [Na^+] to 120 mEq/L?

Answer: Since the patient is symptomatic, he should be treated with hypertonic saline (3%) to slowly raise his serum [Na^+] to 120 mEq/L. Restriction of fluids alone is incorrect at this time.

Four days later, the patient started urinating 3-4 L a day and his serum [Na^+] was corrected to 140 mEq/L. Fluids were restricted. Two days later, his serum [Na^+] was 150 mEq/L and his urine output rose to 6 L/day.

Question 3. Why did the patient subsequently develop hypernatremia and polyuria?

Answer: Since the patient had sustained head trauma, his posterior pituitary or neurohypophysis may have been damaged or destroyed. As a result, he does not produce any ADH, which leads to polyuria. His hypernatremia is related to inadequate replacement of fluids (output is greater than input).

One week later, the results of plasma ADH levels showed that the patient had no detectable level of ADH.

Question 4. How would you treat this patient?

Answer: The patient should be treated with desmopressin, the synthetic analogue of ADH. The patient should be advised to drink fluids as required.

Case 2

A 50-year-old male on maintenance hemodialysis (artificial kidney machine) gained 10 lbs between two dialysis treatments. His serum chemistry is:

Na^+	=	130 mEq/L
K^+	=	5.6 mEq/L
Cl^-	=	100 mEq/L
HCO_3^-	=	15.0 mEq/L
Creatinine	=	15.0 mg/dL
BUN	=	210 mg/dL
Glucose	=	90 mg/dL

Question 1. Is the serum osmolality isotonic or hypertonic?

Answer: The calculated serum osmolality is 340 mOsm/kg H_2O, which is hypertonic.

Question 2. Does this hypertonicity stimulate thirst?

Answer: No. The hypertonicity is largely contributed by BUN, which is an ineffective osmolyte. Therefore, thirst mechanism is not stimulated.

Question 3. Is hyponatremia a Na^+ or water problem?

Answer: Hyponatremia in this patient is due to water rather than Na^+ problem. There is too much water relative to Na^+ because of kidneys's inability to excrete excess water because of renal failure.

SUGGESTED READING

1. Zerbe, R.L. and Robertson, G.L. Osmotic and nonosmotic regulation of thirst and vasopressin secretion. In: Clinical Disorders of Fluid and Electrolyte Metabolism. 5th edition. R.G. Narins (ed.). McGraw-Hill, Inc. New York, 1994; 81-100 (*A detailed review describing the synthesis, regulation, and mechanism of vasopressin in water balance*).
2. Harris, H.W. and Zeidel, M.L. Cell biology of vasopressin. In: The Kidney. 5th edition. B.M. Brenner (ed.). W.B. Saunders Company, Philadelphia, 1996; pp.516-531 (*This chapter discusses the effects of vasopressin on permeability of epithelial cells*).

CHAPTER 11

ACID-BASE PHYSIOLOGY AND DISORDERS

Objectives

After reading this chapter, the student should be able to:

1. Define pH, pK_a, acid, base, buffer, and the relationship between pH and H^+ ion concentration.
2. State and explain the Henderson-Hasselbalch equation with application to the HCO_3^- buffer system.
3. Discuss how the lungs and kidneys regulate normal blood pH.
4. Describe the mechanisms and factors that regulate HCO_3^- reabsorption and NH_4^+ synthesis and excretion by the tubules of the nephron.
5. Discuss net acid excretion and its importance in the maintenance of blood pH.
6. Identify the four primary acid-base disorders.
7. Define and explain the Henderson equation and anion gap.
8. Describe the primary and secondary changes that occur in metabolic and respiratory acid-base disorders.
9. State the causes and treatment modalities of metabolic acidosis and alkalosis and respiratory acidosis and alkalosis.
10. Discuss the mixed acid-base disturbances.

Acid-base physiology deals with the maintenance of normal hydrogen ion concentration (abbreviated as $[H^+]$) in the body fluids. The normal $[H^+]$ in the extracellular fluid is about 40 nmol/L or 40 nEq/L (range 38-42 nmol/L), which is precisely regulated by an interplay between body buffers, lungs, and kidneys. Since many functions of the cell are dependent on the optimum $[H^+]$, it is extremely important to maintain $[H^+]$ in blood around 40 nmol/L. Any deviation from this $[H^+]$ results either in acidemia ($[H^+]>40$ nmol/L) or alkalemia ($[H^+]<40$ nmol/L).

This chapter provides an overview of the role of buffers, lungs, and kidneys in regulating $[H^+]$ in body fluids. In addition, a pathophysiologic approach to the diagnosis and management of disturbances of $[H^+]$ is presented.

The $[H^+]$ in blood is so low that it is not measured routinely. However, the $[H^+]$ is measured as pH, which is expressed as:

$$pH = -\log [H^+] \quad (1)$$

Thus pH is defined as the negative logarithm of the $[H^+]$. An inverse relationship exists between pH and $[H^+]$. In other words, as the pH increases, the $[H^+]$ decreases and vice versa. This relationship is shown in Table 11-1. Cells cannot function at a pH below 6.8 and above 7.8. The normal arterial pH ranges from 7.38 to 7.42, which translates to a $[H^+]$ of 38-42 nmol/L.

Table 11-1. Relationship between pH and $[H^+]$

pH (Units)	$[H^+]$ (nmol/L)
7.90	13
7.80	16
7.70	20
7.60	25
7.50	32
7.40	40
7.30	50
7.20	63
7.10	79
7.00	100
6.90	126
6.80	159
6.70	199
6.60	251

Blood pH is under constant threat by endogenous acid and base loads. If not removed, these loads can cause severe disturbances in blood pH, and thus impair cellular function. However, three important regulatory systems prevent changes in pH and thus maintain blood pH in the normal range. These protective systems, as stated above, are buffers, lungs, and kidneys. The following sections discuss how these acids and bases are formed and how the protective systems operate to maintain pH in the normal range.

PRODUCTION OF ENDOGENOUS ACIDS AND BASES

An acid is a proton donor, whereas a base is a proton acceptor. Under physiological conditions, the diet is a major contributor to endogenous acid and base production.

Endogenous Acids

The oxidation of dietary carbohydrates, fats, and amino acids yields CO_2. About

15,000 mmol of CO_2 are produced by cellular metabolism daily. This CO_2 combines with water in the blood to form carbonic acid (H_2CO_3):

$$CO_2 + H_2O \overset{CA}{\Leftrightarrow} H_2CO_3 \Leftrightarrow H^+ + HCO_3^- \qquad (2)$$

This reaction is catalyzed by carbonic anhydrase (CA), an enzyme present in tissues and red blood cells but absent in plasma. When H_2CO_3 dissociates into CO_2 and H_2O (a process called dehydration), the CO_2 is eliminated by the lungs. For this reason, H_2CO_3 is called a **volatile acid.**

In addition to volatile acid, the body also generates **nonvolatile (fixed) acids** from cellular metabolism. These nonvolatile acids are produced from sulfur-containing amino acids (i.e., cysteine and methionine) and phosphoproteins. The acids produced are sulfuric acid and phosphoric acid, respectively. Other sources of endogenous nonvolatile acids include glucose, which yields lactic and pyruvic acids; triglycerides, which yield acetoacetic and beta-hydroxybutyric acids; and nucleoproteins, which yield uric acid. Hydrochloric acid is also formed from the metabolism of cationic amino acids (i.e., lysine, arginine, and histidine). Sulfuric acid accounts for 50% of all acids produced. A typical North American diet produces 1 mmol/kg/day of endogenous nonvolatile acid.

Under certain conditions, acids are produced from sources other than the diet. For example, starvation produces ketoacids, which can accumulate in the blood. Similarly, strenuous exercise generates lactic acid. Drugs such as corticosteroids cause endogenous acid production by enhancing catabolism of muscle proteins.

Endogenous Bases

Endogenous base (HCO_3^-) is generated from anionic amino acids (glutamate and aspartate) in the diet. Also, citrate or lactate generated during metabolism of carbohydrate yields HCO_3^-. Vegetarian diets contain high amounts of anionic amino acids and small amounts of sulfur and phosphate-containing proteins. Therefore, these diets generate more base than acid. In general, the production of acid exceeds that of base in a person ingesting a typical North American diet.

MAINTENANCE OF NORMAL pH

All acids that are produced must be removed from the body in order to maintain normal blood pH. Although the kidneys eliminate most of these acids, it takes hours to days to complete the process. Buffers (both cellular and extracellular) are the first line of defense against wide fluctuations in pH.

Buffers

A buffer consists of two parts: a weak acid and its conjugate base. In solution, the buffer can either accept or donate a proton, and thus is able to act as an acid or a base. This property, called buffering, can be expressed as follows:

$$HA \Leftrightarrow H^+ + A^- \qquad (3)$$

where HA is a weak acid and A^- is its conjugate base. Addition of H^+ permits the base to accept the H^+ ion to form the acid (HA). This reaction reduces the $[H^+]$ and thus prevents changes in pH. In other words, the H^+ ions are buffered.

A weak acid dissociates partially, whereas a strong acid dissociates completely and offers little buffering capacity. Each buffer has a dissociation constant (K_a), which expresses the acid strength in terms of its dissociation into positive H^+ ions and negative anions. K_a is, therefore, expressed as:

$$K_a = \frac{[H^+]\,[A^-]}{[HA]} \quad \text{or} \quad K_a = \frac{[\text{Products}]}{[\text{Reactants}]} \qquad (4)$$

When solved for $[H^+]$, the equation becomes:

$$[H^+] = K_a \frac{[HA]}{[A^-]} \qquad (5)$$

Taking the negative logarithm of each side of the equation yields:

$$-\log [H^+] = -\log K_a - \log \frac{[HA]}{[A^-]} \qquad (6)$$

Since $-\log [H^+]$ equals pH, $-\log K_a$ defines pK_a. Substituting $-\log [HA]/[A^-]$ for $+\log [A^-]/[HA]$, the above equation becomes:

$$pH = pK_a + \log \frac{[A^-]}{[HA]} \qquad (7)$$

This equation, called the **Henderson-Hasselbalch equation**, can be used to define the dissociation of any weak acid. This equation can be rewritten as:

$$pH = pK_a + \log \frac{(\text{Proton acceptor})}{(\text{Proton donor})} \qquad (8)$$

A buffer is very effective when the pH of the solution is within 1 pH unit of the pK_a of that buffer, whereas a buffer is less effective if the pK_a and pH are disparate. The pK_a, which is defined as the pH at which the acid is half dissociated, is unique for any acid of a buffer pair and is influenced by the temperature and pH.

Let us consider how extracellular (blood) buffers prevent changes in blood pH. There are three important buffers in the plasma: bicarbonate/carbonic acid (HCO_3^-/H_2CO_3), disodium phosphate/monosodium phosphate ($Na_2HPO_4^{2-}/NaH_2PO_4^-$), and plasma proteins. In addition, erythrocytes contain the important hemoglobin (Hb) system, reduced Hb (HHb^-) and oxyhemoglobin (HbO_2^{2-}).

Of the plasma buffers, the HCO_3^-/H_2CO_3 system provides the first line of defense in protecting pH. Its role as a buffer can be described by incorporating this system into the Henderson-Hasselbalch equation as follows:

$$pH = pK_a + \log \frac{[HCO_3^-]}{[H_2CO_3]} \qquad (9)$$

Although H_2CO_3 cannot be measured directly, its concentration can be estimated from the partial pressure of CO_2 (PCO_2) and the solubility coefficient (α) of CO_2 at known temperature and pH. At normal temperature of 37°C and pH of 7.4, the PCO_2 is 40 mm Hg, the α is 0.03, and the pK_a is 6.1. The Henderson-Hasselbalch equation can be appropriately written as:

$$pH = 6.1 + \log \frac{[HCO_3^-]}{0.03 \times PCO_2} \qquad (10)$$

Normal plasma [HCO_3^-] is 24 mEq/L. Therefore,

$$pH = 6.1 + \log \frac{24}{0.03 \times 40} \qquad (11)$$

$$pH = 6.1 + \log \frac{24}{1.2} = \frac{20}{1}$$

$$\log 20 = 1.3$$

$$pH = 6.1 + 1.3 = 7.40$$

It should be noted from the Henderson-Hasselbalch equation that the pH of a solution is determined by the pK_a and the ratio of [HCO_3^-] to PCO_2, and not by their absolute values. Thus, because the kidneys regulate the [HCO_3^-] and the lungs PCO_2, the kidneys and lungs determine the pH of extracellular fluids.

Red blood cells play an important role in handling CO_2 transport. CO_2 is lipid soluble and diffuses into red blood cells where it undergoes two important reactions. First, it is hydrated to form H_2CO_3 by the enzyme carbonic anhydrase. Second, it partially combines with Hb to form carboxyhemoglobin; some of the H_2CO_3 dissociates to form H^+ ions and HCO_3^-. H^+ ions are titrated by histidine groups of Hb, and HCO_3^- is transported into plasma in exchange for Cl^-. Some of the dissolved CO_2 diffuses into the alveoli during passage of red blood cells through the lung capillaries. Thus, CO_2 is eliminated from the body.

Phosphate buffers are effective in regulating intracellular pH more efficiently than extracellular pH. Their increased effectiveness intracellularly is due to their higher concentrations inside the cell. Also, the pK_a of this system is 6.8, which is close to the intracellular pH.

Plasma proteins contain several ionizable groups in their amino acids that buffer either acids or bases. For example, the imidazole groups of histidine and the N-terminal amino groups have pK_as that are close to extracellular pH and thus function as effective buffers. In blood, Hb is an important protein buffer because of its abundance in red blood cells.

Extracellular buffering to an acid load is complete within 30 minutes. Subsequent buffering occurs intracellularly and takes several hours to complete. Most of this intracellular buffering occurs in bone.

It is apparent from the Henderson-Hasselbalch Eq. 10 that any change either in $[HCO_3^-]$ or PCO_2 can cause a change in blood pH. The acid-base disturbance that results form a change in plasma $[HCO_3^-]$ is termed a **metabolic acid-base disorder**, whereas that due to a change in PCO_2 is called a **respiratory acid-base disorder**.

Lungs

After buffers, the lungs are the second line of defense against pH disturbance. In a normal individual, PCO_2 is maintained around 40 mm Hg. This PCO_2 is achieved by expelling the CO_2 that is produced by cellular metabolism through the lungs. Any disturbance in the elimination of CO_2 may cause a change in blood pH. Thus, alveolar ventilation maintains normal PCO_2 to prevent an acute change in pH. Alveolar ventilation is controlled by chemoreceptors located centrally in the medulla and peripherally in the carotid body and aortic arch. Blood $[H^+]$ and PCO_2 are important regulators of alveolar ventilation. The chemoreceptors sense the changes in $[H^+]$ or PCO_2 and alter alveolar ventilatory rate. For example, an increase in $[H^+]$; i.e., a decrease in pH, stimulates ventilatory rate and decreases PCO_2. These responses, in turn, raise pH (see equation 10). Conversely, a decrease in $[H^+]$ or an increase in pH depresses alveolar ventilation and causes retention of PCO_2 so that the pH is returned to near normal. An increase in PCO_2 stimulates, whereas a decrease depresses the ventilatory rate. The respiratory response to changes in $[H^+]$ takes several hours to complete.

Kidneys

As stated above, 1 mmol/kg/day of fixed acid is produced from the diet. If not removed, this acid is retained and plasma $[HCO_3^-]$ decreases. The result is metabolic acidosis. In a healthy individual, metabolic acidosis does not occur because the kidneys excrete the acid load and maintain plasma $[HCO_3^-]$ around

24 mEq/L. The maintenance of [HCO_3^-] is achieved by three renal mechanisms:

1. Reabsorption of filtered HCO_3^-
2. Generation of new HCO_3^- by titratable acid excretion
3. Formation of HCO_3^- from generation of NH_4^+

Reabsorption of Filtered HCO_3^-

HCO_3^- is freely filtered at the glomerulus. The daily filtered load (plasma concentration x glomerular filtration rate) of HCO_3^- is 4320 mEq (24 mEq/L x 180 L/day = 4320 mEq/day). Almost all of this HCO_3^- is reabsorbed by the tubular segments of the nephron, and urinary excretion is negligible (< 3 mEq). HCO_3^- reabsorption by various segments of the nephron can be summarized as follows:

Proximal tubule:	80%
Loop of Henle:	10%
Distal tubule :	6%
Collecting duct:	4%

Proximal Tubule

As stated above, the proximal tubule has a high capacity for HCO_3^- reabsorption. This reabsorption occurs because of H^+ ion secretion into the tubular lumen via the Na/H exchanger (Figure 11-1). Another transporter, called H-ATPase, is also responsible for transport of some protons into the lumen (see Figure 11-1). The H^+ ion combines with the filtered HCO_3^- to form H_2CO_3. The apical membrane is rich in carbonic anhydrase, which splits H_2CO_3 into H_2O and CO_2. The CO_2 diffuses into the cell where it is hydrated to form H_2CO_3 in the presence of carbonic anhydrase. H_2CO_3 is dehydrated to form H^+ and HCO_3^-. H^+ ions are subsequently secreted into the lumen via the Na/H exchanger and H-ATPase to start the cycle again.

HCO_3^- exit across the basolateral membrane occurs via an Na/HCO_3 symporter, in which 2-3 HCO_3^- ions are transported for each Na^+ ion. Another mechanism occurs through the Cl/HCO_3 antiporter, in which one HCO_3^- is exchanged for one Cl^- ion. Both the energy and electrochemical gradient for H^+ ion secretion and HCO_3^- exit are provided by the Na/K-ATPase pump located in the basolateral membrane.

Loop of Henle

Most HCO_3^- reabsorption occurs in the thick ascending Henle's loop. The mechanisms for H^+ ion secretion into the lumen and HCO_3^- exit across the basolateral membrane appear to be similar to those described for the proximal tubule.

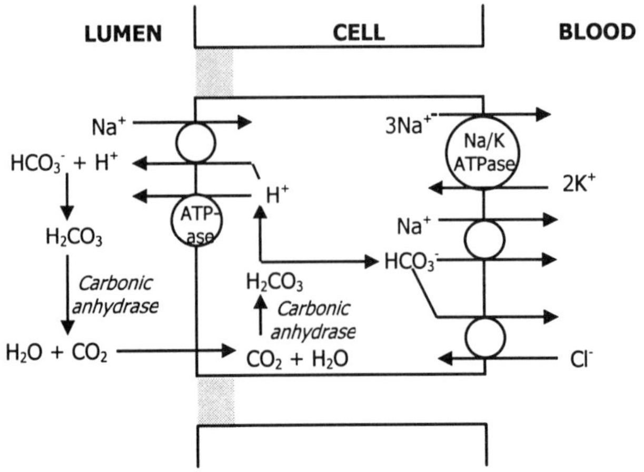

Figure 11-1. Schematic representation of H^+ ion secretion and HCO_3^- reabsorption by the proximal tubule cell.

Distal Tubule

For the purpose of understanding HCO_3^- reabsorption, it is helpful to divide the distal tubule into three distinct segments: (1) distal convoluted tubule; (2) connecting tubule; and (3) cortical collecting duct. Very little is known about H^+ ion secretion and HCO_3^- reabsorption by the distal convoluted tubule. This tubule consists of only one cell type, which contains H-ATPase in its apical membrane. The other two segments of the distal tubule consist of principal cells and intercalated cells. The latter cells are responsible for acid-base transport. The intercalated cells in the cortical collecting duct are of two types: Type A and B cells. Type A intercalated cells contain H-ATPase in the apical membrane. H^+ ions that are formed inside the cell from dehydration of H_2CO_3 are secreted into the lumen by this transporter (Figure 11-2). HCO_3^- exit is facilitated by the Cl/HCO_3 antiporter.

In contrast, Type B intercalated cells secrete HCO_3^- into the lumen (Figure 11-3). These cells possess an Cl/HCO_3 antiporter in the apical membrane and H-ATPase in the basolateral membrane. HCO_3^- secretion is stimulated by alkali loading and inhibited by depletion of luminal Cl^-.

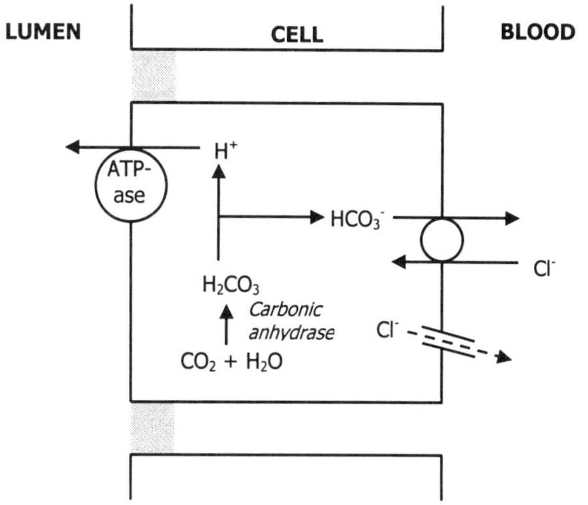

Figure 11-2. Cellular model for H^+ ion secretion and HCO_3^- reabsorption by Type A intercalated cell of the cortical collecting duct. Broken arrow represents a conductance channel.

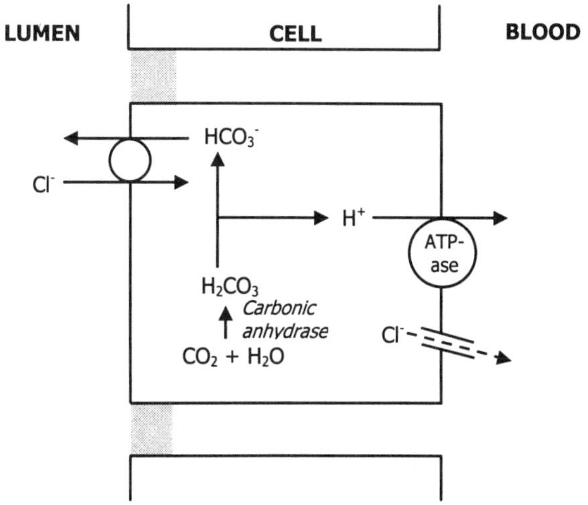

Figure 11-3. Cellular model for HCO_3^- secretion and H^+ ion reabsorption by Type B intercalated cell of the cortical collecting duct. Broken arrow represents a conductance channel.

Collecting Duct

The collecting duct includes the cortical portion and outer and inner medullary portions. The cellular mechanisms of HCO_3^- reabsorption in the cortical collecting duct were discussed in the previous paragraph. The intercalated cells of the outer medullary and inner medullary collecting duct reabsorb HCO_3^- and secrete protons similar to the A-type cell mechanisms (see Figure 11-2). The cells of outer medullary and inner medullary collecting duct do not secrete HCO_3^- into the lumen.

Regulation of HCO_3^- Reabsorption

A number of factors influence HCO_3^- reabsorption both in the proximal tubule and distal segments of the nephron. These factors are summarized in Tables 11-2 and 11-3. Since the Na/H antiporter is the major mechanism for H^+ secretion, any factor that enhances or inhibits this antiporter stimulates or decreases HCO_3^- reabsorption.

Aldosterone plays an important role in HCO_3^- reabsorption and H^+ ion secretion by the intercalated (Type A) cell. It also stimulates Na^+ reabsorption by the principal cell. As a result of this Na^+ reabsorption, the lumen becomes electrically negative, which promotes H^+ ion secretion. Aldosterone seems to have little effect on HCO_3^- reabsorption by the proximal tubule.

Generation of New HCO_3^- by Titratable Acid Excretion

The filtered load of HCO_3^- (i.e., 4320 mEq/day) must be reclaimed entirely in order to maintain normal plasma [HCO_3^-] of 24 mEq/L. As discussed above, this reclamation is dependent on H^+ ion secretion. In general, one HCO_3^- ion is reclaimed for each H^+ ion that is secreted into the lumen. This mechanism alone does not replenish the HCO_3^- lost in buffering the daily acid load. Additional HCO_3^- has to be added. How does the new HCO_3^- form? The answer is as follows: whenever a H^+ ion is secreted into the tubule, it combines with the filtered HCO_3^- or with two important urinary buffers, namely, HPO_4^{2-} and NH_3, to form $H_2PO_4^-$ and NH_4^+, respectively. For each H^+ ion that combines with HPO_4^{2-}, one new HCO_3^- is formed and reabsorbed. The process is different when NH_3 is converted into NH_4^+. In this conversion, HCO_3^- is produced from glutamine metabolism. This process is discussed in the next section. In addition to the generation of new HCO_3^-, the urinary buffers also help to maintain urinary pH acidic (i.e., 4.5-6.0). If these buffers did not exist, the daily acid load would be excreted into the urine and its pH would be < 4.5. The amount of free H^+ ions in the urine is about 0.04 mmol/L. In the absence of urinary buffers, an individual has to excrete 1,750 L of urine to eliminate 70 mmol/L of acid load. Obviously, this amount of urine excretion is impossible. Let us now see how urinary buffers replenish the HCO_3^- load.

Table 11-2. Factors affecting HCO_3^- reabsorption (or H^+ ion secretion) by the proximal tubule

Factor	HCO_3^- reabsorption	Possible mechanism
Increase in filtered load of HCO_3^-	↑	Glomerulotubular balance (G-T) is maintained so that a constant fraction of filtered load of HCO_3^- is reabsorbed
Volume Contraction	↑	↓ Volume promotes HCO_3^- reabsorption by ↑ Na/H exchange
Hypokalemia	↑	↓ Intracellular pH increases $[H^+]$ and promotes proton secretion by stimulation of Na/H antiporter
↑ PCO_2	↑	↓ Intracellular pH and ↑ Na/H antiporter
↑ Plasma $[H^+]$	↑	↓ Intracellular pH and ↑ Na/H antiporter
Cl^- depletion	↑	↓ Volume and GFR
Hypercalcemia	↑	Probable ↓ volume and GFR
Volume expansion	↓	↑ GFR. Although G-T balance is maintained, still some HCO_3^- escapes from reabsorption
Parathyroid hormone	↓	Probable ↑ in cytosolic Ca^{2+}. No effect on GFR
↓ PCO_2	↓	↑ Intracellular pH
↓ Phosphate	↓	↑ Intracellular pH
Carbonic anhydrase inhibitor (acetazolamide)	↓	↓ Carbonic anhydrase activity

↑ = increase; ↓ = decrease

Table 11-3. Factors affecting HCO_3^- reabsorption by the distal tubule

Factor	HCO_3^- reabsorption	Possible mechanism
Aldosterone	↑	↑ H^+ secretion
↑ PCO_2	↑	↓ intracellular pH
↑ Plasma $[H^+]$	↑	↓ intracellular pH
Impermeant anions (sulfate, phosphate, etc)	↑	↑ H^+ excretion
Hypokalemia (man and rat)	↑	↓ GFR
↓ PCO_2	↓	↑ intracellular pH
↓ Plasma $[H^+]$	↓	↑ intracellular pH
Adrenalectomy	↓	↓ H^+ secretion

↑ = increase; ↓ = decrease

As mentioned previously, the two major urinary buffers are HPO_4^{2-} / $H_2PO_4^-$ and NH_3/NH_4^+. About 40% of H^+ ions that are excreted are buffered by phosphate ions, whereas the remaining 60% are buffered by ammonium ions. The contribution of phosphate to urinary acid excretion is termed **titratable acidity**, which is defined as the number of equivalents of hydroxyl ions required to titrate a unit volume of acidic urine to the pH of the blood (i.e., pH of 7.4). Thus, the amount of hydroxyl ions used in the titration is equal to the amount of H^+ ions that were buffered in the tubular lumen. If 30 mmol of hydroxyl ions are used to raise urine pH to 7.4, then 30 mmol of H^+ ions are titrated, and 30 mmol of HCO_3^- are generated. Other organic substances, such as creatinine and urate, also contribute to titratable acid excretion to a minor degree. Compared to creatinine and urate, the phosphate buffer pair has a pK_a of 6.8 and thus appears to be an ideal urinary buffer. Figure 11-4. shows the mechanisms by which titratable acid excretion occurs in the collecting duct cell. The filtered phosphate (HPO_4^{2-}) combines with the H^+ ions secreted in the lumen via ATPase to form $H_2PO_4^-$. The H^+ ions are formed inside the cell due to dehydration of H_2CO_3 by the catalytic action of carbonic anhydrase. Note that one HCO_3^- ion is formed for each H^+ ion secreted.

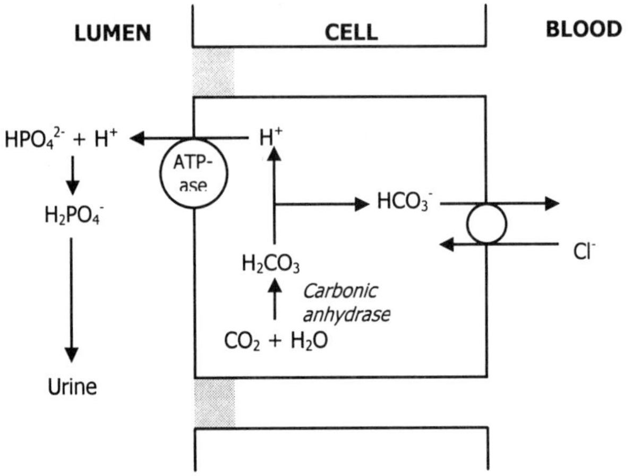

Figure 11-4. Schematic representation for titratable acid formation in the collecting duct cell.

Formation of HCO_3^- From Generation of NH_4^+

Recent research indicates that renal handling of NH_4^+ is rather different from the widely accepted earlier view. The current view is summarized below, and the details follow.

1. ***NH_4^+ (not NH_3) is formed from glutamine in the proximal tubule. It is secreted into the tubular lumen via the Na/H antiporter replacing H^+ in this transporter.***
2. ***NH_4^+ is subsequently reabsorbed in the thick ascending Henle's loop via the Na/K/2Cl cotransporter by replacing K^+. In the medulla, NH_4^+ is split into NH_3 and H^+. As a result, NH_3 accumulates. NH_3 then diffuses into the collecting tubule where it combines with H^+ to form NH_4^+, which is excreted in the urine.***
3. ***The excretion of NH_4^+ per se does not generate HCO_3^-. Instead, new HCO_3^- is formed from the metabolism of glutamine and its***

organic anions (α-ketoglutarate). Both NH_4^+ formation and excretion are necessary to prevent HCO_3^- loss. If all NH_4^+ formed in the proximal tubule were returned to the general circulation, it would be used for urea synthesis in the liver. During urea synthesis, H^+ ions are formed which would neutralize the HCO_3^- generated from glutamine. This neutralization would lower [HCO_3^-], and thus negate the beneficial effect of NH_4^+ generation.

Only a small quantity of NH_4^+ is filtered at the glomerulus. Most of this NH_4^+ is formed in the proximal tubule from glutamine. Glutamine, an amino acid derived from dietary protein, is metabolized to yield NH_3, H^+, and glutamate. Because the pK_a of NH_3 is about 9.0, most of this uncharged ion combines with the H^+ ion to form charged NH_4^+. Glutamate is deaminated to α-ketoglutarate with the formation of another NH_4^+ ion. The α-ketoglutarate is subsequently metabolized to yield either glucose or CO_2. During this reaction, 2 HCO_3^- ions are formed. The overall reaction can be written as:

$$\text{Glutamine} \overset{(1)}{\leftrightarrow} NH_4^+ + \text{glutamate} \overset{(2)}{\leftrightarrow} NH_4^+ + \alpha\text{-ketoglutarate} \leftrightarrow 2\ HCO_3^-.$$

The first reaction is catalyzed by a phosphate-dependent glutaminase and the second reaction by glutamate dehydrogenase. The net result is the formation of 2 NH_4^+ and 2 HCO_3^- ions. Renal excretion of NH_4^+ prevents the formation of H^+ ions in the liver during urea synthesis, as follows:

$$2\ NH_4^+ + CO_2 \leftrightarrow \text{Urea} + H_2O + 2\ H^+$$

Thus, NH_4^+ excretion aids in the formation of new HCO_3^- from glutamine and α-ketoglutarate. NH_4^+ is also synthesized from other sources, particularly glycine and purines. However, the pathway involving glutamine is the most significant in NH_4^+ synthesis.

Renal handling of NH_4^+ involves secretion by the proximal tubule, reabsorption by the medullary thick ascending limb of Henle's loop, and secretion of NH_3 (not NH_4^+) by the cortical and medullary collecting duct. Once NH_4^+ is formed in the proximal tubule cell, it is transported into the lumen by a secondary active transport system involving Na/H antiporter (Figure 11-5A). Here H^+ is replaced by NH_4^+. Following the secretion of NH_4^+, the next segment to participate in NH_4^+ handling is the medullary thick ascending limb of Henle's loop (Figure 11-5B). Most of the NH_4^+ reabsorption occurs by active transport and mediated by the Na/K/2Cl cotransporter. Here NH_4^+ substitutes for K^+. In addition to active transport, NH_4^+ also enters the cell by passive reabsorption through the paracellular pathway (see Figure 11-5B). As a result of these two processes, the tubular fluid in the distal tubule contains very little NH_4^+.

NH_4^+ formation in the lumen of the collecting duct occurs by combination of NH_3 with H^+ ions. This NH_3 comes directly from the medulla by diffusion and the H^+ ions are derived by secretion via H-ATPase (Figure 11-5C). The NH_4^+ thus formed is excreted in the urine. Two observations are pertinent to this reaction. First, because no luminal carbonic anhydrase is present in the collecting duct, the rate of dehydration of H_2CO_3 is reduced. Therefore, accumulation of H_2CO_3 lowers the luminal pH, which stimulates NH_3 diffusion into the lumen. Second, H^+ ions are actively secreted, which enhance the formation of NH_4^+ and reduces NH_3 diffusion back into the cell. Thus, absence of luminal carbonic anhydrase favors NH_4^+ formation.

The supply of NH_3 to the collecting duct does not depend on the glomerular filtration rate of NH_4^+. Most of the NH_4^+ is produced in the proximal tubule, which reaches the collecting duct from the loops of Henle through the medullary interstitium. Thus, the $[NH_4^+]$ must be high in the medulla. The high $[NH_4^+]$ is achieved by the active reabsorption of NH_4^+ by the thick ascending limb. The pH of the medullary interstitium is slightly alkaline and NH_4^+ dissociates into NH_3 and H^+. If this NH_3 diffuses back into the blood, excretion of NH_4^+ into the urine is diminished. This back-leak of NH_3 is prevented by its recirculation in the medullary interstitium. The descending and ascending limbs of Henle's loop are shown to participate in this recycling as a countercurrent multiplication system (Figure 11-6). This recycling of NH_3/ NH_4^+ serves two major functions: (1) maintenance of high medullary concentration of NH_3/ NH_4^+; and (2) prevention of NH_3 diffusion into the blood. A number of factors regulate NH_4^+ synthesis and its excretion. Table 11-4 summarizes these factors.

NET ACID EXCRETION

As mentioned previously, the H^+ ions (protons) that are generated as fixed acids must be excreted daily in the urine to maintain normal acid-base balance. These H^+ ions are not excreted as free ions. Instead, they are excreted in the form of titratable acid (TA) and NH_4^+. Only a small amount of H^+ is excreted as free ions. Each liter of urine contains approximately 0.04 mmol of free H^+ ions. Because of this negligible amount of free H^+ ions, the urine pH is maintained between 4.5 and 6.0. Another reason for the maintenance of acidic urine pH is the relatively low concentration of HCO_3^- (< 3 mEq/L of urine). Urinary loss of HCO_3^- greater than 5 mEq would generally raise the pH above 6.0 and make the urine alkaline. HCO_3^- loss in the urine is generally equated as a gain of H^+ to the body.

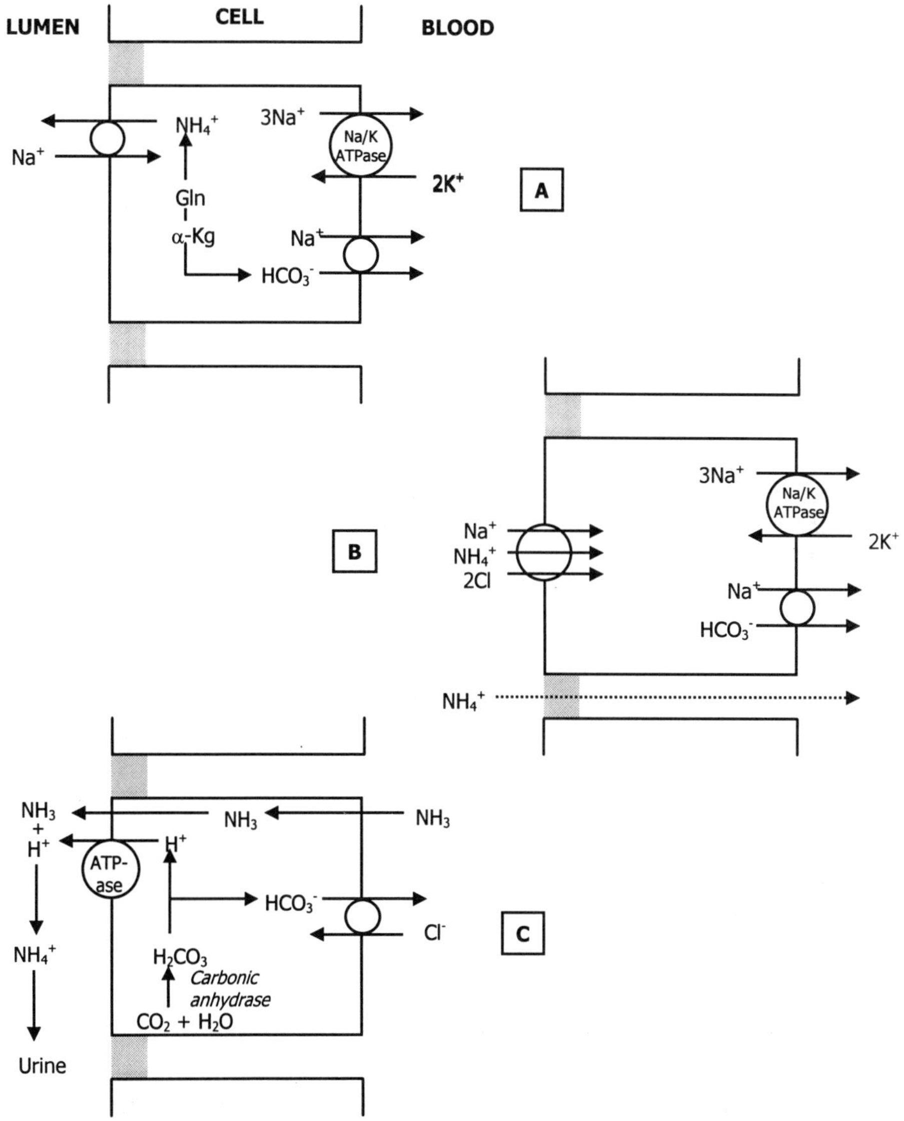

Figure 11-5. Cellular model for NH_4^+ transport in the proximal tubule (A); thick ascending limb of Henle's loop (B); and NH_4^+ excretion in the medullary collecting duct (C). Gln = glutamine; α-Kg = α-ketoglutarate.

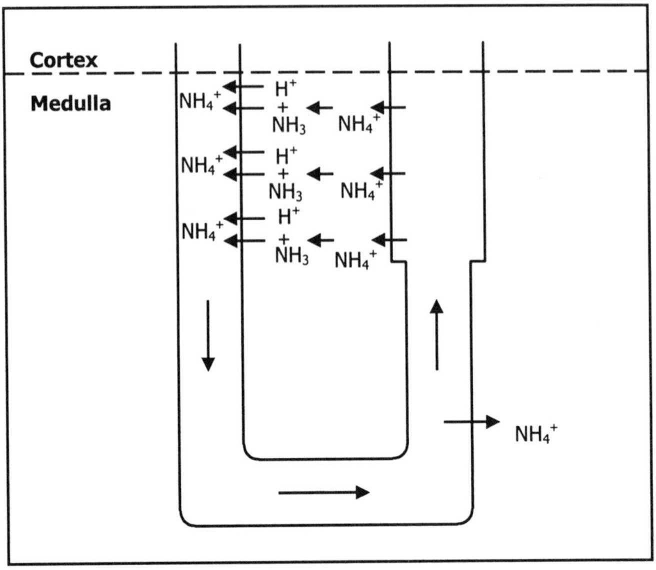

Figure 11-6. Recycling of NH_3/NH_4^+ in the renal medulla.

Table 11-4. Conditions regulating NH_4^+ synthesis and its excretion

Conditions	Synthesis	Excretion
Metabolic acidosis	↑	↑
Metabolic alkalosis	↓	↓
High urine pH	↓ (?)	↓
Low urine pH	↑ (?)	↑
High glutamine delivery	↑	↑
Low glutamine delivery	↓	↓
High urine flow	-	↑
Hypokalemia	↑	↑
Hyperkalemia	↓	↓
Mineralocorticoids	↑	↑
Glucocorticoids	↑	↑

↑ = increase; ↓ = decrease

The excretion of H^+ as TA and NH_4^+ is quantified as **net acid excretion** (NAE). NAE is defined as the sum of TA and NH_4^+ minus any H^+ that is added to the body because of urinary loss of HCO_3^-. Therefore, NAE is calculated as follows:

$$NAE = TA + NH_4^+ - HCO_3^-$$

Metabolic acidosis due to excess lactic acid production or diarrhea (see below) increases the NAE because the excretion of both TA and NH_4^+ increase. Thus,

NAE reflects the amount of proton excretion in the form of urinary buffers.

ACID-BASE DISORDERS

Previously, we described that a change in plasma [HCO_3^-] results in a metabolic acid-base disturbance, whereas a change in arterial PCO_2 results in a respiratory acid-base disorder. Clinically, four primary acid-base disorders can be recognized: (1) **metabolic acidosis**; (2) **metabolic alkalosis**; (3) **respiratory acidosis**; and (4) **respiratory alkalosis** (Table 11-5).

Table 11-5. Primary acid-base disturbances and their secondary response

Acid-base disorder	pH	Primary change	Secondary change	Mechanism
Metabolic acidosis	< 7.40	↓ HCO_3^-	↓ PCO_2	Hyperventilation
Metabolic alkalosis	> 7.40	↑ HCO_3^-	↑ PCO_2	Hypoventilation
Respiratory acidosis	< 7.40	↑ PCO_2	↑ HCO_3^-	↑ HCO_3^- reabsorption
Respiratory alkalosis	> 7.40	↓ PCO_2	↓ HCO_3^-	↓ HCO_3^- reabsorption

Before we discuss each of the above acid-base disorders, it is essential to define terms that are frequently used in acid-base physiology. These terms appear in the At a Glance Box as well as in the glossary. Three concepts that you should know in more detail are the **Henderson equation,** the **anion gap**, and **compensation.**

Henderson equation

In clinical practice, the Henderson-Hasselbalch equation is a rather cumbersome way to calculate the pH using logarithms. The same information can be obtained by using the **Henderson equation**, which relates [H^+] to pH. This equation, which calculates [H^+], is expressed as:

$$H^+ \text{ (nmol/L)} = 24 \times \frac{PCO_2}{[HCO_3^-]}$$

As an example of how this equation can be used, consider the following normal arterial blood gas (ABG) values:

pH = 7.40
PCO_2 = 40 mm Hg
HCO_3^- = 24 mEq/L

$$[H^+] = 24 \times PCO_2 / [HCO_3^-] = 24 \times (40/24) = 40.$$

This $[H^+]$ of 40 corresponds to the pH of 7.40. The Henderson equation is thus used clinically to check the validity of pH obtained from the clinical laboratory. This equation can also be used to calculate the $[HCO_3^-]$:

$$[HCO_3^-](mEq/L) = 24 \times \frac{PCO_2}{[H^+]}$$

> **At a Glance Box 11-1**
> Acid-base terminology
>
> **Acidemia**: an increase in blood $[H^+]$
> **Alkalemia**: a decrease in blood $[H^+]$
> **Acidosis**: a pathophysiologic process that tends to acidify body fluids
> **Alkalosis**: a pathophysiologic process that tends to alkalinize body fluids
> **Arterial blood gas** (ABG): includes pH, PCO_2 and plasma $[HCO_3^-]$
> **Normocapnia**: normal arterial PCO_2
> **Hypocapnia**: a decrease in arterial PCO_2
> **Hypercapnia**: an increase in arterial PCO_2
> **Normobicarbonatemia**: normal plasma $[HCO_3^-]$
> **Hypobicarbonatemia**: a decrease in plasma $[HCO_3^-]$
> **Hyperbicarbonatemia**: an increase in plasma $[HCO_3^-]$
> **Primary change**: an abnormality in either the $[HCO_3^-]$ or PCO_2 resulting from a primary change in body function/metabolism or additions to/losses from the body fluids
> **Secondary change**: a compensatory response that acts to minimize alterations in pH produced by the primary disorder. It is also called compensation
> **Simple acid-base disorder**: presence of one primary disturbance with appropriate secondary response
> **Mixed acid-base disorder**: simultaneous occurrence of two or more primary acid-base disorders

Anion gap

In plasma, the number of cations must equal the number of anions to maintain electroneutrality. However, measurement of all of these cations and anions is not done routinely. Generally, only Na^+, K^+, Cl^-, and HCO_3^- are measured. From these measurements, the number of unmeasured anions can be calculated. This sum of unmeasured anions is called the **anion gap** (AG). Since the change in serum $[K^+]$ in either health or disease is minimal, this cation is not routinely included in the calculation of AG. Thus, the AG is defined as the difference between Na^+ and the sum of Cl^- and HCO_3^-:

$$AG = (mEq/L) = Na^+ - (Cl^- + HCO_3^-)$$

The normal AG ranges between 8 and 12. It represents mostly sulfate, phosphate, proteins, and organic acids (citrate, lactate). The AG is useful in classifying the metabolic acidosis and evaluating mixed acid-base disorders.

Compensation

It is a physiologic process that minimizes changes in $[H^+]$ brought about by a primary change. Two types of compensatory responses are involved: respiratory and renal. In a metabolic acid-base disorder, the compensatory response is respiratory. For example, in metabolic acidosis, the primary change is a decrease in plasma $[HCO_3^-]$, and an increase in $[H^+]$. The compensatory response is a decrease in PCO_2 due to hyperventilation. This decrease in PCO_2 limits the rise in $[H^+]$, and thus the pH is returned toward normal. The observed hyperventilation represents the normal physiologic response to an increase in $[H^+]$. Conversely, hypoventilation is an appropriate physiologic response to metabolic alkalosis (see Table 11-5). In a respiratory acid-base disorder, the compensatory response is renal. In respiratory acidosis, the primary change is an increase in PCO_2, and a decrease in pH or an increase in $[H^+]$. The renal compensation increases the plasma $[HCO_3^-]$ with a resultant increase in pH *toward* normal. It should be pointed out that these compensatory mechanisms do not increase the pH to normal, but rather return the pH *toward* normal.

METABOLIC ACIDOSIS

Metabolic acidosis is characterized by a primary reduction in plasma $[HCO_3^-]$ and a pH < 7.40. This acidemia stimulates the medullary respiratory center causing hyperventilation. As a result, the PCO_2 is decreased, which in turn minimizes the decrease in pH (see Table 11-5).

The three most important mechanisms that can cause the plasma $[HCO_3^-]$ to decrease are: (1) loss of HCO_3^- from the body (for example, diarrhea); (2) addition of acid (as in diabetic ketoacidosis, where ketones are produced, or in severe hypoxia, where lactic acid is produced); and (3) failure of the kidney to excrete acid, as in acute or chronic renal failure.

Based on the AG, the metabolic acidosis is classified as normal AG (12 mEq/L) or high AG (> 16 mEq/L) metabolic acidosis (see At a Glance Box 11-2). In acidosis caused by diarrhea, the AG remains normal because the loss in HCO_3^- is replaced by Cl^- to maintain electroneutrality. However, in acidosis caused by excessive accumulation of ketoacids or lactic acid, $[HCO_3^-]$ falls because it buffers these acids. $[Cl^-]$ does not change. Therefore, the accumulated anions maintain the electroneutrality and thereby increase the AG.

At a Glance Box 11-2
Anion gap in metabolic acidosis

Normal AG metabolic acidosis
- Diarrhea
- Renal tubular acidosis

High AG metabolic acidosis
- Renal failure
- Ketoacidosis (due to diabetes mellitus, starvation or alcohol intake)
- Lactic acidosis
- Intoxicants (methanol, ethylene glycol, aspirin overdose)

Renal tubular acidosis (RTA) is a group of metabolic acidoses characterized by defective tubular reabsorption of HCO_3^- and H^+ ion secretion. As a result, the NAE is decreased. RTAs are classified into proximal and distal types. Distal RTAs are further divided into hypokalemic (low serum [K^+]) and hyperkalemic (high serum [K^+]) types. Proximal RTA, also called type II RTA, is characterized by impairment in proximal tubular reabsorption of HCO_3^-. Hypokalemic distal RTA, also called type I or classical RTA, is due to a defect in the distal nephron secretion of H^+ ions. As a result, the urine is not acidified despite severe acidemia. Hyperkalemic distal RTA, also called type IV RTA, can be due to either low aldosterone levels, tubular resistance to aldosterone action or urinary tract obstruction, causes decreased NH_3 production. Therefore, the urinary excretion of NAE is decreased. Type IV RTA is more common in adults than the other types of RTAs.

Patients with severe metabolic acidosis present with hyperventilation. Hypotension due to decreased myocardial contractility and peripheral vasodilation is not uncommon. Severe acidemia may cause nausea, vomiting, abdominal pain, fatigue, and weakness.

For metabolic acidosis of any cause, an appropriate respiratory compensation is initiated. Therefore, the expected PCO_2 for any given pH can be calculated from the formulas shown in Table 11-6.

How to Evaluate an Acid-Base Disorder

A 30-year-old male with a long history of intravenous drug abuse was admitted for weakness and abdominal pain. His respiratory rate was 24 per minute (normal = 12-14 per minute). Initial electrolyte and ABG values were:

Na^+ = 138 mEq/L	pH = 7.28
K^+ = 5.1 mEq/L	PCO_2 = 30 mm Hg
Cl^- = 100 mEq/L	PO_2 = 100 mm Hg
HCO_3^- = 14 mEq/L	HCO_3^- = 13 mEq/L

BUN = 120 mg/dL
Creatinine = 10 mg/dL

Table 11-6. Normal compensatory responses to primary acid-base disorders

Acid-base disorder	Compensatory response
Metabolic acidosis	$PCO_2 = HCO_3 \times 1.5 + 8 \pm 2$ or for each mEq/L decrease in HCO_3^-, PCO_2 decreases by 1.2 mm Hg.
Metabolic alkalosis	For each mEq/L increase in HCO_3^-, PCO_2 increases by 0.7 mm Hg.
Respiratory acidosis	
Acute	For each mm Hg increase in PCO_2, HCO_3^- increases by 0.1 mEq/L.
Chronic	For each mm Hg increase in PCO_2, HCO_3^- increases by 0.4 mEq/L.
Respiratory alkalosis	
Acute	For each mm Hg decrease in PCO_2, HCO_3^- decreases by 0.2 mEq/L.
Chronic	For each mm Hg decrease in PCO_2, HCO_3^- decreases by 0.4 mEq/L.

Any acid-base disturbance can be approached with the following system.
1. Check the validity of blood pH - use Henderson equation, and Table 11-1
2. Identify the primary disorder - use Table 11-5
3. Calculate the AG
4. Identify the causes of the primary disorder
5. Calculate the expected compensation (also called secondary response) - use Table 11-6
6. Determine the appropriate treatment

Step 1: Check the validity of blood pH
Using the Henderson equation:

$$[H^+] = 24 \times (PCO_2 / [HCO_3^-]) = 24 \times (30/14) = 51.43$$

From Table 11-1, it is evident that the corresponding pH for the $[H^+]$ of 51.43 is approximately 7.28. Therefore, the reported pH for the patient is correct.

Step 2: Identify the primary disorder
From Table 11-5, the primary disorder is metabolic acidosis because both pH and HCO_3^- are less than normal.

Step 3: Calculate the AG

$$Na^+ - (Cl^- + HCO_3^-)$$
$$138 - (100 + 14) = 24$$

Step 4: Identify the cause of the primary disorder
Because the AG is 24, this disorder is a high AG metabolic acidosis. From the causes listed in the At a Glance Box 11-2 and the laboratory values of the patient, it is evident that the cause is renal failure.

Step 5: Calculate the expected compensation

Since hyperventilation is an appropriate compensatory (secondary response), the PCO_2 should be lower than the normal value of 40 mm Hg. This patient's PCO_2 is 30. The following formula is used to determine whether this value is the expected (or predicted) PCO_2.

$$PCO_2 = HCO_3^- \times 1.5 + 8 \pm 2$$
$$= 14 \times 1.5 + 8 \pm 2 = 29$$

If the patient has an appropriate respiratory response for acidemia of 51.43 $[H^+]$, the expected PCO_2 should be between 27 and 31 mm Hg. Since the patient's PCO_2 is 30, his respiratory response is appropriate. Therefore, the acid-base disturbance in this patient is a simple metabolic acidosis with appropriate physiologic compensation.

If the patient's PCO_2 is different from the expected PCO_2, then a coexisting respiratory acid-base disorder is present. For example, if the patient's PCO_2 is lower than the expected PCO_2, a respiratory alkalosis is present in addition to metabolic acidosis. If, on the other hand, the patient's PCO_2 is higher than the expected PCO_2, a coexisting respiratory acidosis is present.

Step 6: Determine the appropriate treatment

Generally, the treatment for metabolic acidosis with pH less than 7.20 is $NaHCO_3$. In this patient, the pH > 7.20, and thus no treatment is necessary. The patient is symptomatic from his renal failure and needs dialysis to relieve his symptoms. Dialysis will also improve his plasma $[HCO_3^-]$ and blood pH.

METABOLIC ALKALOSIS

Metabolic alkalosis is characterized by an increase in plasma $[HCO_3^-]$ and a pH > 7.40. The resultant alkalemia depresses ventilation, and thereby increases PCO_2 to blunt the increase in pH (see Table 11-5).

There are 2 important mechanisms by which $[HCO_3^-]$ is increased: (1) loss of H^+ ions from the body; and (2) addition of alkali to the body. The loss of H^+ ions can occur either from the gastrointestinal tract, as in vomiting, or from the kidney, as a result of diuretic administration or aldosterone excess syndromes. Addition of alkali to the body can occur as a result of milk-alkali syndrome, formation of HCO_3^- from lactate or ketone bodies, or simply by taking antacids containing HCO_3^-.

Based on the response to saline administration and urinary $[Cl^-]$, metabolic alkalosis is classified into chloride-responsive and chloride-resistant types (Table 11-7).

The development of metabolic alkalosis includes a generation phase and a maintenance phase. During the generation phase, HCl loss occurs. Maintenance of alkalosis occurs after HCl loss stops. Persistence of alkalosis is maintained by continuous renal reabsorption of HCO_3^- as a result of volume contraction and depletion of Cl^-.

Clinical manifestations of metabolic alkalosis include those related to the central nervous system (disorientation, lethargy, seizures); neuromuscular system (muscle weakness, cramping); cardiovascular system (hypotension, increased myocardial contractility, arrythmias); and metabolism (increased affinity between oxygen and Hb). It is not uncommon for the AG to be elevated in metabolic alkalosis. The reason for the elevated AG is two-fold. First, the serum albumin concentration increases as a result of volume countraction most commonly seen in alkalotic patients. This albumin releases H^+ ions and becomes more negatively charged. Second, alkaline pH stimulates glycolysis by enhancing the activity of the rate-limiting enzyme phosphofructokinase. As a result, the production of lactic, citric, and other organic acids production increases. The physiologic significance of elevated AG in metabolic alkalosis is not known. As shown in Table 11-5, hypoventilation is the secondary response to metabolic alkalosis. The resultant increase in PCO_2 lowers pH toward near normal. Appropriate compensation for metabolic alkalosis is shown in Table 11-6.

Table 11-7. Causes and mechanisms of metabolic alkalosis

Cause	Mechanism	Urine [Cl^-]
Chloride-Responsive		
Vomiting	Loss of H^+ ions as HCl	< 10 mEq/L
Nasogastric suction	Loss of H^+ ions as HCl	< 10 mEq/L
Diuretics (Furosemide, Thiazides)	Loss of H^+ ions from the kidney and decreased HCO_3^- space in the body	< 10 mEq/L (after diuretic action wears off)
Congenital chloridorrhea	Loss of H^+ ions in the stool as NH_4Cl	< 10 mEq/L
Laxatives	Loss of H^+ ions in the stool as NH_4Cl	< 10 mEq/L
Chloride-Resistant		
Primary aldosteronism	Loss of H^+ ions from the kidney as NH_4Cl	> 20 mEq/L
Secondary aldosteronism (licorice or chewing tobacco)	Renal loss of H^+ ions	> 20 mEq/L
Bartter's syndrome	Urinary loss of Cl^- and H^+ ions	> 20 mEq/L
K^+ depletion	Increased renal HCO_3^- absorption	> 20 mEq/L
Hypercalcemia	Increased renal HCO_3^- absorption	> 20 mEq/L
Liddle's syndrome	Increased renal HCO_3^- absorption	> 20 mEq/L

Chloride-responsive alkalosis is generally treated with normal saline and replacement of K^+. Volume repletion improves the glomerular filtration rate, which, in turn augments HCO_3^- excretion. Chloride-resistant alkalosis can be treated with K^+ replacement and HCl administration or correction of the underlying disorders. Volume replacement is not necessary since patients with chloride-resistant alkalosis have slight volume expansion.

RESPIRATORY ACIDOSIS

Respiratory acidosis is characterized by hypercapnia and pH < 7.40. Hypercapnia is due to hypoventilation or impaired gas exchange. Acute respiratory acidosis causes only a small increase in plasma [HCO_3^-]. In chronic respiratory acidosis, renal reabsorption of HCO_3^- increases with the resultant hyperbicarbonatemia. The various causes of respiratory acidosis are listed in the accompanying At a Glance Box 11-3.

At a Glance Box 11-3
Causes of respiratory acidosis

1. **Depression of medullary respiratory center**
   Central sleep apnea
   Stroke
   Extreme obesity
   Drugs (opiates, anesthetics, sedatives)
2. **Disorders of chest wall movement**
   Respiratory muscle weakness (myasthenia gravis, Guillain-Barré syndrome, poliomyelitis)
   Kyphoscoliosis
   Trauma
   Drugs (aminoglycosides)
   Hypokalemia or hypophosphatemia
3. **Pulmonary disorders**
   Chronic obstructive pulmonary disease (bronchitis, emphysema)
   Asthma
   Pneumonia
   Adult respiratory distress syndrome

Clinically, patients with respiratory acidosis are hypoxemic (low PO_2), which is more important than hypercapnia. Renal compensatory response for acute or chronic respiratory acidosis is shown in Table 11-6.

Treatment of acute respiratory acidosis is prompt removal of the underlying cause. Improving ventilation is the treatment of choice for chronic respiratory acidosis. O_2 therapy, mechanical ventilation support, bronchodilators, or use of antibiotics for respiratory infections are all used to improve ventilation in these patients.

RESPIRATORY ALKALOSIS

Respiratory alkalosis is characterized by hypocapnia and pH > 7.40. Hypocapnia results from hyperventilation due to stimulation of the medullary respiratory center. Acute respiratory alkalosis causes a minor reduction in plasma [HCO_3^-]. With chronic alkalemia, renal reabsorption of HCO_3^- decreases and a much more severe reduction in plasma [HCO_3^-] occurs (see Table 11-4). The most common causes of respiratory alkalosis are listed in the At a Glance Box 11-4.

Clinical manifestations of respiratory alkalosis include irritability, light-headedness, parasthesias of the circumoral area and extremities, tetany, arrhythmias, and even loss of consciousness.

Removal of the underlying disorder prevents hypoventilation. Acutely, hyperventilation and lowering of pH can be achieved by asking the patient to rebreath into a paper bag. This procedure can increase PCO_2, thereby lowering blood pH to an acceptable level.

At a Glance Box 11-4
Causes of respiratory alkalosis

1. **Direct stimulation of medullary respiratory center**
   Voluntary or psychogenic hyperventilation
   Stroke
   Encephalitis
   Gram negative sepsis
   Liver failure
   Hypermetabolic state (fever, thyrotoxicosis)
   Drugs (salicylates, progesterone)
   Pregnancy
2. **Hypoxemic stimulation of medullary respiratory center**
   Pulmonary disease (pneumonia, interstitial fibrosis, edema)
   Cyanotic heart disease
   High altitude
3. **Mechanical ventilation**

MIXED ACID-BASE DISORDERS

It is not uncommon for two or three simple acid-base disturbances to coexist in hospitalized patients. Mixed acid-base disorders should be suspected whenever:

(1) there is no compensatory response or overcompensation for a primary simple acid-base disorder
(2) the pH and [HCO_3^-] are normal, but the AG is high (mixed metabolic acidosis and metabolic alkalosis)
(3) the pH is near normal, but [HCO_3^-] is high (mixed metabolic alkalosis and

respiratory acidosis)

(4) the pH is near normal, but [HCO_3^-] is low (mixed metabolic acidosis and respiratory alkalosis)

(5) the pH is low (< 7.4), but [HCO_3^-] is normal (mixed metabolic acidosis and respiratory acidosis)

(6) the pH is high (> 7.4), but [HCO_3^-] is normal (mixed respiratory alkalosis and metabolic alkalosis)

How to Evaluate a Mixed Acid-Base Disorder

A 31-year-old female with AIDS was admitted for weakness and poor appetite. Her respiratory rate is 26 per minute. Lung examination revealed crackles bilaterally, and chest x-ray confirms pulmonary edema. Her initial laboratory values are:

Na^+ = 129 mEq/L	<u>ABG</u>
K^+ = 3.4 mEq/L	pH = 7.36
Cl^- = 90 mEq/L	PCO_2 = 22 mm Hg
HCO_3^- = 12 mEq/L	PO_2 = 90 mm Hg
Creatinine = 8.2 mg/dL	HCO_3^- = 11 mEq/L
BUN = 82 mg/dL	
Glucose = 100 mg/dL	

To analyze this acid-base disorder, follow the steps 1-6 shown before.

Step 1: Check the validity of blood pH

Using the Henderson equation, the [H^+] is 44, which corresponds to the pH of 7.36.

Step 2: Identify the primary disorder

The dominant acid-base disturbance is metabolic acidosis because the pH< 7.40 and the HCO_3^- is < 24 mEq/L.

Step 3: Calculate the AG

The AG is 27, which is elevated. This high AG metabolic acidosis seems to be the result of renal failure (see At a Glance Box 11-2).

Step 4: Identify the causes of the primary disorder

From the laboratory values, the cause for the patient's metabolic acidosis is renal failure.

Step 5: Calculate the expected compensation

For a simple metabolic acidosis, the expected PCO_2 is between 24 and 28 mm Hg. However, the patient's PCO_2 is below 24, suggesting the coexistence of respiratory alkalosis. The patient, therefore, has a mixed metabolic acidosis and respiratory alkalosis.

Step 6: Determine the appropriate treatment

Administration of $NaHCO_3$ to raise serum [HCO_3^-] is not appropriate because of pulmonary edema. The appropriate treatment is hemodialysis, which not only removes fluid from the lungs but also increases serum [HCO_3^-] and blood pH.

SUMMARY

1. Many functions of the cell are dependent on optimum [H^+] or pH. pH is defined as the negative logarithm of the [H^+]. The normal arterial pH varies from 7.38 to 7.42, which corresponds to a [H^+] of 38-42 nmol/L.
2. The pH is maintained within narrow limits by interplay between body buffers, lungs, and kidneys. Bicarbonate/carbonic acid is the most important extracellular buffer system in the body. The lungs excrete PCO_2 generated from volatile acids, whereas the kidneys excrete H^+ ions generated from nonvolatile acids to maintain serum [HCO_3^-] and pH in the normal range.
3. Maintenance of normal serum [HCO_3^-] by the kidneys is accomplished by three mechanisms: (1) reabsorption of all the filtered load of HCO_3^-; (2) excretion of titratable acid; and (3) generation of HCO_3^- from NH_4^+.
4. Acid-base disorders include changes in blood pH or [H^+]. There are four primary acid-base disorders: (1) metabolic acidosis; (2) metabolic alkalosis; (3) respiratory acidosis; and (4) respiratory alkalosis. Metabolic acid-base disorders result from changes in serum [HCO_3^-], whereas respiratory acid-base disorders result from changes in arterial PCO_2. Whenever a primary acid-base disorder occurs, either a respiratory or renal compensatory response occurs to minimize changes in pH. Frequently, two or three primary acid-base disorders coexist, called mixed acid-base disorder, in a hospitalized patient. A systematic approach to ABG can identify such a mixed or primary acid-base disorder.

STUDY QUESTIONS

Case 1

A 70-kg-man on a normal diet has a GFR of 125 ml/min and plasma [HCO_3^-] of 24 mmol/L (24 μmol/ml).

Question 1. Assuming this person generates an acid urine (pH 5.0) and net acid excretion (NAE) of 70 mmol, calculate his: (a) HCO_3^- reabsorption; (b) HCO_3^- regeneration from titratable acid (TA); and (c) HCO_3^- generation from NH_4^+ excretion.

Answer: This man will generate 1 mmol of fixed acid per kg body weight. Therefore, he generates 70 mmol of acid. Since this man is able to acidify the urine to pH 5.0, the urine contains no HCO_3^-. Therefore, the NAE includes only TA plus NH_4^+. The subject is eating a diet containing adequate amounts of phosphate, and the TA equals approximately 30 mmol. The remaining 40 mmol of NAE account for NH_4^+ excretion.

a. <u>HCO_3^- reabsorption</u>

HCO_3^- reabsorption equals the filtered load of HCO_3^- (i.e., GFR x [HCO_3^-])

125 ml/min x 24 μmol/ml = 3000 μmol/min.

b. <u>HCO_3^- generation from TA</u>

$$TA = 30 \text{ mmol or } \frac{30{,}000\ \mu mol}{1440\ min/day} = 20.8\ \mu mol/min$$

c. <u>HCO_3^- generation from NH_4^+</u>

(Note that NH_4^+ forms from glutamine metabolism)

$$NH_4^+ = 40 \text{ mmol or } \frac{40{,}000\ \mu mol}{1440\ min/day} = 27.8.\ \mu mol/min$$

Total HCO_3^- reabsorption and generation

= 3000 + 20.8 + 27.8 = 3,048.6 μmol/min

or 4,390 mmol/day

Case 2

The following values were obtained from a 72-kg person:

24-hour volume = 1.5 L

Titratable acid (TA) = 20 mmol/L

[NH_4^+] = 30 mmol/L

[HCO_3^-] = 2 mmol/L

Question 1. Calculate net acid excretion (NAE).

Answer: NAE = TA + NH_4^+ - HCO_3^-

TA = 20 x 1.5 = 30 mmol/day

NH_4^+ = 30 x 1.5 = 45 mmol/day

HCO_3^- = 2 x 1.5 = 3 mmol/day

NAE = 30 + 45 - 3 = 72 mmol/day

Case 3

A 42-year-old man was admitted because of dizziness and weakness. His blood pressure was 120/80 and pulse 90 while sitting, and 100/64 and pulse 110, while standing. He was not on any medications, but admits to vomiting. Admitting laboratory values were:

Na^+ = 129 mEq/L	ABG
K^+ = 2.5 mEq/L	pH = 7.53
Cl^- = 58 mEq/L	PCO_2 = 63 mm Hg
HCO_3^- = 58 mEq/L	PO_2 = 63 mm Hg
Creatinine = 1.9 mg/dL	HCO_3^- = 58 mEq/L
BUN = 32 mg/dL	
Glucose = 94 mg/dL	

Question 1. Analyze the acid-base disturbance.

Answer: To analyze this acid-base disorder, follow the steps 1-5 shown before.
Step 1: According to the Henderson equation, the $[H^+]$ is 26, which corresponds to a pH of 7.53. Therefore, the reported pH is correct.
Step 2: From Table 11-5, the primary acid-base disturbance is metabolic alkalosis.
Step 3: The AG is 13, which is normal.
Step 4: The cause for metabolic alkalosis is vomiting.
Step 5: The respiratory compensation is appropriate (Table 11-6), suggesting that this acid-base disturbance is a simple metabolic alkalosis.

Question 2. What other laboratory test should you order?

Answer: The laboratory test that is pertinent to this acid-base disorder is determination of urinary Cl^-, which was 5 mEq/L. The patient, therefore, has chloride-responsive metabolic alkalosis.

Question 3. How would you treat this acid-base disturbance?

Answer: The treatment is normal saline with K^+ supplementation.

Case 4

A 65-year-old man with a history of chronic obstructive pulmonary disease (COPD) was admitted for evaluation of shortness of breath. On admission, his laboratory values were:

Na^+ = 134 mEq/L	ABG
K^+ = 3.6 mEq/L	pH = 7.35
Cl^- = 90 mEq/L	PCO_2 = 64 mm Hg

HCO_3^- = 34 mEq/L	PO_2 = 70 mm Hg
Creatinine = 1.1 mg/dL	HCO_3^- = 33 mEq/L
BUN = 12 mg/dL	
Glucose = 100 mg/dL	

Question 1. Characterize the acid-base disorder.

Answer: As above, follow step by step to analyze this acid-base disorder.
Step 1: According to the Henderson equation, the $[H^+]$ is 45 nmol/L, which corresponds to a pH of 7.35.
Step 2: From Table 11-4, the primary acid-base disturbance is respiratory acidosis.
Step 3: The AG is 10, which is normal.
Step 4: The cause for this patient's respiratory acidosis is COPD.
Step 5: The compensation for respiratory acidosis is renal reabsorption of HCO_3^-. From Table 11-6, the patient has a primary chronic rather than acute respiratory acidosis.
Step 6: The immediate treatment is administration of oxygen by nasal cannula, and subsequent correction of the precipitating factor.

Case 5
A 72-year-old female with a history of non insulin-dependent diabetes mellitus, congestive heart failure, and renal failure was admitted for nausea, vomiting, and shortness of breath. She was taking insulin and furosemide. Her weight was 60 kg. Admission laboratory values were as follows:

Na^+= 140 mEq/L	<u>ABG</u>
K^+ = 4.1 mEq/L	pH = 7.40
Cl^- = 95 mEq/L	PCO_2 = 40 mm Hg
HCO_3^- = 24 mEq/L	PO_2 = 90 mm Hg
Creatinine = 4.1 mg/dL	HCO_3^- = 24 mEq/L
BUN = 52 mg/dL	
Glucose = 145 mg/dL	

Question 1. Characterize the acid-base disturbance in this patient.

Answer: The electrolytes and ABG values reveal no abnormalities. However, a step by step approach reveals that a mixed acid-base disturbance is present.
Step 1: From the Henderson equation, the $[H^+]$ is 40 nmol/L, which is equal to a pH of 7.40.
Step 2: From ABG values, no apparent acid-base disturbance is present.
Step 3: The AG is 21, which suggests the presence of a high AG metabolic acidosis.
Step 4: The cause for this metabolic acidosis is renal failure.

Step 5: If this were a pure metabolic acidosis, the pH, serum [HCO_3^-], and PCO_2 levels would be lower than normal. Since the patient was vomiting and was also taking furosemide for her congestive heart failure, she developed metabolic alkalosis. The coexistence of metabolic acidosis and metabolic alkalosis normalizes ABG values and gives the impression of no underlying disturbance. The clue for the diagnosis of this mixed metabolic acidosis and metabolic alkalosis is the presence of a high AG. Thus, this case emphasizes the importance of calculating AG in the analysis of any acid-base disturbance.

SUGGESTED READING

1. Seldin, D.W. and Giebisch, G. (eds.). The Regulation of Acid-Base Balance. Raven Press, New York, 1989 (*A multi-authored text with emphasis on basic and clinical aspects of acid-base disturbance*).
2. Abelow, B. Understanding Acid-Base. Williams & Wilkins, Baltimore, 1997 (*A monograph with easy and clear understanding of both basic and clinical concepts of acid-base disturbance*).

CHAPTER 12

POTASSIUM REGULATION AND DISORDERS

Objectives

After reading this chapter, the student should be able to:

1. Discuss the distribution and functions of K^+ in the body.
2. Describe the various factors influencing the transcellular distribution of K^+.
3. Explain the cellular mechanisms of reabsorption and secretion of K^+.
4. Discuss the causes, clinical consequences, and treatment of hypo- and hyperkalemia.

GENERAL FEATURES

Potassium (K^+) is the predominant intracellular cation in the body. Maintenance of a high cellular concentration of K^+ is necessary for several cellular functions, including growth, nucleic acid and protein synthesis, and regulation of cell volume, as well as pH and enzyme activation. In addition, a high intracellular concentration of K^+ is essential to the maintenance of the resting membrane potential for cellular excitability and contraction.

The high intracellular K^+ concentration is maintained by the Na/K-ATPase located in the cell membranes of all animal cells. This enzyme uses the energy derived from the hydrolysis of ATP to pump 2 K^+ ions into the cell and 3 Na^+ ions out of the cell. Ouabain and other cardiac glycosides, such as digitalis, inhibit this enzyme system and prevent the transport of these ions. As a result, the extracellular (blood) K^+ concentration (abbreviated as $[K^+]$) increases. The activity of this enzyme is influenced by a variety of hormones.

The total body $[K^+]$ varies with age, sex, and body weight of an individual. The total $[K^+]$ of 20-year-old male is approximately 58 mEq/kg body weight; an elderly male has 20% less K^+. Females have 25% less total body K^+ than males of a comparable age presumably, due to their smaller muscle mass. K^+ is readily absorbed from the gastrointestinal tract and enters the blood. About 98% of K^+ is located within cells of the muscle, liver, bone, and red blood cells. The remaining 2% is found in the extracellular compartment. The intracellular

$[K^+]$ is 140 to 150 mEq/L; in blood it is 3.5 to 5 mEq/L. Serum contains a slightly higher concentration of K^+ than plasma because K^+ is released from red blood cells during clot formation.

The kidney is the primary route for K^+ excretion. Generally, K^+ excretion in the urine, called **kaliuresis**, parallels dietary intake. The other route for K^+ excretion is the colon. Under conditions of decreased renal function, K^+ excretion by the colon is enhanced.

RESTING MEMBRANE POTENTIAL AND K^+

Electrophysiology studies from nerve have demonstrated that there is a transmembrane potential difference of about 70 mV, with the inside being negative to the outside. Thus, the resting membrane potential is -70 mV. The resting membrane potential takes into account the permeabilities of ions (Na^+, K^+, and Cl^-) across the cell membrane at rest. Since K^+ permeabilty is highest compared to other ions at rest, K^+ is the major determinant of the resting membrane potential.

The membrane potential of either a nerve or muscle cell depends on three factors: (1) the electrical charge present on each ion; (2) the permeability (P) of the membrane to each ion; and (3) the concentration of each ion on the outside (o) and inside (i) of the membrane. The following equation (called Goldman-Hodgkin-Katz equation) calculates the membrane potential (E_m) on the inside of the membrane when Na^+ and K^+ are involved:

$$E_m\ (\text{mV}) = -61 \log \frac{[K^+]i + 0.01\ [Na^+]\ i}{[K^+]o + 0.01\ [Na^+]\ o}$$

where, 0.01 is the relative membrane permeability of Na^+ to K^+, and the subscripts i and o denote inside and outside concentrations of the corresponding ions. The E_m can be calculated by using Na^+ and K^+ concentrations as follows:

$$Em\ (\text{mV}) = -61 \log \frac{(140) + 0.01\ (12)}{(4.5) + 0.01\ (145)} = -86$$

Thus, the cell interior is - 86 mV, which is largely contributed by the movement of K^+ out of the cell. An additional - 4 mV is contributed to the membrane potential by Na/K- ATPase, making the net resting membrane potential - 90 mV. In nerve and muscle cells, the resting membrane potential is the prerequisite for membrane depolarization, i.e., the generation of an action potential. Therefore, any change in plasma $[K^+]$ can alter the action potential and thus the excitability of the cell. A decrease in plasma $[K^+]$ increases the resting membrane potential so that the cell becomes less excitable. An increase in plasma $[K^+]$ causes an opposite effect. The Goldman-Hodgkin-Katz equation takes into account the contributions of all permeant ions, whereas the Nernst equation applies only to one permeant ion at a time.

TRANSCELLULAR DISTRIBUTION OF K^+

A number of physiologic and pathophysiologic factors can affect the transcellular distribution of K^+ (see At a Glance Box 12-1). Physiologic factors such as insulin are important to maintain normal plasma $[K^+]$ following a meal because renal excretion of K^+ does not occur immediately. Insulin promotes K^+ uptake into the cell by stimulating Na/K-ATPase. Conversely, insulin deficiency, as seen in patients with diabetes mellitus, impairs cellular uptake of K^+. Similar to insulin, epinephrine stimulates K^+ uptake into the cell via activation of β_2-receptors. Consequently, β_2-agonists, such as albuterol (used to treat asthma) transiently cause low plasma $[K^+]$. β_2-antagonists, such as propranolol, inhibit cellular uptake of K^+, and cause elevated plasma $[K^+]$. Exercise causes a transient increase in plasma $[K^+]$; however, epinephrine release due to exercise stimulates K^+ uptake into the cell. As a result, no change in plasma $[K^+]$ is observed during exercise. When a patient is on propranolol, vigorous exercise may cause severe increase in plasma $[K^+]$. During metabolic alkalosis, H^+ ions leave the cell to buffer the extracellular pH, and K^+ enters the cell. Generally, plasma $[K^+]$ falls by 0.4 mEq/L for every 0.1 unit increase in blood pH. The effect of aldosterone on K^+ uptake has not been conclusively demonstrated. An increase in plasma osmolality due to mannitol infusion or hyperglycemia in a diabetic subject increases plasma $[K^+]$. This increase in plasma $[K^+]$ is attributed to movement of water from the intracellular to extracellular compartment with accompanying K^+ due to solvent drag.

RENAL HANDLING AND CELLULAR MECHANISMS OF K^+ TRANSPORT

Renal handling of K^+ involves filtration, reabsorption, and secretion. Most of the filtered K^+ is reabsorbed in segments of the proximal nephron, and the K^+ that is found in the urine is secreted by the distal segments of the nephron (Figure 12-1).

Proximal Nephron

Proximal Tubule

K^+ is freely filtered at the glomerulus. About 60-80% of this filtered K^+ is reabsorbed by the proximal tubule. Reabsorption of K^+ is mostly passive and occurs via a K^+ transporter. Also, passive reabsorption of K^+ occurs through the paracellular pathway (Figure 12-2). This passive transport of K^+ is coupled with Na^+ and water transport. Volume expansion and osmotic diuretics (e.g., mannitol) inhibit this passive diffusion of Na^+ -coupled K^+ transport.

> **At a Glance Box 12-1**
> Factors influencing transcellular distribution of K^+
>
> **Factors that promote cellular uptake of K^+**
> - Insulin
> - β-adrenergic agonists (epinephrine)
> - α-adrenergic blockers (phentolamine)
> - Aldosterone (?)
> - Alkalosis
>
> **Factors that reduce cellular uptake of K^+ or increase its efflux**
> - Glucagon
> - β-adrenergic blockers (propranolol)
> - α-adrenergic agonists (phenylephrine)
> - Aldosterone deficiency (?)
> - Acidosis (mineral)
> - Vigorous exercise
> - Plasma hyperosomolality

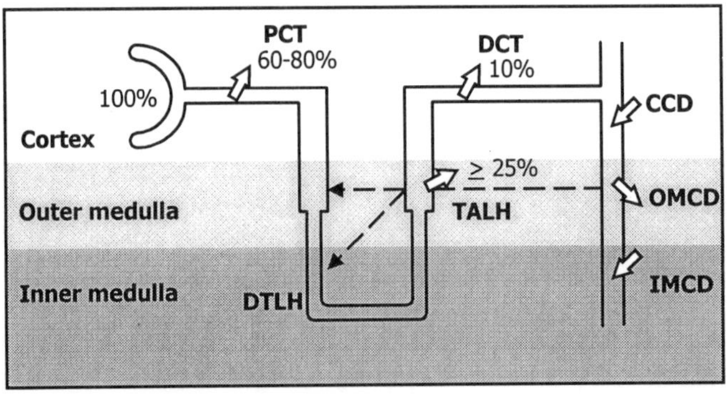

Figure 12-1. Handling of K^+ by various segments of the nephron. Sixty to eighty percent of K^+ is reabsorbed by the proximal convoluted tubule (PCT) and about 25% by the medullary thick ascending limb of Henle's loop (TALH). Only 10% of filtered K^+ is delivered to the distal convoluted tubule (DCT). CCD, OMCD, and IMCD refer to cortical collecting, outer medullary collecting and inner medullary collecting ducts, respectively. Broken arrows denote K^+ secretion into the late segment of the proximal tubule and descending thin limb of Henle's loop (DTHL).

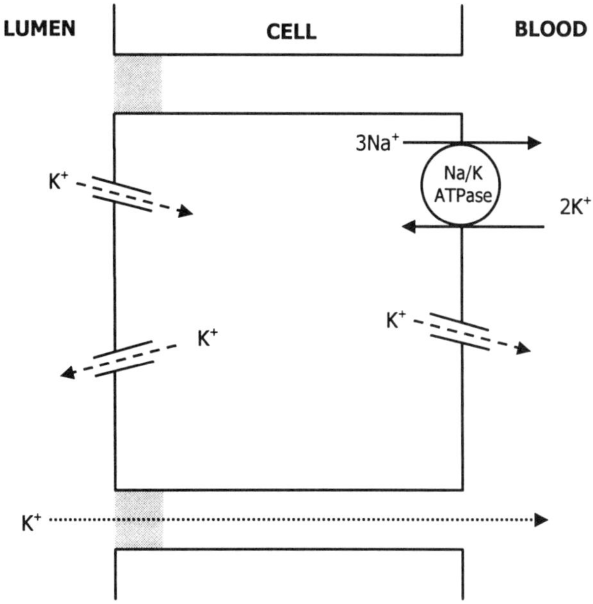

Figure 12-2. Cellular model for transepithelial K^+ transport in the proximal tubule. Thick broken arrows indicate diffusion of K^+ through conductance channels.

Loop of Henle

In this segment of the nephron, both secretion and reabsorption of K^+ occur. K^+ enters the late segment of the proximal tubule and the descending thin limb of the Henle's loop. This observation is based on evidence that the [K^+] is higher in the lumen of the hairpin turn of the Henle's loop than the plasma [K^+], suggesting that K^+ enters passively from the medullary interstitium.

The thick ascending limb of Henle's loop actively reabsorbs K^+. This segment also reabsorbs Na^+ and Cl^-. K^+ reabsorption occurs mostly in the medullary thick ascending limb and could account for as much as 25% of the filtered K^+.

K^+ transport in this segment of the nephron occurs by secondary active transport as well as by passive diffusion through the paracellular pathway. The secondary active transport mechanism involves the cotransport of 1 Na^+, 1 K^+, and 2 Cl^- ions (Figure 12-3). The driving force for this cotransport is provided by the Na/K-ATPase located in the basolateral membrane. This enzyme decreases the intracellular concentration of Na^+, thereby creating a steep Na^+ gradient across the apical membrane. In order to stimulate Na^+ entry, K^+ must leak back into the lumen. Indeed, K^+ diffuses back into the lumen through K^+ conductance channels to provide a continuous supply of K^+ ions for cotransport with Na^+ and Cl^-. Without this back-leak of K^+, the low luminal K^+ concentration would limit the reabsorption of Na^+ and Cl^-. This cotransport system is inhibited by the loop diuretics (furosemide, bumetanide, etc.).

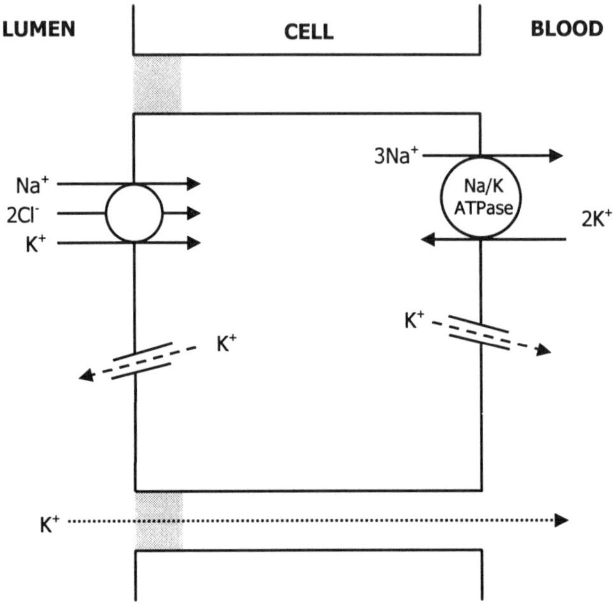

Figure 12-3. Cellular model for transepithelial K^+ transport in the thick ascending limb of Henle's loop. Thick broken arrows indicate diffusion of K^+ through conductance channels.

Distal Nephron

Distal Tubule

About 10% of the filtered K^+ reaches the distal tubule. K^+ secretion occurs in this segment because of low luminal Cl^- and high luminal Na^+ concentration. In this segment, a luminal K/Cl cotransporter is responsible for K^+ secretion (Figure 12-4). This cotransporter operates in cooperation with a luminal Na/Cl cotransporter. It has been shown that delivery of Na^+ to the distal tubule promotes secretion of K^+ through the K/Cl cotransporter. Thiazide diuretics (hydrochlorothiazide) inhibit Na/Cl cotransporter as well as K^+ secretion. K^+ secretion is unaffected by aldosterone.

Connecting Tubule

The connecting tubule secretes K^+ at a higher rate than the rate at which it is excreted in the urine. K^+ secretion is sensitive to aldosterone.

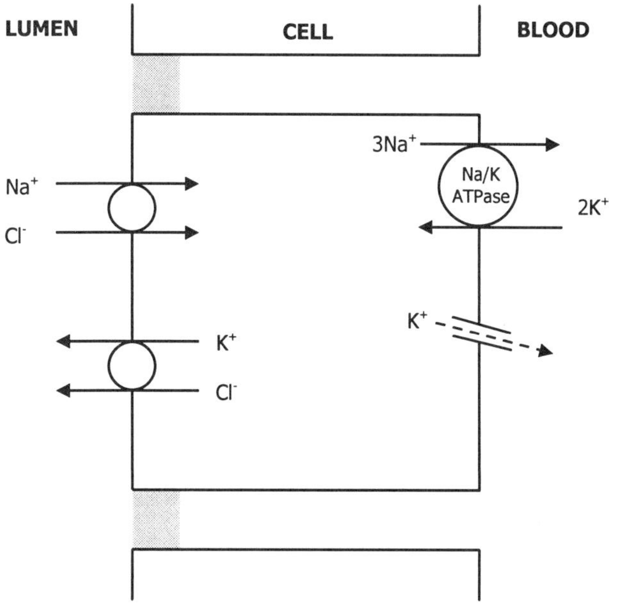

Figure 12-4. Cellular model for transepithelial K^+ transport in the distal tubule. Broken arrow indicates diffusion of K^+ through conductance channel.

Cortical Collecting Duct

The collecting duct is the major site for K^+ secretion. Two types of cells are found in this segment: principal cells and intercalated cells. Principal cells are the primary cells for K^+ secretion. They possess two secretory pathways for K^+ in the apical membrane (Figure 12-5A). One pathway is through the K^+ conductance channel and the other is through the K/Cl cotransporter. A conductance channel for Na^+ also exists. K^+ secretion into the lumen occurs in association with a Na/K-ATPase located in the basolateral membrane, which pumps 2 K^+ into and 3 Na^+ ions out of the cell. Blockage of Na^+ uptake by amiloride inhibits K^+ secretion. Thus, K^+ secretion is dependent on Na^+ uptake from the lumen. Aldosterone promotes K^+ secretion by stimulating basolateral Na/K-ATPase. The A-type intercalated cell may be involved in K^+ reabsorption.

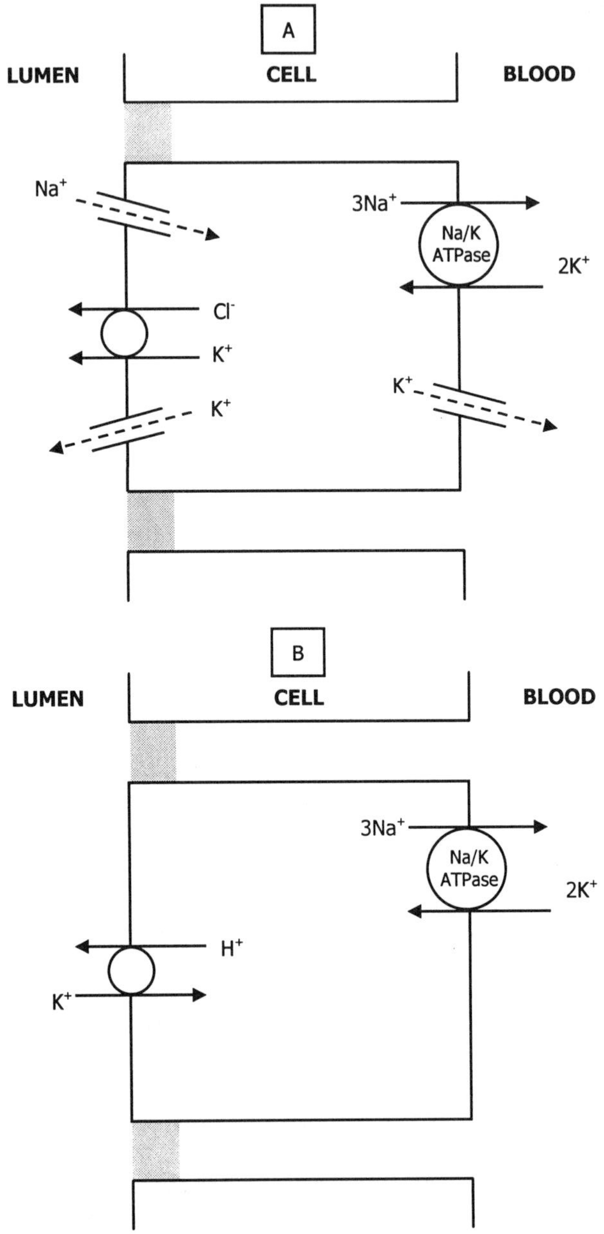

Figure 12-5. Cellular model for transepithelial K^+ transport in the cortical collecting duct. A = principal cell; B = intercalated cell. Broken arrows indicate diffusion of respective ions through specific conductance channels.

This cell reabsorbs K^+ in exchange for H^+ ion secretion via an H/K-ATPase (Figure 12-5B). For each H^+ ion secreted, one HCO_3^- is generated. Thus, the H/K-ATPase may participate in acid-base balance.

Outer Medullary Collecting Duct

The lumen of this segment contains a high concentration of K^+ because of K^+ secretion in the cortical collecting duct. The lumen, therefore, becomes electro-positive. The combination of a high concentration of K^+ in the lumen and its electro-positivity creates a driving force for passive reabsorption of K^+.

Inner Medullary Collecting Duct

Under normal conditions, this segment plays only a minor role in K^+ secretion. However, in K^+-loaded animals, the inner medullary collecting duct secretes significant amounts of K^+. Aldosterone potentiates the secretion of K^+ in this segment.

K^+ RECYCLING

K^+ recycling plays an important role in determining the excretion of ingested K^+ in the diet. In order to excrete this ingested K^+, the secreted K^+ in the cortical collecting duct must undergo minimal reabsorption in the outer medullary collecting duct (see Figure 12-1). Minimal reabsorption is possible only when the $[K^+]$ in the medullary interstitium is high. The events leading to this high $[K^+]$ are as follows: (1) K^+ is secreted by the cortical collecting duct; (2) part of this secreted K^+ is reabsorbed by the outer medullary collecting duct into the interstitium; (3) some of the interstitial K^+ diffuses into the later portion of the proximal tubule and the descending limb of Henle's loop; (4) K^+ is then transported at a high flow rate to the thick ascending limb, where it is reabsorbed with Cl^- and Na^+; (5) the remaining K^+ is delivered to the cortical collecting duct, which adds K^+ to the lumen by secretion; (6) K^+ is again reabsorbed by the outer medullary collecting duct until the $[K^+]$ in the interstitium equilibrates with the tubular $[K^+]$; and (7) at this time, some K^+ secreted by the cortical collecting duct escapes reabsorption and thus appears in the urine. This sequence of events reveals that K^+ is concentrated in the medullary interstitium by countercurrent exchange between the ascending and descending limbs of Henle's loop.

K^+ recycling is activated when K^+ intake is increased. Due to the increased intake, K^+ excretion must be enhanced. Conversely, K^+ recycling is decreased when K^+ intake is decreased.

FACTORS AFFECTING K^+ EXCRETION

As stated earlier, K^+ secretion occurs in the cortical collecting ducts which accounts for the K^+ excreted in the urine. A number of factors (see At a Glance Box 12-2) influence K^+ excretion.

At a Glance Box 12-2
Factors that influence K^+ excretion

- Dietary K^+ intake and plasma [K^+]
- Urine flow rate and Na^+ delivery
- Hormones
- Acid-base balance
- Anions
- Diuretics

Dietary Intake and Plasma [K^+]

An increase in K^+ intake has been shown to raise plasma as well as intracellular [K^+]. This increase in plasma [K^+] stimulates aldosterone synthesis and secretion, which enhances K^+ secretion and excretion. Increased K^+ excretion by the kidney is due to decreased reabsorption by Henle's loop and enhanced secretion by the cortical and inner medullary collecting ducts. A decrease in K^+ intake causes an opposite effect on K^+ excretion and aldosterone synthesis.

Urine Flow Rate and Na^+ Delivery

K^+ secretion depends on the urine flow rate to the distal nephron. In turn, the distal urine flow rate depends on Na^+ intake and glomerular filtration rate. If these factors are decreased, all of the filtrate is reabsorbed in the proximal tubule, and little is delivered to the distal nephron. Delivery of Na^+ therefore decreases, and thus exchange of Na^+ for K^+ also decreases. As a result, K^+ is retained.

Increase in Na^+ intake or parenteral infusion of saline tends to expand the extracellular fluid volume. Both GFR and Na^+ delivery to the distal nephron are increased, which stimulate K^+ excretion. This kaliuresis is independent of aldosterone effect or increase in plasma [K^+], but can be attributed to increased Na^+ delivery to the distal nephron. In this situation, Na^+ excretion is also increased.

Hormones

Two important hormones are involved in K^+ secretion and excretion:

aldosterone and antidiuretic hormone (ADH). Aldosterone acts on the principal cells of the cortical collecting duct and stimulates the absorption of Na^+ in exchange for K^+. Consequently, adrenal insufficiency (a condition in which aldosterone synthesis and secretion are low) causes K^+ retention and Na^+ wasting, which are reversed by administration of aldosterone. Glucocorticoid hormones seem to have little effect on either K^+ secretion or excretion. ADH has been shown to promote K^+ secretion despite a reduction in urine flow rate. This effect of ADH seems to occur in the medullary collecting duct. Other hormones have also been shown to influence K^+ secretion. Epinephrine decreases and norepinephrine increases K^+ secretion in the cortical collecting duct.

Acid-Base Balance

A number of studies have shown that changes in systemic pH alter K^+ excretion. Infusion of NH_4Cl causes metabolic acidosis (pH < 7.20) acutely, which reduces K^+ excretion. This reduction may be related to inhibition of K^+ secretion by the cortical collecting duct, possibly by closing pH sensitive K^+ channels in the luminal membrane. In contrast, chronic acidosis promotes K^+ secretion due to increased fluid delivery to the cortical collecting duct.

Induction of metabolic alkalosis (pH > 7.50) acutely by infusion of $NaHCO_3$ increases K^+ excretion. Chronic alkalosis also augments K^+ excretion. This augmented excretion is presumably due to enhanced K^+ entry into the principal cell across the basolateral membrane and by accelerated exit across the apical membrane through K^+ channels into the lumen.

Acute respiratory acidosis decreases and respiratory alkalosis increases K^+ excretion. However, chronic acidosis and alkalosis may increase K^+ excretion. In chronic respiratory acidosis, the plasma $[HCO_3^-]$ is elevated, which increases the distal delivery of $NaHCO_3$, and thus promotes K^+ excretion.

Anions

When Na^+ with nonchloride anions such as sulfate or bicarbonate is infused into the body, K^+ excretion by the cortical collecting duct can be markedly augmented. Delivery of impermeant anions (sulfate, some penicillins) to the distal nephron creates a lumen-negative voltage gradient favoring K^+ secretion. K^+ secretion can also be augmented when the luminal $[Cl^-]$ is decreased independently of the transepithelial potential difference. This effect suggests the presence of a K/Cl cotransporter that is stimulated by the increased cellular luminal gradient.

Diuretics

In general, diuretics promote K^+ excretion by increasing distal delivery of fluid and Na^+. Osmotic diuretics, such as mannitol, inhibit Na^+ and water reabsorption by the proximal tubule and increase distal rates of flow. Acetazolamide, a carbonic anhydrase inhibitor, reduces $NaHCO_3$ reabsorption by the proximal tubule, and thus creates a lumen-negative potential difference in the distal nephron that promotes K^+ secretion. Loop diuretics, such as furosemide or bumetanide, inhibit the Na/K/2Cl cotransporter in the thick ascending limb of Henle's loop, and thus promote kaliuresis. Thiazide diuretics act on the distal tubule and inhibit NaCl reabsorption. Kaliuresis occurs due to increased fluid delivery to the cortical collecting duct.

Spironolactone, triamterene, and amiloride inhibit secretion, and thus inhibit urinary loss of K^+. Spironolactone antagonizes the effects of aldosterone, whereas triamterene and amiloride inhibit Na^+ conductance channels and impede the entry of Na^+. Because Na^+ entry is blocked, the luminal membrane of the principal cells becomes hyperpolarized, which prevents K^+ secretion.

At a Glance Box 12-3
Causes of hypokalemia

Dietary
Inadequate dietary intake
High carbohydrate intake
Uptake by cells
Insulin
Catecholamines (β_2-agonists)
Alkalemia
Hypokalemic periodic paralysis (an inherited defect in skeletal muscle Ca^{2+} channel)
B_{12} injections
Renal loss
Primary or secondary hyperaldosteronism
Corticosteroid excess
Renal tubular acidosis
Bartter's syndrome (due to a mutation in Na/K/2Cl cotransporter)
Liddle's syndrome (due to a mutation in renal epithelial Na^+ channel)
Gitelman's syndrome (due to mutation in NaCl cotransporter)
Drugs
Diuretics, Penicillins, Aminoglycosides, Amphotericin B, Lithium, Cisplatin, Licorice
Gastrointestinal loss
Vomiting, Diarrhea
Skin loss (Excessive heat, Strenuous exercise)

DISORDERS OF K^+

Hypokalemia

Hypokalemia is defined as a serum $[K^+] < 3.5$ mEq/L. The important causes of hypokalemia (see At a Glance Box 12-3) can be divided into 5 major categories: (1) dietary, (2) K^+ uptake by cells, (3) renal loss, (4) gastrointestinal loss; and (5) skin loss. The physiologic and clinical manifestations of hypokalemia include metabolic, cardiovascular, neuromuscular, and renal effects (see At a Glance box 12-4).

At a Glance Box 12-4
Physiologic and clinical manifestations of hypokalemia

Metabolic effects
- Decreased insulin release
- Impaired hepatic glycogen and protein synthesis
- Abnormal tolerance to glucose causing hyperglycemia
- Decreased aldosterone and growth hormone secretion
- Maintenance of metabolic alkalosis

Cardiovascular effects
- Abnormal EKG changes resulting in arrhythmias
- Abnormal contractility
- Potentiation of digitalis toxicity

Neuromuscular effects
- Muscle weakness and paralysis due to depolarization of the cell membrane
- Tetany
- Ileus (decreased intestinal mobility)

Renal effects
- Impaired urine concentration resulting in polyuria and polydipsia
- Increased renal ammonia production
- Increased renal HCO_3^- reabsorption
- Rhabdomyolysis (muscle necrosis) causing acute renal failure

Treatment of hypokalemia depends on its severity and associated clinical manifestations. Treatment of mild to moderate hypokalemia (3-3.5 mEq/L) includes oral administration of 40 to 80 mEq of KCl/day and correction of the underlying cause, such as diarrhea. Severe hypokalemia (< 2.5 mEq/L) can be life-threatening in a patient with cardiac disease, and thus warrants immediate treatment. Intravenous administration of KCl is preferred to oral administration. Generally, 20-40 mEq of KCl in 1 L of normal or half-normal saline given over an hour is considered safe. Higher concentrations of KCl may lead to hyperkalemia and pain and sclerosis of peripheral veins. KCl should not be given with dextrose solution for initial therapy because of the risk of dextrose-induced hypokalemia through insulin release.

Hyperkalemia

Hyperkalemia is defined as a serum [K^+] > 5.5 mEq/L. True hyperkalemia is caused by an excessive exogenous load of K^+ or can result from a decrease in cellular uptake, massive release following cell lysis, or a decrease in renal excretion. A number of drugs also cause hyperkalemia (see At a Glance Box 12-5). **Pseudohyperkalemia** refers to a condition in which K^+ is released from cells during venipuncture following prolonged application of a tourniquet in the arm. Hemolysis of red blood cells and an increased number of white blood cells (> 100,000 cells) and platelets (> 1,000,000 platelets) also release K^+ and cause pseudohyperkalemia.

At a Glance Box 12-5
Causes of hyperkalemia

Exogenous intake
- Oral
- Intravenous

Reduced cellular uptake
- Insulin deficiency
- β-adrenergic blockade
- Aldosterone deficiency
- Digitalis overdose
- Hyperkalemic periodic paralysis (an inherited defect in skeletal muscle Na^+ channels)

Increased cellular release
- Cell breakdown as in rhabdomyolysis or increased catabolism or tumor lysis syndrome
- Severe exercise
- Hyperosmolality due to hyperglycemia

Decreased renal excretion
- Advanced renal failure
- Addison's disease with aldosterone deficiency
- Tubular resistance to aldosterone effect
- Diseases causing a defect in K^+ secretion (sickle cell disease, lupus, obstructive uropathy)
- Volume depletion with decreased distal delivery of Na^+

Drugs
- K^+-sparing diuretics (inhibits K^+ secretion)
- Amiloride (blocks Na^+ channel)
- Pentamidine (blocks Na^+ channel)
- Trimethoprim (blocks Na^+ channel)
- Angiotensin-converting enzyme inhibitors (↓ aldosterone synthesis)
- Nonsteroidal anti-inflammatory agents (↓ aldosterone synthesis)
- Heparin (↓ aldosterone secretion)
- Cyclosporine (↓ aldosterone synthesis)

The adverse effects of hyperkalemia are limited to skeletal and cardiac muscle. Neuromuscular abnormalities include muscle weakness and paralysis. These symptoms are due to reduced membrane potential caused by a reduction in the ratio of intracellular to extracellular [K^+].

Cardiac effects include abnormalities in the rate and rhythm of the heart conduction system. Therefore, EKG monitoring is essential in the patient with hyperkalemia. The magnitude of EKG changes is related to serum [K^+] (Figure 12-6). Initial EKG changes include peaked T waves with a shortened QT interval due to rapid repolarization. As the serum [K^+] rises, the QRS complex becomes widened; the P wave then disappears. The widened QRS complex merges with the peaked T wave to form a sine wave; then ventricular fibrillation and finally a flat line ensues.

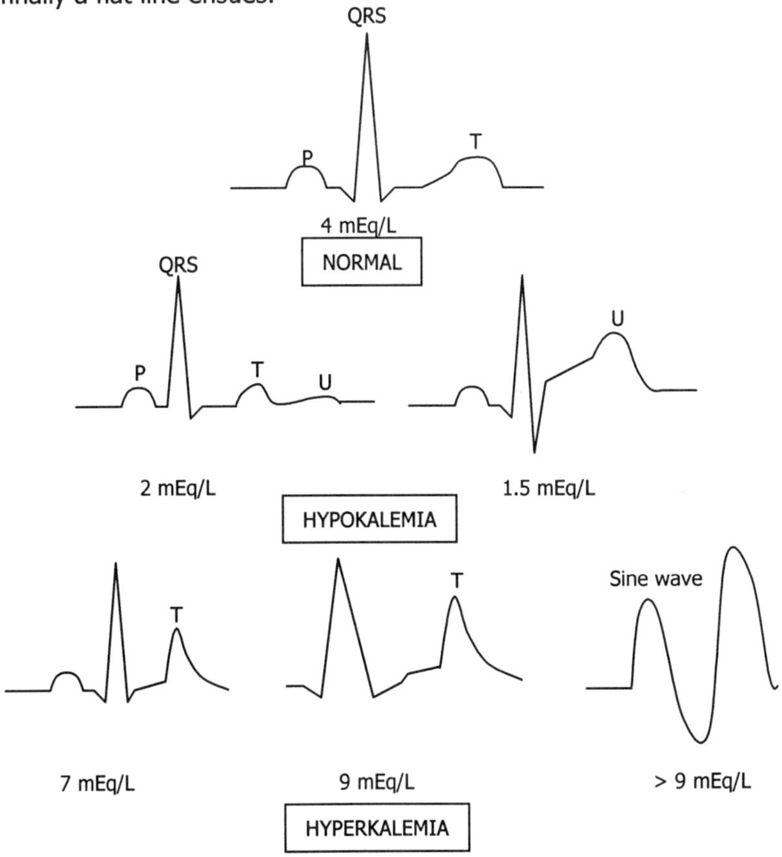

Figure 12-6. EKG changes in hypo- and hyperkalemia. A normal EKG is also shown for comparison. Hypokalemia produces ST segment depression with a prominent U wave. The earliest change in hyperkalemia is the peaked (tented) T wave. With an increase in plasma [K^+], the QRS complex widens, the P wave disappears, and finally a sine wave pattern appears, leading to asystole.

Hyperkalemia is an acute emergency. Its management depends on the serum [K^+] and EKG changes. In many cases, hyperkalemia without EKG changes warrants treatment. The goals of acute therapy are four-fold: (1) counteracting the membrane effects of hyperkalemia; (2) promoting cellular uptake of K^+; and (3) removal of K^+ from the body slowly by cation exchange resin or (4) rapidly by hemodialysis using the dialysate containing either no K^+ or 2 mEq/L (Table 12-1).

Table 12-1. Acute treatment of hyperkalemia

Treatment	Dose	Onset	Duration of effect	Mechanism
Calcium gluconate (10%)	10-20 ml IV	1-3 min	30-60 min	Counteract the membrane effects of K^+
$NaHCO_3$	44-88 mEq IV	5-10 min	1-6 hr	K^+ uptake by cells
Insulin + glucose	25-50 g of glucose + 10-20 U of insulin IV	$\geq$ 30 min	4-6 hr	K^+ uptake by cells
Albuterol (β_2-agonist)	0.5 mg in 100 ml of D5W IV	20-30 min	1-2 hr	K^+ uptake by cells
	20 mg in 4 ml of normal saline by nebulization	30 min	1-2 hr	K^+ uptake by cells
Kayexalate (cation exchange resin)	Oral (30- 45 g) or enema (50-100 g)	$\geq$ 2 hr	2-6 hr	Exchange of Na^+ for K^+ and removal by gut
Hemodialysis	--	Immediate	2-8 hr	Removal of K^+ from body

IV = intravenous administration

SUMMARY

1. K^+ is the most abundant intracellular cation and plays an important role in cell growth, nucleic acid and protein synthesis, regulation of cell volume, and maintenance of the resting membrane potential of excitable cells.
2. Two mechanisms regulate plasma [K^+]: (1) transfer of K^+ between the intracellular fluid (ICF) and extracellular fluid (ECF) compartments; and (2) renal excretion. Insulin, epinephrine, and metabolic acidosis promote cellular uptake of K^+, whereas insulin deficiency, β-adrenergic blockade, and hyperosmolality cause efflux of K^+ from the ICF to ECF compartment.
3. The proximal tubule reabsorbs about 50-70% of the filtered K^+, whereas the thick ascending limb and distal tubule reabsorb about 25% and 10%,

respectively, of the filtered K^+. K^+ secretion occurs mostly in the cortical collecting duct by the principal cells, and this secretion matches dietary intake of K^+. Aldosterone primarily regulates K^+ secretion and excretion. In addition, a variety of factors regulate K^+ excretion.

4. Hypo -and hyperkalemia are two clinical disorders of K^+, which are defined as serum $[K^+]$ of < 3.5 mEq/L and > 5.5 mEq/L, respectively. The clinical manifestations of both disorders include neuromuscular and cardiac effects, which present as muscle weakness, paralysis, and arrhythmias. Hyperkalemia is an emergency, and the treatment depends on changes in the EKG.

STUDY QUESTIONS

Case 1

A 45-year-old male is admitted to the hospital because of weakness, nausea, and vomiting. He has been drinking alcohol for 1 week without adequate dietary intake. His blood pressure is 110/70 with a pulse rate of 100. Physical examination is otherwise normal. The following serum chemistry is obtained:

Na^+ = 130 mEq/L
K^+ = 2.8 mEq/L
Cl^- = 86 mEq/L
HCO_3^- = 30 mEq/L
BUN = 40 mg/dL
Creatinine = 1.6 mg/dL
Glucose = 60 mg/dL

Question 1. What will happen to this patient's serum $[K^+]$ if a 5% dextrose solution is administered?

Answer: The serum $[K^+]$ will decrease even further because glucose infusion stimulates pancreatic beta cells to secrete insulin, which promotes the cellular uptake of K^+. If glucose infusion is continued, this patient's symptoms will worsen. The proper treatment for this patient is to give normal saline initially, which will improve his volume status and blood pressure, followed by K^+ supplementation.

Case 2

A 20-year-old white female is admitted for headache and visual disturbance. Her blood pressure is 200/130 with a pulse rate of 80. Physical examination is normal except for retinal changes and an abdominal bruit. The following serum chemistry is obtained:

Na^+ = 140 mEq/L
K^+ = 2.7 mEq/L
Cl^- = 95 mEq/L
HCO_3^- = 26 mEq/L
BUN = 12 mg/dL
Creatinine = 1.0 mg/dL
Glucose = 90 mg/dL

Question 1. Explain the reason for this patient's hypokalemia. Why is her blood pressure elevated?

Answer: Based on abnormal retinal findings and abdominal bruit, the diagnosis of renovascular hypertension is most likely. This form of hypertension causes renal ischemia, which stimulates the production of renin. Renin acts on angiotensinogen and converts it to angiotensin I (AI). AI is converted into AII by angiotensin converting enzyme. AII causes severe vasoconstriction and stimulates aldosterone synthesis (see Chapter 3). Aldosterone promotes K^+ secretion in the cortical collecting duct, and thus causes hypokalemia. The reason for this patient's hypertension is increased production of AII. A renal arteriogram showed fibromuscular dysplasia of the renal arteries, which confirmed the diagnosis of renovascular hypertension.

Question 2. Discuss the consequences of hypo- and hyperkalemia on cell excitability.

Answer: The cell is said to be hyperpolarized when the resting membrane potential (RMP) becomes more negative and depolarized when the (RMP) becomes less negative. Hypokalemia hyperpolarizes the cell, i.e, the RMP becomes more negative, (> -90 mV). As a result, the cell becomes less excitable and flaccid paralysis may develop. In contrast, hyperkalemia depolarizes the cell, causing more excitability. However, in severe hyperkalemia, the cell is unable to repolarize after a single action potential. The result is less excitability of the cell and flaccid paralysis as seen in hypokalemia.

Case 3

A 40-year-old female with noninsulin-dependent diabetes mellitus is admitted for uncontrolled hyperglycemia. Her blood pressure is 180/100 mm Hg. Her medications include glipizide (oral hypoglycemic drug), enalapril (angiotensin converting enzyme-inhibitor), and a nonsteroidal anti-inflammatory drug. Admission serum (unhemolyzed sample) chemistry is as follows:

Na^+ = 128 mEq/L
K^+ = 6.5 mEq/L
Cl^- = 108 mEq/L

HCO_3^- = 14 mEq/L
BUN = 30 mg/dL
Creatinine = 2.0 mg/dL
Glucose = 500 mg/dL
Arterial pH = 7.30

Question 1. Discuss the factors that contributed to this patient's hyperkalemia.

Answer: Several factors have contributed to this patient's hyperkalemia: (1) relative insulin deficiency or defective insulin action; (2) hyperglycemia; (3) hyporeninemic hypoaldosteronism; (4) enalapril; and (5) a nonsteroidal anti - inflammatory drug.

Relative insulin deficiency causes a decrease in cellular uptake of K^+. However, the associated hyperglycemia and hyperosmolality play an important role. Hyperosmolality pulls water out of the cells, and K^+ comes along with water movement. This phenomenon, called solvent drag, is responsible for hyperkalemia. Diabetes in some patients causes a state of hyporeninemic hypoaldosteronism. Hypoaldosteronism could contribute to hyperkalemia. Furthermore, the angiotensin converting enzyme-inhibitor and nonsteroidal anti-inflammatory drug induce functional hyporeninemic hypoaldosteronism, which inhibits K^+ secretion and causes hyperkalemia. Although advanced renal failure may impair K^+ secretion, the extent of renal failure is not sufficient to cause hyperkalemia.

Question 2. How would you manage this patient's hyperkalemia?

Answer: The chronic treatment of hyperkalemia in this patient includes control of her blood glucose level with insulin, administration of oral $NaHCO_3$, and judicious use of angiotensin converting enzyme-inhibitors or nonsteroidal anti-inflammatory drugs. Daily oral kayexalate may control her hyperkalemia. Some patients may benefit from a loop diuretic or mineralocorticoid administration.

Case 4

A hemodialysis-dependent patient comes to the emergency room with muscle weakness and shortness of breath. He missed two dialysis treatments. His serum [K^+] is 7.1 mEq/L. An EKG shows peaked T waves.

Question 1. What is the resting membrane potential (E_m) of this patient's muscle cell (assuming an intracellular [K^+] of 140 mEq/L).

Answer: Since the major determinant of the E_m is K^+, one can use the following equation (called the Nernst equation) for any univalent ion:

$$E_m\ (mV) = -61 \log \frac{[K^+]_i}{[K^+]_o}$$

substituting K^+ values

$$E_m\ (mV) = -61 \log \frac{[140]}{[7.1]} = -79$$

The resting membrane potential is -79 mV, which is much lower than -86 mV when plasma $[K^+]$ is 4.5 mEq/L.

Question 2. How would you treat this patient's hyperkalemia?

Answer: The EKG shows peaked T waves and the immediate treatment of choice is intravenous administration of calcium chloride. Calcium chloride counteracts the membrane effects of hyperkalemia, and the T waves return to baseline. However, serum $[K^+]$ remains at 7.1 mEq/L. Administration of glucose and insulin promotes cellular K^+ uptake and transiently lowers plasma $[K^+]$ until hemodialysis can be performed. Hemodialysis for an hour with a dialysate containing no K^+ removes a substantial amount of K^+. Continuation of hemodialysis for 2 to 3 hours with low K^+ dialysate not only normalizes serum $[K^+]$ but improves shortness of breath by removing fluid from the patient.

SUGGESTED READING

1. Seldin, D.W. and Giebisch, G.H. (eds.). The Regulation of Potassium Balance. Raven Press, New York, 1989 (*An excellent multi-authored volume on various aspects of potassium*).
2. Giebisch, G., Malnic, G. and Berliner, R. Control of renal potassium excretion. In: The Kidney. 5th edition. B.M. Brenner (ed.). W.B. Saunders Company, Philadelphia, 1996; pp. 371-407 (*A comprehensive review on tubular transport and regulation of potassium*).
3. Jamison, R.L. Potassium. In: Nephrology. R.L. Jamison and R. Wilkinson, (eds.). Chapman & Hall, London, 1997; pp. 102-108 (*Another short review of renal tubular transport and regulation of potassium balance*).

CHAPTER 13

CALCIUM REGULATION AND DISORDERS

Objectives

After reading this chapter, the student should be able to:

1. Discuss the distribution and functions of Ca^{2+}.
2. Discuss the importance of the intestine, bone, and the kidney in Ca^{2+} homeostasis.
3. Explain how Ca^{2+} is handled by the kidney.
4. Discuss the various factors that regulate Ca^{2+} excretion.
5. Discuss the causes, clinical manifestations, and treatment modalities of hyper- and hypocalcemia.

GENERAL FEATURES

Calcium (Ca^{2+}) is the most abundant divalent ion in the body. Approximately 1.2 to 1.3 kg of Ca^{2+} is present in a 70-kg individual. Of this amount, 99% is present in the bone in the form of hydroxyapatite ($Ca_{10}(PO_4)_6(OH)_2$), and the remaining 1% is found in the teeth, soft tissues, plasma, and cells. The plasma Ca^{2+} concentration (abbreviated as $[Ca^{2+}]$) is 10 mg/dL (range 8.5 - 10.5 mg/dL) and exists in three forms. About 50% of Ca^{2+} exist as a free or ionized form. Approximately 40% of Ca^{2+} is bound to proteins, mostly to albumin and to some extent globulins. The remaining 10% is complexed with anions such as phosphate, bicarbonate, and citrate. Only the ionized and anion-complexed Ca^{2+} is filterable by the glomerulus. Protein-bound Ca^{2+} is not filtered. Only the ionized (free) Ca^{2+} is physiologically active. The free intracellular $[Ca^{2+}]$ is about 10,000-fold lower than the extracellular free $[Ca^{2+}]$; this concentration gradient is maintained by Ca^{2+}-specific channels, Ca-ATPase and a Na/Ca exchanger.

Ca^{2+} plays a significant role in cellular metabolic functions; such as muscle and nerve contraction, enzyme activities, blood coagulation, and cell growth. Consequently, a low plasma $[Ca^{2+}]$ (hypocalcemia) or high plasma $[Ca^{2+}]$ (hypercalcemia) may lead to severe cellular dysfunction.

Ca^{2+} HOMEOSTASIS

The plasma [Ca^{2+}] is maintained within narrow limits by the interplay between resorption and formation of Ca^{2+} by the intestine, bone, and kidney (Figure 13-1). The daily intake of Ca^{2+} is between 600 and 1000 mg. Of this amount, about 400 mg is reabsorbed by the intestine. Evidence suggests that about 200 mg of Ca^{2+} are secreted into the intestine from the extracellular Ca^{2+}. These amounts, plus the nonreabsorbed Ca^{2+} (600 mg), are eliminated in the feces. Intestinal Ca^{2+} absorption is both passive and active. Active reabsorption is stimulated by the metabolite of vitamin D, namely, 1,25-dihydroxycholecalciferol (also called **calcitriol**), the active form of vitamin D_3, and it is inhibited by glucocorticoids.

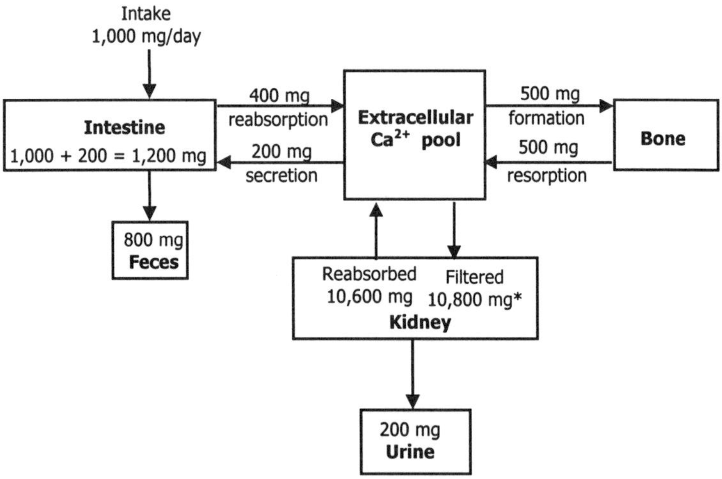

Figure 13-1. Processes involved in Ca^{2+} homeostasis in an adult subject. *Of 10 mg/dL plasma Ca^{2+}, only 6 mg/dL are filtered which amount to the filtered load of 10,800 mg/day (60 mg/L x 180 L = 10,800 mg) (Modified with permission from Nordin B.E.C., (ed.). Calcium, Phosphate, and Magnesium Metabolism. Churchill Livingston, Edinburgh, 1976).

Net Ca^{2+} turnover (resorption and formation) in bone is important in the maintenance of plasma [Ca^{2+}]. The daily turnover rate of Ca^{2+} between extracellular fluid and bone, which varies from 250 to 1000 mg, is influenced primarily by parathyroid hormone (PTH), active vitamin D_3, and calcitonin. PTH regulates plasma [Ca^{2+}] by three mechanisms: (1) it stimulates bone resorption (demineralization) by activating osteoclasts (cells that break down bone mineral); (2) it increases the synthesis of active vitamin D_3 by enhancing the activity of 25-hydroxycholecalciferol-1α–hydroxylase (see Chapter 3); and (3) it increases Ca^{2+} reabsorption in the distal tubule. Active vitamin D_3 increases bone resorption in concert with PTH and also promotes Ca^{2+} absorption from the intestine. Calcitonin, a 32-amino acid peptide synthesized by the parafollicular or C cells of the thyroid gland, is released in response to elevated plasma [Ca^{2+}]. Calcitonin inhibits bone resorption directly by inhibiting the activity of osteoclasts.

The kidney is another important organ that participates in Ca^{2+} homeostasis. About 10,800 mg of Ca^{2+} are filtered at the glomerulus. Of this amount, 10,600 mg (98%) are reabsorbed by the various segments of the nephron, and the remaining 200 mg (< 2%) are excreted in the urine. This obligatory loss equals the amount absorbed by the intestine.

Intestinal absorption of Ca^{2+} is influenced by certain physiologic conditions. Normal pregnancy and growth are associated with increased absorption, whereas aging causes decreased absorption. Foods containing oxalates and phytates also decrease intestinal absorption of Ca^{2+}.

Several physiologic adaptations occur during low or high plasma [Ca^{2+}] to maintain normocalcemia. When plasma [Ca^{2+}] is low, PTH synthesis and secretion are increased. In turn, PTH acts on the bone, kidney, and intestine to increase plasma [Ca^{2+}] to normal (Figure 13-2). The opposite sequence of events occurs when plasma [Ca^{2+}] is increased (Figure 13-3).

Thus, the coordinated interactions of the hormones that regulate intestinal absorption, bone turnover, and renal reabsorption maintain the plasma [Ca^{2+}] within narrow limits.

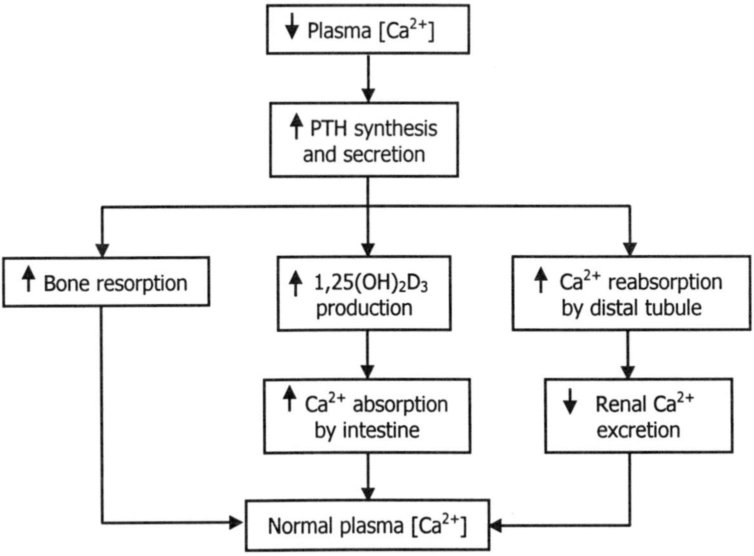

Figure 13-2. Physiologic mechanisms to restore normocalcemia during low plasma [Ca^{2+}].

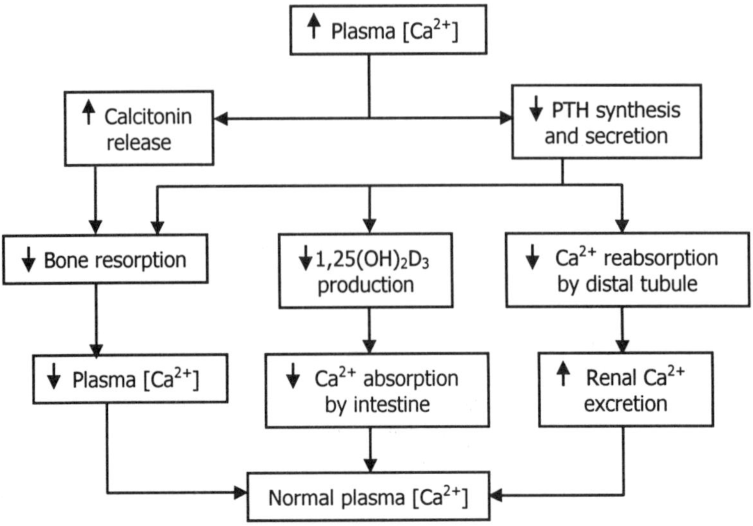

Figure 13-3. Physiologic mechanisms to restore normocalcemia during high plasma [Ca^{2+}].

Renal Handling of Ca^{2+}

As stated earlier, only ionized and anion-complexed Ca^{2+} is filtered. Filtered Ca^{2+} amounts to 60% of the total Ca^{2+}, or approximately 6 mg/dL. If the GFR is 180 L per day and filterable Ca^{2+} is 6 mg/dL or 60 mg/L, the filtered load of Ca^{2+} is 10,800 mg (60 mg/L x 180 L = 10,800 mg). In order to maintain Ca^{2+} balance, 98% of the filtered Ca^{2+} must be reabsorbed by the kidney. Approximately 70% of the filtered Ca^{2+} is reabsorbed by the proximal tubule, 20% by the thick ascending limb of Henle's loop, 5 to 10% by the distal convoluted tubule, and 5% by the collecting duct. Less than 2% of Ca^{2+} is excreted in the urine (Figure 13-4). The thin descending and thin ascending limb of Henle's loop do not participate in Ca^{2+} transport.

The amount of Ca^{2+} filtered at the glomerulus is influenced by a number of factors. Increases in the plasma [Ca^{2+}] up to 15 mg/dL increase the amount of filtered Ca^{2+}. Severe acidosis increases ionized [Ca^{2+}], which in turn, enhances filtration of Ca^{2+}. Alkalosis causes an opposite effect. Acid-base changes induce changes in protein binding of Ca^{2+} because H^+ ions compete with Ca^{2+} for the ionic-binding sites on the protein. In acidosis, Ca^{2+} binding to protein is reduced, and therefore the ionized [Ca^{2+}] is increased. Alkalemia increases Ca^{2+} binding to protein, and thus reduces ionized [Ca^{2+}].

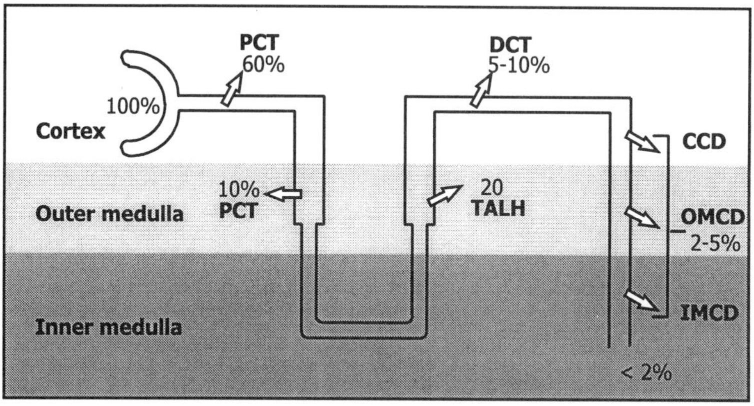

Figure 13-4. Ca^{2+} reabsorption in various segments of the nephron. The numbers represent approximate percentages of Ca^{2+} reabsorption. PCT = proximal convoluted tubule; TALH = thick ascending loop of Henle; DCT = distal convoluted tubule; CCD = cortical collecting duct.

CELLULAR MECHANISMS OF Ca^{2+} TRANSPORT

In the proximal tubule, the transport of Ca^{2+} from the lumen to the cell occurs by transcellular and paracellular pathways (Figure 13-5). About one-third of Ca^{2+} entry into proximal tubule cells is mediated by the transcellular pathway. This transport occurs via several mechanisms. First, Ca^{2+} is reabsorbed in conjunction with Na^+ and water. Second, a chemical gradient for Ca^{2+} exists between the lumen and the cell that favors Ca^{2+} transport into the cell. Third, Ca^{2+} may enter through Ca^{2+}-specific channels. The transport via the paracellular pathway occurs by solvent drag.

The exit of Ca^{2+} from the cell at the basolateral membrane appears to be a partly active process. The mechanism by which this exit occurs is controversial. However, some evidence suggests the presence of a Ca-ATPase and a Na/Ca exchanger (see Figure 13-5). The transport of Ca^{2+} from the lumen to the blood appears to be largely due to solvent drag via the paracellular pathway.

In the thick ascending limb of Henle's loop, the lumen is electropositive due to Na/K/2Cl cotransport, which causes Ca^{2+} to diffuse passively via the paracellular pathway into the blood. Studies also have suggested that Ca^{2+} is actively transported in the cortical thick limb of Henle's loop. However, the existence of this active component of Ca^{2+} transport is controversial. Furosemide (a loop diuretic) abolishes the lumen-positive transepithelial voltage by inhibiting Na/K/2Cl cotransport, thus inhibiting Ca^{2+} reabsorption in this segment. As in the proximal tubule, Ca^{2+} reabsorption closely parallels that of Na^+ reabsorption.

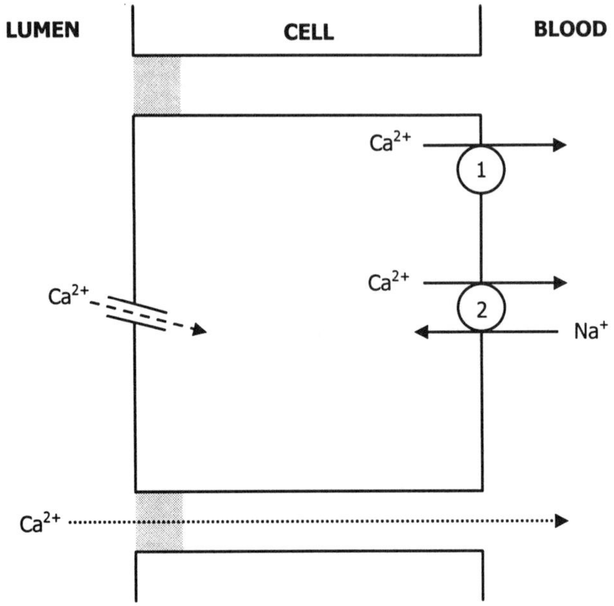

Figure 13-5. Possible cellular mechanisms for Ca^{2+} entry into the cell via transcellular and paracellular pathways in the proximal tubule. The transcellular exit of Ca^{2+} seems to occur via Ca-ATPase (1) and Na/Ca exchanger (2). Thick broken arrow indicates Ca^{2+} entry via a Ca^{2+} conductance channel.

In the distal convoluted tubule, Ca^{2+} transport is an active process, and therefore occurs against an electrochemical gradient. Very little or no reabsorption occurs through the paracellular pathway. The mechanism of Ca^{2+} transport in this segment is not clearly understood. However, a recent study demonstrates that hormonal (PTH and calcitonin) stimulation of Ca^{2+} transport produces insertion of voltage-gated Ca^{2+} channels in the apical membrane. Thus, Ca^{2+} entry is not dependent on Na^+ entry.

Ca^{2+} exit across the basolateral membrane is mediated by two enzyme systems, namely, Ca/Mg-ATPase and the Na/Ca exchanger. Unique to this segment of the nephron is the presence of a vitamin D-stimulated Ca^{2+}-binding protein, which seems to participate in Ca^{2+} transport, probably by stimulating Ca/Mg-ATPase.

In the distal convoluted tubule, the transport of Ca^{2+} and Na^+ occur independently of each other. This segment is the major regulatory site for Ca^{2+} excretion in the urine. Ca^{2+} transport in the collecting duct is minor compared to the other segments of the nephron. The transport may be active in the cortical collecting duct and passive in the medullary segment.

FACTORS INFLUENCING Ca^{2+} TRANSPORT

A number of factors, as listed in Table 13-1, either decrease or increase Ca^{2+} reabsorption in various segments of the nephron. As a result, the urinary excretion of Ca^{2+} varies. Among the hormones, PTH is an important regulator. It promotes Ca^{2+} reabsorption by the thick ascending limb of Henle's loop and the distal convoluted tubule. The effects of PTH on the proximal tubule are variable (increase, decrease, or no effect). Calcitonin also has variable effects. Vitamin D may stimulate Ca^{2+} reabsorption in the distal convoluted tubule probably by stimulating the production of Ca^{2+}-binding protein. Hypercalcemia decreases Ca^{2+} reabsorption via a decrease in PTH secretion and enhances Ca^{2+} excretion (see Figure 13-4). Volume expansion reduces Ca^{2+} reabsorption, whereas volume contraction promotes Ca^{2+} reabsorption.

Table 13-1. Effect of various factors on Ca^{2+} reabsorption in the nephron

Factor	PCT	TALH	DCT	Urinary excretion
PTH	Variable	↑	↑	↓
Vitamin D	?	No effect	↑	↓
Hypercalcemia	↓	↓	↓	↑
Volume expansion	↓	?	↓	↑
Volume contraction	↑	?	?	↓
Metabolic acidosis	↓	?	↓	↑
Metabolic alkalosis	↑	?	↑	↓
Loop diuretics	?	↓	No effect	↑
Thiazide diuretics (acute)	?	?	↑	↑
Thiazide diuretics (chronic)	↑	No effect	?	↓
Amiloride	No effect	No effect	↑	↓

PCT = proximal convoluted tubule; TALH = thick ascending limb of Henle's loop; DCT = distal convoluted tubule. ↑ = increase; ↓ = decrease.

Metabolic acidosis inhibits Ca^{2+} reabsorption in the proximal and distal convoluted tubule and promotes Ca^{2+} excretion. Metabolic alkalosis has an opposite effect. Diuretics influence Ca^{2+} reabsorption and its excretion. Most importantly, loop diuretics, such as furosemide and bumetamide, inhibit Ca^{2+} reabsorption in the thick ascending limb of Henle's loop and thereby promote Ca^{2+} excretion. Acute administration of thiazides promotes Ca^{2+} reabsorption in the distal convoluted tubule. The urinary excretion of Ca^{2+} may transiently increase due to marked natriuresis. Conversely, chronic administration of thiazides causes hypocalciuria due to enhanced Ca^{2+} reabsorption in the proximal tubule caused by volume contraction. Amiloride also promotes Ca^{2+} reabsorption in the distal convoluted tubule.

DISORDERS OF Ca^{2+}

As stated earlier, Ca^{2+} homeostasis is maintained by the interrelationship between intestinal absorption, bone turnover, and renal excretion. Alterations in any of these functions may lead to changes in the extracellular $[Ca^{2+}]$. A plasma $[Ca^{2+}]$> 11 mg/dL is called **hypercalcemia**, and a concentration < 8.5 mg/dL is called **hypocalcemia.**

Hypercalcemia

Although causes of hypercalcemia are varied, they fall into three major categories (see At a Glance Box 13-1): (1) hypercalcemia secondary to increased Ca^{2+} mobilization from the bone; (2) hypercalcemia due to increased reabsorption of Ca^{2+} from the gastrointestinal tract; and (3) hypercalcemia due to decreased urinary excretion of Ca^{2+}. Primary hyperparathyroidism is the leading cause of hypercalcemia. It occurs in middle-aged and older individuals, and is due most commonly to a benign adenoma or infrequently to hyperplasia of the parathyroid glands. Clinically symptomatic patients present with kidney stones and bone pain. Kidney stones are more common in younger than in older patients. Treatment includes removal of the adenoma or seven-eighths of the hyperplastic parathyroid glands.

Malignancy is the second leading cause of hypercalcemia. The mechanisms for malignancy-induced hypercalcemia include: (1) invasion of the tumor into the bone, which causes lysis of the bone matrix; (2) production of a PTH-related protein or peptide by tumor cells; (3) production of bone-resorbing prostaglandins; and (4) release of cytokines such as interleukin-1, lymphotoxin, and osteoclast-activating factor. These cytokines cause bone resorption, and thus cause hypercalcemia.

Many granulomatous diseases, such as sarcoidosis and tuberculosis, release active vitamin D_3 and cause hypercalcemia. Familial hypocalciuric hypercalcemia (FHH) is another condition that deserves mention. This autosomal dominant disease occurs in several adolescents of the same family. FHH is characterized by mild elevations in the plasma $[Ca^{2+}]$ and a mild degree of hyperparathyroidism. Decreased urinary excretion of Ca^{2+} is the major characteristic of this syndrome. The genetic mutation that is linked to FHH causes the Ca^{2+} receptor in the parathyroid gland to be unresponsive to hypercalcemia. FHH is a benign condition and no treatment is necessary. The clinical manifestations of hypercalcemia vary from individual to individual, and are listed in the accompanying At a Glance Box 13-2.

The treatment of acute hypercalcemia includes: (1) hydration with normal saline and then administration of furosemide; (2) inhibit bone resorption of Ca^{2+}; (3) decrease intestinal absorption of Ca^{2+}; and (4) removal of Ca^{2+} by hemodialysis using a dialysate solution containing low Ca^{2+}. These treatment modalities are shown in Table 13-2. Following acute correction, chronic management of hypercalcemia includes removal of the cause. Newer treatments include gallium nitrate, which inhibits PTH-mediated bone resorption; cis-platinum; and chloroquine. The latter drug decreases active vitamin D_3 levels.

At a Glance Box 13-1
Some major causes of hypercalcemia

Hypercalcemia due to increased bone resorption
- Hyperparathyroidism
- Malignancy
  - Metastatic
  - Nonmetastatic
- Immobilization
- Vitamin D intoxication
- Vitamin A intoxication

Hypercalcemia due to increased Ca^{2+} absorption from intestine
- Granulomatous diseases
  - Tuberculosis
  - Sarcoidosis
- Addison's disease
- Milk-alkali syndrome
- Vitamin D intoxication

Hypercalcemia due to decreased Ca^{2+} excretion
- Thiazide diuretics
- Familial hypocalciuric hypercalcemic syndrome

At a Glance Box 13-2
Clinical features of hypercalcemia

General: Weakness, lethargy
Neuromuscular: Headache, confusion, coma, myalgia, muscle weakness
Cardiovascular: Arrhythmias, shortened Q-T interval on EKG, vascular calcifications, hypertension
Renal: Polyuria, impaired urine concentration, renal stones, renal failure
Gastrointestinal: Nausea, vomiting, abdominal pain, constipation, pancreatitis
Eyes: Band keratopathy (calcification in the medial and lateral limbic margins of the cornea)

Table 13-2. Treatment modalities of hypercalcemia

Treatment	Dosage	Route of administration	Duration of effect	Mechanism
Promote Ca^{2+} excretion				
Normal saline	1-2 L every 6 hr	IV	4-6 hr	Improves GFR and promotes Ca^{2+} excretion
Furosemide	40-12 mg every 2-4 hr	IV	2-4 hr	Inhibits Ca^{2+} reabsorption in the TALH
Decrease bone resorption				
Calcitonin	2-4 MRC units/kg every 4-8 hr	IV	4-12 hr	Inhibits bone resorption
Mithramycin	25 g/kg in 500 ml saline	IV	12-72 hr	Same as above
Biphosphorates	300 mg every 8 hr	Oral	3-10 days	Same as above
Indomethacin	75 mg every 12 hr	Oral	2-4 days	Decreases bone resorption through inhibition of PGE_2
Decrease intestinal absorption				
Prednisone	20-30 mg every 12 hr	Oral	2-4 days	Inhibits gut absorption
Decrease plasma [Ca^{2+}]				
Hemodialysis	Use dialysate containing low Ca^{2+}			

IV = intravenous; MRC = Medical Research Council

Hypocalcemia

Hypocalcemia is less common than hypercalcemia. Like hypercalcemia, the causes of hypocalcemia are varied (see At a Glance box 13-3). Since Ca^{2+} is bound to albumin, a decrease in plasma albumin concentration may cause hypocalcemia. For each gram decrease of albumin from normal (i.e., 4.0 g/dL), [Ca^{2+}] decreases by 0.8 mg/dL. The important causes of hypocalcemia include: (1) low levels of PTH; (2) a decrease in vitamin D metabolites; (3) a decrease in gastrointestinal absorption of Ca^{2+}; (4) increased renal excretion of Ca^{2+}; (5) hypomagnesemia, which inhibits PTH secretion and also causes PTH-resistance to bone resorption; and (6) pseudohypoparathyroidism, a genetic disorder that causes end organ resistance to PTH action. The PTH levels in this disorder are high (see At a Glance Box 13-3).

Most of the symptoms of hypocalcemia involve the neuromuscular system. The clinical hallmark of hypocalcemia is tetany, which can be elicited by Chvostek's sign (tapping over the facial nerve produces contraction of facial muscles) or Trousseau's sign (inflating a blood pressure cuff above systolic blood pressure for 2-3 minutes results in carpal spasm).

Parasthesias, muscle cramps, seizures, and proximal myopathy may also be seen in a hypocalcemic patient. The cardiovascular system can also be affected by hypocalcemia. A prolonged Q-T interval on EKG, hypotension, and arrhythmias are frequently observed in hypocalcemia.

At a Glance Box 13-3
Major causes of hypocalcemia

Low albumin level
Low or absent PTH levels
- Hypoparathyroidism
- Hypomagnesemia

Disturbances in vitamin D
- Decreased intake (due to nutritional deficiency)
- Decreased intestinal absorption (due to gastrectomy, intestinal bypass)
- Decreased production of $25(OH)D_3$ (due to liver disease)
- Increased metabolism of $25(OH)D_3$ (due to dilantin, phenobarbital, alcohol)
- Increased urinary loss of $25(OH)D_3$ (due to nephrotic syndrome)
- Decreased synthesis of $1,25(OH)_2D_3$(due to renal failure, hyperphosphatemia)

Increased resistance to PTH action
- Pseudohypoparathyroidism (a genetic disorder)

Preparations of calcium salts (calcium gluconate, calcium chloride) and vitamin D are used to treat either acute or chronic hypocalcemia. If hypocalcemia is due to hyperphosphatemia, the goal of therapy is to decrease the phosphates concentration rather than institution of calcium salts.

SUMMARY

1. Calcium (Ca^{2+}) plays an important role in cellular functions, including muscle contraction, blood coagulation, and cell growth. Only the ionized and anion-complexed Ca^{2+} is filtered at the glomerulus. The proximal tubule reabsorbs most of this filtered Ca^{2+}, and less than 2% of Ca^{2+} is excreted in the urine.
2. The plasma $[Ca^{2+}]$ is maintained within narrow limits by the interaction between resorption and formation of Ca^{2+} by the intestine, bone, and kidney. Parathyroid hormone (PTH), active vitamin D_3 and calcitonin regulate intestinal absorption, bone resorption, and renal reabsorption of Ca^{2+}. Thus, these three hormones play an important role in Ca^{2+} homeostasis.

3. Although PTH is the main regulator of Ca^{2+} excretion, other factors such as volume status, acid-base balance, and diuretics play an important role in Ca^{2+} excretion.
4. Hypercalcemia is more common than hypocalcemia. The major cause of hypercalcemia in middle-aged subjects is primary hyperparathyroidism. Malignancy is the second leading cause of hypercalcemia. Initial treatment of acute hypercalcemia includes hydration with normal saline followed by administration of a loop diuretic such as furosemide. Severe hypocalcemia causes tetany, and preparations of calcium salts are used to treat tetany and other signs of acute or chronic hypocalcemia.

STUDY QUESTIONS

Case 1

A 38-year-old white female is brought to the emergency room for agitation, weakness, severe abdominal pain, and frequent urination. According to her husband, she is well but has been acting "funny" for the last 7 days. She is not taking any medications. On physical examination, her blood pressure is normal but her pulse rate is 100 beats per minute. Except for a lump in her right breast, the remainder of the physical examination is within normal limits. The laboratory values are:

Na^+ = 138 mEq/L
K^+ = 4.1 mEq/L
Cl^- = 100 mEq/L
HCO_3^- = 24 mEq/L
BUN = 34 mg/dL
Creatinine = 1.4 mg/dL
Glucose = 100 mg/dL

Chest x-ray is normal. An EKG shows a shortened Q-T interval.

Question 1. What other laboratory tests would you order at this time and why?

Answer: Serum Ca^{2+}, phosphate, Mg^{2+}, and albumin concentrations are needed to rule out hypercalcemia and hypophosphatemia as a cause of weakness, and hypermagnesemia for the shortened Q-T interval. Albumin levels are required to evaluate serum [Ca^{2+}].

One hour later the above values are available:

Ca^{2+} = 14.2 mg/dL
Phosphate = 3.5 mg/dL
Mg^{2+} = 2.0 mg/dL
Albumin = 4.0 g/dL

Question 1. Explain the cause of this patient's hypercalcemia.

Answer: Two potential causes should be considered in this patient. One is primary hyperparathyroidism. Both the physical examination and laboratory values (eitherHCO_3^- or phosphate) are not consistent with primary hyperparathyroidism. The other cause is malignancy. The lump in her breast suggests breast cancer. If the cancer metastasizes to the bone, hypercalcemia can result due to increased bone resorption of Ca^{2+}.

Question 2. Skeletal x-rays of the patient reveal evidence of metastasis. How would you treat this patient's hypercalcemia acutely?

Answer: The choice of initial treatment is intravenous normal saline. The patient is mildly dehydrated (volume contracted) because her creatinine and BUN are elevated. Because of this volume depletion, proximal tubular reabsorption of Ca^{2+} is increased. This tubular reabsorption is inhibited by volume expansion, and thus Ca^{2+} excretion is increased. About 4 to 5 L of normal saline should be given over a 24-hour period.

If volume expansion does not decrease the plasma [Ca^{2+}] significantly, 40 to 80 mg of intravenous furosemide should be given to block Ca^{2+} reabsorption in the thick ascending limb of Henle's loop. Furosemide should not be given without adequate hydration.

Case 2

A 30-year-old male is admitted for nausea, vomiting, and weakness. He has had insulin-dependent diabetes for 20 years, and hypertension for 5 years. His medications are insulin and a calcium-blocker. On admission, his laboratory values are:

Na^+ = 136 mEq/L	Ca^{2+} = 6.5 mg/dL
K^+ = 5.0 mEq/L	Phosphate = 7.5 mg/dL
Cl^- = 100 mEq/L	Albumin = 2.5 g/dL
HCO_3^- = 20 mEq/L	Urinary protein = 5.5 g/day
BUN = 100 mg/dL	Creatinine = 10 mg/dL
Glucose = 150 mg/dL	

Question 1. Explain the causes for this patient's hypocalcemia.

Answer: The important causes to be considered are: (1) hypoalbuminemia; (2) hyperphosphatemia; (3) nephrotic syndrome; and (4) renal failure.

Hypoalbuminemia decreases total serum [Ca^{2+}] by 0.8 mg per 1.0 g of albumin. This patient has a decrease of 1.5 g of albumin (normal: 4.0 g/dL).

The corrected total serum [Ca^{2+}], therefore, is 7.7 mg/dL (6.5 + 1.2 = 7.7 mg/dL).

Hyperphosphatemia causes hypocalcemia in several ways. First, hyperphosphatemia decreases the production of active vitamin D_3. Second, it inhibits bone resorption of Ca^{2+}. Finally, phosphate combines with Ca^{2+}; if the product of these two exceeds 60 (both in mg/dL), precipitation of Ca^{2+} and phosphate occurs in the myocardium, skin, and skeletal muscle.

Nephrotic syndrome (see Chapter 8) causes urinary loss of Ca^{2+}-binding vitamin D protein. This loss results in a decrease in total serum [Ca^{2+}].

Renal failure, either acute or chronic, causes decreased production of active vitamin D_3, i.e.,calcitriol. As a result, the intestinal absorption of Ca^{2+} and bone resorption of Ca^{2+} by PTH are greatly reduced, which causes hypocalcemia even in the presence of excess PTH levels.

Question 2. How would you treat this patient's hypocalcemia?

Answer: First, the serum phosphate levels must be decreased, which can be achieved by dietary restriction of phosphate and phosphate-binders such as calcium acetate. If the serum phosphate level is reduced but hypocalcemia persists, treatment with active vitamin D_3 (calcitriol) should begin. Both treatment modalities are required to raise the serum [Ca^{2+}] to a desired level.

SUGGESTED READING

1. Suki, W.N. and Rouse, D. Renal transport of calcium, magnesium, and phosphate. In The Kidney. B.M. Brenner (ed.). 5th edition. W.B. sauders Company, Philadelphia, 1996; pp. 472-515 (*A detailed review of renal transport mechanisms and regulation of calcium, magnesium, and phosphate balance*).
2. Hruska, K.A. and Slatopolsky, E. Disorders of phosphorus, calcium, and magnesium metabolism. In: Diseases of the Kidney. 6th edition. R.W. Schrier and C.W. Gottschalk (eds.). Little, Brown and Company, Boston, 1997; pp. 2477-2526 (*Another excellent review that deals with renal transport and clinical disorders of phosphorus, calcium, and magnesium*).

CHAPTER 14

PHOSPHORUS REGULATION AND DISORDERS

Objectives

After reading this chapter, the student should be able to:

1. Discuss the distribution and functions of phosphate.
2. Explain the integrated actions of the intestine, kidney, and bone to maintain phosphate homeostasis.
3. Describe how phosphate is handled by the kidney.
4. Discuss the various factors that alter phosphate reabsorption and excretion.
5. Explain the causes and treatment of hypo- and hyperphosphatemia.

GENERAL FEATURES

Phosphorus, although not as abundant as Ca^{2+}, is an important constituent of the body. It plays a significant role in mitochondrial respiration and oxidative phosphorylation. Phosphorus constitutes approximately 1% of the body weight. A 70-kg man contains about 700 g of phosphorus. Of this amount, 85% is present in bones and teeth, 14% in soft tissues, and the remaining 1% in the extracellular fluid.

Phosphorus and phosphate are generally used interchangeably. In biologic fluids, phosphate is measured as elemental phosphorus. However, the latter participates in biologic functions as phosphate. For example, it is phosphate that is filtered at the glomerulus or transported across the renal tubules, not phosphorus. In plasma, the concentration of phosphorus is expressed as mg/dL, and in transport and other processes it is generally expressed as mEq or mmol/L.

In plasma, phosphate exists as **organic** (70%) and **inorganic** (30%) forms. The inorganic form is physiologically active. Only 10% of inorganic phosphate is bound to albumin. However, unlike Ca^{2+}, phosphate concentration is not influenced by changes in plasma albumin concentration. At a pH of 7.40, inorganic phosphate exists predominantly as dibasic phosphate (HPO_4^{2-}) and monobasic phosphate ($H_2PO_4^-$) in the ratio of 4:1. However, at a pH of 6.8, which is the pK_a of this buffer pair, the ratio falls to 1:1.

The concentration of intracellular phosphate is several-fold higher than the plasma concentration. Inside the cell, 75% of phosphate exists as organic phosphate compounds such as adenosine triphosphate (ATP), creatinine phosphate, and adenosine monophosphate. In red blood cells, it occurs predominantly as 2,3-diphosphoglycerate. Free phosphate in the cytosol accounts for 25% of the intracellular concentrations of phosphate, and only this fraction is available for transport mechanisms.

PHOSPHATE HOMEOSTASIS

As in Ca^{2+} homeostasis, three main organs are involved in phosphate homeostasis: the intestine, the kidney, and the bone (Figure 14-1).

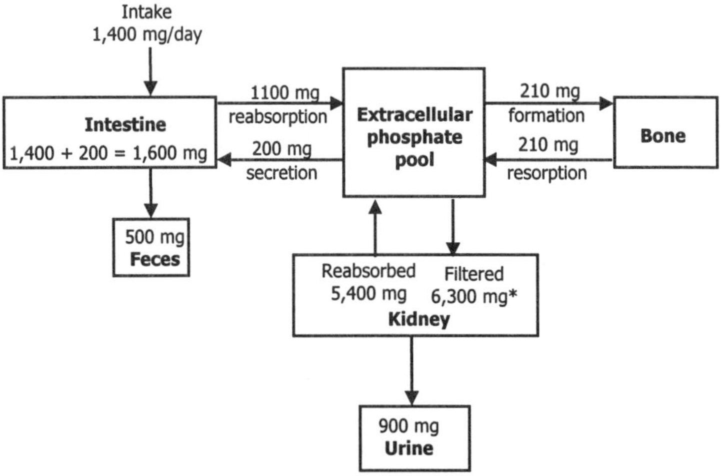

Figure 14-1. Phosphate homeostasis in an adult subject. * The filtered load of phosphate equals the free plasma concentration of 3.5 mg/dL multiplied by the GFR of 180 L per day , i.e., 180 L x 35 mg/L = 6,300 mg/day. (Modified with permission from Nordin B.E.C., (ed.). Calcium, Phosphate, and Magnesium Metabolism. Churchill Livingston, Edinburgh, 1976).

The dietary intake of phosphate varies from 1000 mg to 1400 mg daily. Of this amount, 300-500 mg are excreted in the feces and 700-900 mg in the urine to maintain a plasma phosphate concentration (abbreviated as [Pi]) between 3.0 and 4.5 mg/dL. Although phosphate exchange occurs between the extracellular fluid and bone, it is the balance between gut absorption and renal excretion that maintains phosphate homeostasis. For example, when gut absorption of phosphate increases, a transient increase in plasma [Pi] occurs. The kidneys excrete this excess amount in order to maintain the normal plasma [Pi].

In the intestine, both absorption and secretion of phosphate occurs. Most of the dietary phosphate is absorbed in the duodenum and jejunum. Approximately 200 mg of phosphate is secreted into the gastrointestinal tract, mainly into saliva and bile. The net result is that about 65% of phosphate is absorbed in the gastrointestinal tract. Two important mechanisms seem to participate in this process. One, localized in the duodenum, is a Na^+-dependent secondary active transport system that is influenced by a number of factors. Arsenate, mercury, and calcitonin inhibit, whereas 1,25-dihydroxyvitamin D_3 stimulates this transport process. The second mechanism is phosphate-dependent and is located in the jejunum and ileum. Phosphate absorption in these segments of the intestine depends on the luminal phosphate concentration. Absorption seems to be predominantly passive under normal circumstances and occurs through the paracellular pathway. Active transport becomes prominent when dietary phosphate is extremely low.

Ca^{2+} and aluminum are two important elements that complex with phosphate and decrease its intestinal absorption. These two compounds are thus used to treat increased plasma [Pi] in clinical practice. Under normal conditions, the exchange of phosphate between the bone and the extracellular pool is rather small (see Figure 14-1), and the release of phosphate is always accompanied by the release of Ca^{2+}. Thus, the release of phosphate is stimulated by the same hormones that stimulate the release of Ca^{2+}.

The kidneys play a significant role in the maintenance of phosphate homeostasis. Since the dietary intake of phosphate varies daily, the total body phosphate concentration would also vary were it not for the kidneys. The kidneys vary their excretion of phosphate to the absorption of phosphate by the intestine, thus maintaining the proper phosphate balance.

Physiologic adaptations to low or high plasma [Pi] occur as in low or high plasma [Ca^{2+}] to maintain normal plasma [Pi]. These adaptations occur independent of parathyroid hormone (PTH), but involve changes in synthesis of 1,25-dihydroxyvitamin D_3 (Figures 14-2 and 14-3).

RENAL HANDLING OF PHOSPHATE

Renal handling of phosphate involves filtration and reabsorption. No secretion of phosphate probably occurs in humans. Plasma phosphate is filtered freely at the glomerulus. Of this filtered amount, about 80-90% is reabsorbed by the proximal tubule. Approximately 10% is reabsorbed by the distal convoluted tubule. Little or no phosphate transport occurs in the Henle's loop and collecting ducts. Therefore, the urine contains only 10% of the filtered phosphate. In conditions of excess phosphate intake, urinary excretion may approach 20%.

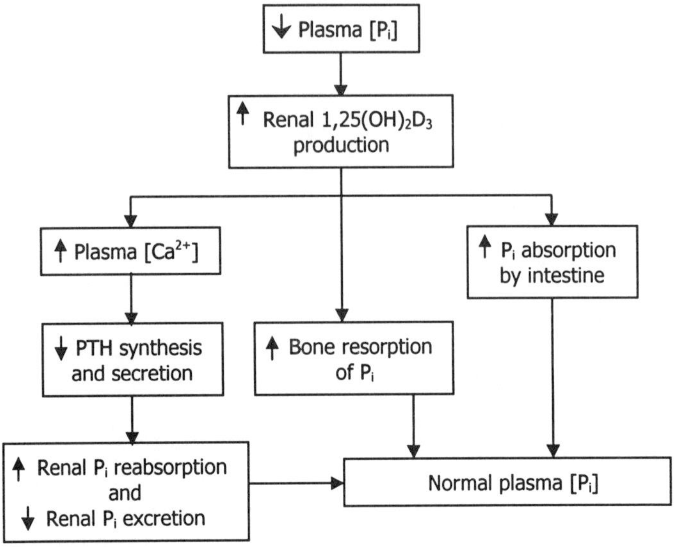

Figure 14-2. Physiologic adaptation to maintain normal plasma [Pi] during hypophosphatemia.

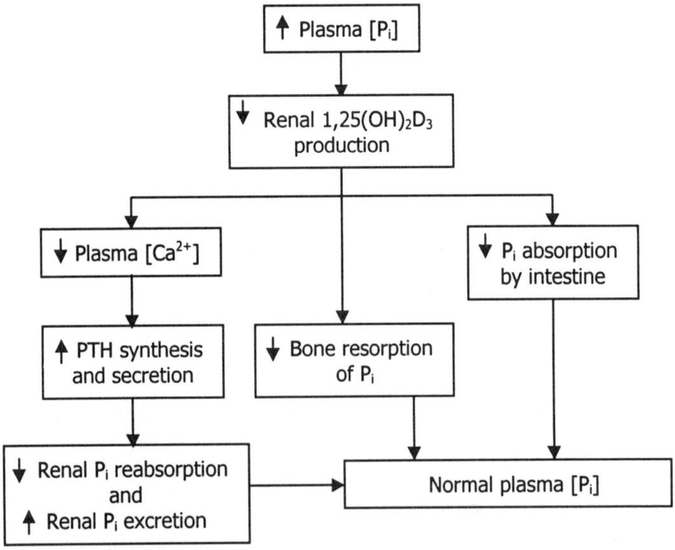

Figure 14-3. Physiologic adaptation to maintain normal plasma [Pi] during hyperphosphatemia.

CELLULAR MECHANISMS OF PHOSPHATE TRANSPORT

Transport of phosphate across the luminal membrane of the proximal tubule is active and occurs transcellularly (Figure 14-4). The transport is unidirectional. There is no passive diffusion. The mechanism of phosphate transport depends on the availability of luminal Na^+. In general, two Na^+ ions are transported with one phosphate ion. The transporter, called the Na/Pi cotransporter (Pi refers to inorganic phosphate), prefers divalent to monovalent phosphate as a cotransporter, so that the monovalent phosphate ($H_2PO_4^-$) is excreted as the major form of phosphate. This cotransport is driven by the energy supplied by the Na/K-ATPase located in the basolateral membrane.

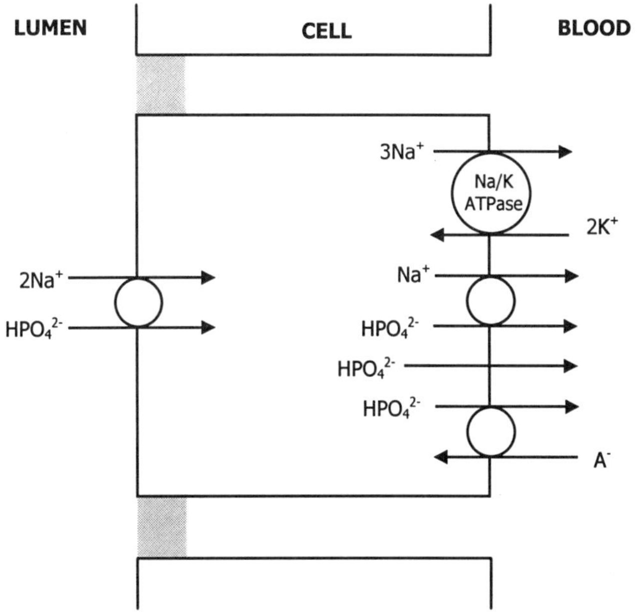

Figure 14-4. Transcellular transport of phosphate across the proximal tubule. A^- = anion.

The nature of the Na/Pi cotransporter proteins of the proximal tubule has been cloned and designated NaPi-1 and NaPi-2. The role of NaPi-1 in species other than the rabbit is not clear. However, the physiologic role of NaPi-2 parallels that of Na/Pi cotransporter in the proximal tubule of several species. Thus, NaPi-2, rather than NaPi-1, seems responsible for phosphate transport in the proximal tubule

A number of factors influence the Na/Pi cotransport system. Of these, PTH, dietary phosphate and the acid-base status deserve mention. PTH decreases

Na/Pi cotransport by decreasing the number of phosphate cotransporters, while parathyroidectomy increases the NaPi-2 protein content of brush border vesicles by two to three-fold. Dietary restriction of phosphate increases and a high phosphate diet decreases proximal tubular reabsorption of phosphate. Phosphate transport is increased by an alkaline pH and decreased by an acid pH. The effect of active vitamin D_3 on phosphate transport is less clear.

Phosphate exit across the basolateral membrane occurs both by Na^+-dependent and Na^+-independent phosphate mechanisms (see Figure 14-4). The Na^+-independent mechanism may involve an anion (Cl^-, lactate, etc.) exchange. Phosphate may also enter the blood by simple diffusion based on the electrochemical gradient.

FACTORS INFLUENCING PHOSPHATE EXCRETION

The proximal tubule has an intrinsic ability to modulate the reabsorption of phosphate depending on the need and the availability of phosphate. A number of factors and hormones influence the reabsorption and excretion of phosphate. Although variable effects have been demonstrated, some generalizations can be made. Excess dietary intake or volume expansion inhibits reabsorption, and thus increases phosphate excretion. Conversely, phosphate restriction and volume contraction promote phosphate transport and diminish urinary excretion. Acute metabolic acidosis has no effect, whereas chronic metabolic acidosis promotes phosphate excretion. Respiratory acidosis enhances while respiratory alkalosis decreases excretion of phosphate. Chronic metabolic alkalosis increases phosphate reabsorption, and thus decrease its excretion. Infusion of Ca^{2+} enhances renal phosphate reabsorption and decreases excretion. Diuretics other than K^+-sparing diuretics promote phosphate excretion. Among hormones, PTH plays an important role in urinary phosphate excretion. Infusion of PTH promotes phosphate excretion (phosphaturia), whereas parathyroidectomy results in diminished phosphate excretion. Active vitamin D_3, like PTH, is also phosphaturic. High doses of calcitonin cause transient hyperphosphaturia. Infusion of glucose inhibits tubular transport of phosphate and causes phosphaturia. Insulin, on the other hand, decreases phosphate excretion. Glucocorticoids and atrial natriuretic peptide are phosphaturic.

DISORDERS OF PHOSPHORUS

Two disorders result from disturbances in plasma [Pi]): **hypophosphatemia** and **hyperphosphatemia**.

Hypophosphatemia

Hypophosphatemia is defined as a plasma [Pi] < 2.5 mg/dL. Patients receiving mannitol develop **pseudohypophosphatemia**, which is caused by the binding of mannitol to the molybdate used to determine the plasma [Pi]. True hypophosphatemia is caused by three important mechanisms: (1) a shift of phosphate from the extracellular to intracellular compartment; (2) a decrease in gastrointestinal absorption of phosphate ; and (3) an increase in renal loss of phosphate (see At a Glance Box 14-1). Hypophosphatemia could be severe (plasma [Pi] < 1.0 mg/dL) or moderate (plasma [Pi] between 1.0 and 2.5 mg/dL). Severe hypophosphatemia can occur in patients with prolonged use of antacids, such as aluminum hydroxide, magnesium hydroxide or calcium carbonate or acetate. Chronic alcoholism can lead to severe hypophosphatemia, and the causes are multifactorial. The causes include poor dietary intake, use of antacids for gastric disturbances, continuous ingestion of alcohol which promotes phosphate excretion, vomiting, diarrhea, and respiratory alkalosis due to liver cirrhosis. Moderate hypophosphatemia may be symptomatic or asymptomatic.

At a Glance Box 14-1
Causes of hypophosphatemia

Shift from extracellular to intracellular compartment
- Glucose
- Insulin
- Catecholamines
- Hyperalimentation
- Respiratory alkalosis

Decreased intestinal absorption
- Prolonged starvation
- Malabsorption
- Phosphate-binding antacids
- Vitamin D deficiency

Increased renal loss
- Hyperparathyroidism
- Fanconi syndrome
- Volume expansion
- Chronic alcoholism
- Hypomagnesemia
- Diuretic (acetazolamide) therapy

The signs and symptoms of hypophosphatemia depend on the onset and severity of the decreased serum [Pi]. Two biochemical abnormalities underlie the manifestations of phosphate deficiency. One is depletion of ATP, and the second is a reduction in erythrocyte 2,3-diphosphoglycerate. Both depletions lead to altered cellular function and hypoxia. An acute drop in plasma [Pi] results in neurologic changes, such as confusion, disorientation, and coma; cardiac dysfunction; hypotension; rhabdomyolysis (destruction of skeletal muscle); and tissue hypoxia. Chronic phosphate depletion presents with decreased mentation; lethargy; muscle weakness; arthralgias; and dysfunction in platelets, and red and white blood cells.

Treatment of hypophosphatemia depends on the severity of symptoms. Symptomatic hypophosphatemia requires intravenous administration of either **sodium** or **potassium phosphate** with frequent monitoring of the plasma [Pi]. Asymptomatic hypophosphatemia can be treated with dietary or oral phosphate supplementation.

Hyperphosphatemia

Hyperphosphatemia is defined as plasma [Pi] > 4.5 mg/dL. Spurious increase in plasma [Pi] is called **pseudohyperphosphatemia.** It is rather rare but has been described in conditions of hyperglobulinemia and hypertriglyceridemia. This spurious increase has been attributed to the interference of proteins and triglycerides in the colorimetric assay of phosphate. Three important mechanisms, which are opposite to those of hypophosphatemia, have been implicated in true hyperphosphatemia. They are (1) release of phosphate from the intracellular to extracellular compartment; (2) an increase in phosphate load; and (3) a decrease in renal loss of phosphate (see At a Glance Box 14-2). In clinical practice, acute and chronic renal failure are probably the most significant causes of hyperphosphatemia.

At a Glance Box 14-2
Major causes of hyperphosphatemia

Release from intracellular to extracellular compartment
- Hemolysis
- Rhabdomyolysis
- Tumor lysis syndrome

Increase in phosphate load
- Excess intake (oral or intravenous)
- Phosphorus-containing laxatives
- Excess vitamin D

Decrease in renal loss of phosphate
- Acute renal failure
- Chronic renal failure
- Hypoparathyroidism

Although the mechanisms of hyperphosphatemia are self-explanatory, the terms **hemolysis, rhabdomyolysis** and **tumor lysis syndrome** deserve mention here. Destruction of red cells (hemolysis) either by mechanical, thermal, or immunologic mechanisms cause release of intracellular contents, especially phosphate and K^+. Similarly, rhabdomyolysis due to trauma, infections, alcoholism, or severe decrease in plasma [Pi] or [K^+] may cause release of phosphate, K^+, and uric acid into the blood. Thus, the plasma concentrations of these substances will increase. Tumor lysis syndrome results from chemotherapy of large and solid tumors such as lymphomas. Destruction of tumor cells releases large quantities of phosphate, uric acid, and K^+.

The signs and symptoms of hyperphosphatemia are related to the resultant hypocalcemia, which include neuromuscular and cardiac abnormalities. As plasma [Pi] increases there is a reciprocal decrease in plasma [Ca^{2+}]. This decrease is due to a decrease in active vitamin D_3 production by hyperphosphatemia. Treatment of chronic asymptomatic hyperphosphatemia involves restriction of dietary phosphate intake and phosphate-binders, such as calcium carbonate or calcium acetate. These binders decrease gastrointestinal absorption of phosphate. Acute symptomatic hyperphosphatemia can be treated with volume expansion if renal function is normal. Also, **high-flux** hemodialysis (artificial kidney) is helpful in removing phosphate and correcting hypocalcemia. Glucose and insulin infusion may be administered to promote cellular uptake of phosphate until hemodialysis is started.

SUMMARY

1. Phosphorus is an important constituent of the body, and plays an important role in mitochondrial respiration and oxidative phosphorylation. Phosphate rather than phosphorus participates in biologic functions. In plasma, phosphate exists as organic and inorganic forms, and the latter is physiologically active. Phosphate homeostasis is maintained by coordinated interactions of the intestine, kidney, and bone.
2. Phosphate is freely filtered at the glomerulus. Of this filtered phosphate, 80% is reabsorbed in the proximal tubule by Na/Pi cotransport system. Only 10% of the filtered phosphate is excreted in the urine. A number of factors either decrease or increase the phosphate transport in the proximal tubule, and thus influence phosphate excretion. PTH decreases transport, and increases phosphate excretion. Dietary phosphate restriction increases transport and decreases phosphate excretion.
3. Hypophosphatemia (plasma [Pi] < 2.5 mg/dL) is caused by either shift of phosphate from the extracellular to intracellular compartment, decreased intestinal absorption of phosphate or increased renal excretion of phosphate. Hypophosphatemia causes multiple organ dysfunction. The

treatment includes elimination of the cause and either oral or intravenous administration of phosphate.

4. Hyperphosphatemia (plasma [Pi] > 4.5 mg/dL) is generally caused by acute or chronic renal failure. The signs and symptoms of hyperphosphatemia are related to the resultant hypocalcemia, which include cardiac and neuromuscular abnormalities. The treatment modalities include elimination of the cause, phosphate-binders, administration of glucose and insulin and high-flux hemodialysis.

STUDY QUESTIONS

Case 1

A 40-year-old male with chronic alcohol abuse is admitted for vomiting, weakness, muscle pain, and diarrhea. He has been drinking one pint of vodka daily for the last 15 days with no food intake. On admission, his serum (plasma) chemistry values are:

Na^+ = 130 mEq/L	Ca^{2+} = 7.2 mg/dL
K^+ = 3.0 mEq/L	Phosphate = 1.6 mg/dL
Cl^- = 84 mEq/L	Mg^{2+} = 1.2 mEq/dL
HCO_3^- = 30 mEq/L	Albumin = 3.0 g/dL
BUN = 32 mg/dL	Serum alcohol = 120 mg
Creatinine = 2.4 mg/dL	
Glucose = 80 mg/dL	

Question 1. Discuss the causes of this patient's hypophosphatemia.

Answer: Possible causes include: (1) dietary phosphate deficiency due to poor intake; (2) decreased intestinal phosphate absorption due to diarrhea, or (3) excessive renal loss of phosphate due to alcohol. All of these mechanisms may be responsible for the patient's chronic alcoholism. This patient's weakness and muscle pain may be due to his hypophosphatemia, although hypokalemia may also contribute to his symptoms.

Question 2. How would you treat the patient's hypophosphatemia?

Answer: Although the patient's hypophosphatemia may be treated with increased dietary phosphate intake by administering milk with supplemental potassium phosphate, vomiting, and diarrhea preclude oral intake. Therefore, intravenous potassium phosphate at a dose of 2.5 to 5.0 mg/kg body weight can be given over 6 hours with monitoring of serum [Pi]. The Mg^{2+} deficiency should also be corrected.

Question 3. What would happen to the urinary excretion of phosphate, if the plasma concentration were raised from 3.5 mg/dL to 5.5 mg/dL?

Answer: Like the glucose titration curve (see Chapter 7), the phosphate titration curve also has a Tm, splay, and renal threshold. The Tm for phosphate is low compared to the Tm for glucose. The increase in plasma [Pi] from 3.5 to 5.5 mg/dL increases the filtered load of phosphate, which exceeds the Tm for phosphate. This results in enhanced excretion of phosphate. Consequently, the plasma [Pi] returns to normal. Thus, the kidneys regulate plasma [Pi].

Case 2

A 30-year-old male is admitted to trauma service following a crush injury. On the third post-operative day, his urine output starts to decline and serum creatinine and BUN start to rise. A renal consult is obtained for evaluation of renal failure. The laboratory values at the time of admission and the third post-operative day are:

	Admission	Post-operative day
Na^+ (mEq/L)	140	134
K^+ (mEq/L)	4.0	5.8
Cl^- (mEq/L)	98	94
HCO_3^- (mEq/L)	24	20
BUN (mg/dL)	12	30
Creatinine (mg/dL)	1.0	4.0
Glucose (mg/dL)	100	110
Ca^{2+} (mg/dL)	9.0	7.50
Phosphate (mg/dL)	3.5	8.00
Uric acid (mg/dL)	6.5	12.50
Albumin (mg/dL)	4.0	4.00
Creatine kinase (U)	50	40,000

Question 1. Explain the causes for this patient's hyperphosphatemia.

Answer: This is a clear-cut case of acute renal failure due to rhabdomyolysis caused by massive injury to the muscle. When muscle is injured due to trauma, infection, or alcohol, intracellular ions and enzymes are released into the blood. These include K^+, phosphate, uric acid, and enzymes such as creatine kinase and aldolase. If renal function is normal, these ions and enzymes are excreted in the urine and only a moderate increase in their serum concentration is observed.

Question 2. How would you treat his hyperphosphatemia?

Answer: First, the patient's volume status and urine output must be improved. The patient should receive 2-4 L of normal saline daily with careful monitoring of his pulmonary and cardiac status. Alkalinization of urine by $NaHCO_3$ may also be helpful. Second, phosphate-binders such as calcium acetate should be given to prevent gastrointestinal absorption of phosphate. If these measures fail, high-flux dialysis with protein restriction (phosphorus content is low in low protein diet) should be initiated.

Answer the following True or False statements.

1. Acute and chronic renal failure are the most common causes of hyperphosphatemia in clinical medicine.
2. Glucose and insulin are the treatment of choice for hypophosphatemia.
3. Chronic alcoholism causes hypophosphatemia.
4. Respiratory alkalosis causes hyperphosphatemia by transporting phosphate from inside to outside of the cell.
5. PTH increases Na/Pi cotransport in the proximal tubule.
6. Calcium acetate can be used as a phosphate binder in patients with renal failure.
7. Rhabdomyolysis and tumor lysis syndrome cause an increase in serum phosphate, uric acid, K^+ and creatine kinase concentrations.

Answer: 1. True; 2. False; 3. True; 4. False; 5. False; 6. True; 7. True.

SUGGESTED READING

1. Yanagawa, N., Nakhoul, F., Kurokawa, K. and Lee, D.B.N. Physiology of phosphorus metabolism. In: Clinical Disorders of Fluid and Electrolyte Metabolism. 5th edition. R.G. Narins (ed.). McGraw-Hill, Inc., New York, 1994; pp. 307-371 (*A detailed review describing the transport of phosphorus metabolism*).
2. Suki, W.N. and Rouse, D. Renal transport of calcium, magnesium, and phosphorus. In: The Kidney. 5th edition. B.M. Brenner (ed.). W.B. Saunders Company, Philadelphia, 1996; pp. 472-515 (*see Suggested Reading in Chapter 13*).
3. Hruska, K.A. and Slatopolsky, E. Disorders of phosphorus, calcium, and magnesium metabolism. In: Disease of the Kidney. 6th edition. R.W. Schrier and C.W. Gottschalk (eds.). Little, Brown and Company, Boston, 1997; pp. 2477-2526 (*see Suggested Reading in Chapter 13*).

CHAPTER 15

MAGNESIUM REGULATION AND DISORDERS

Objectives

After reading this chapter, the student should be able to:

1. Discuss the body distribution and functions of Mg^{2+}.
2. Explain how Mg^{2+} homeostasis is maintained.
3. Discuss the mechanisms involved in renal handling of Mg^{2+}.
4. Discuss the effect of various factors and hormones on Mg^{2+} excretion.
5. List the important causes, clinical manifestations, and treatment modalities of hypo- and hypermagnesemia.

GENERAL FEATURES

Magnesium (Mg^{2+}) is the second most common intracellular cation next to K^+ in the body. A 70- kg individual has approximately 25 g of Mg^{2+}. About 67% of this Mg^{2+} is present in bone, about 20% in muscle, and 12% in other tissues such as the liver. Only 1-2% is present in the extracellular space. In plasma, Mg^{2+} exists as free (60%) and bound (40%) forms. About 10% is bound to HCO_3^-, citrate, and phosphate and 30% to albumin. Only the free and nonprotein-bound Mg^{2+} is filtered at the glomerulus.

Mg^{2+} plays an essential role in cellular metabolism. It is involved in activation of enzymes such as phosphokinases and phosphatases. Mg-ATPase is also involved in the hydrolysis of ATP and thus the generation of energy that is utilized in several ion-pump activities. In addition, Mg^{2+} plays a critical role in protein synthesis and cell volume regulation. Because of its pivotal role in cellular physiology, Mg^{2+} deficiency adversely affects many cellular functions.

Mg^{2+} HOMEOSTASIS

The daily intake of Mg^{2+} in the diet is approximately 300 mg (200-340 mg). However, the plasma concentration of Mg^{2+} (abbreviated as $[Mg^{2+}]$) is maintained between 1.7 and 2.7 mg/dL (1.4-2.3 mEq/L). As in Ca^{2+} and phosphate homeostasis, Mg^{2+} homeostasis is regulated by the intestine, bone, and kidneys. Of ingested Mg^{2+}, 30-40% is reabsorbed by the jejunum and ileum (Figure 15-1). About 30 mg/day are secreted into the gastrointestinal tract. The fecal excretion, which is calculated as the intake plus secretion minus reabsorption, amounts to 200 mg/day. Intestinal absorption of Mg^{2+} occurs by transcellular and paracellular pathways. A carrier-mediated transport system facilitates the movement of Mg^{2+} across the brush border membrane of the intestinal epithelial cell, while the paracellular movement occurs through water reabsorption and solvent drag. The available evidence indicates that the active vitamin D_3 (1,25-$(OH)_2D_3$) increases the intestinal absorption of Mg^{2+}, whereas diets rich in Ca^{2+} and phosphate decrease its absorption.

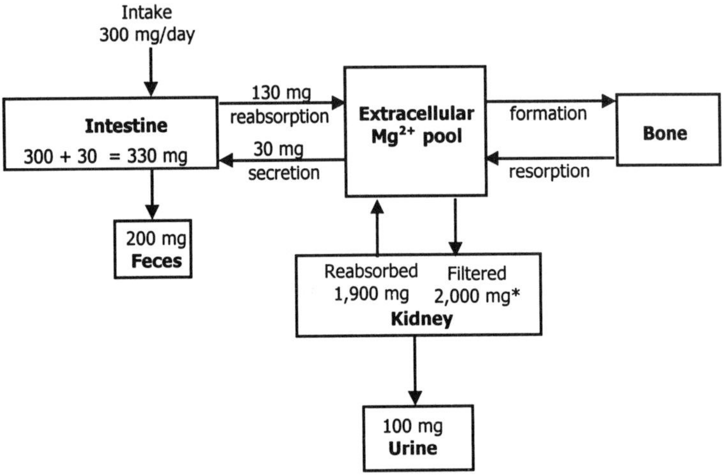

Figure 15-1. Mg^{2+} homeostasis in an adult subject. * Filtered load of Mg^{2+} equals plasma free Mg^{2+} concentration of 1.1 mg/dL times GFR of 180 L/day; i.e., 180 L x 11 mg/L = 1,980 mg/day. Note that the intake of 300 mg/day is excreted in the feces (200 mg) and urine (100 mg) to maintain Mg^{2+} homeostasis. (Modified with permission from Nordin B.E.C., (ed.). Calcium, Phosphate, and Magnesium Metabolism. Churchill Livingston, Edinburgh, 1976).

Mg^{2+} homeostasis is also dependent on the exchange between the extracellular pool and bone. The Mg^{2+} available in the surface pool of the bone is involved in the homeostatic regulation of extracellular Mg^{2+}.

The kidney also maintains Mg^{2+} homeostasis because it regulates the rate of excretion depending on the Mg^{2+} concentration. Normally, the excretory fraction of Mg^{2+} is 5%. In states of Mg^{2+} deficiency, the excretion can be as low as 0.5%. In states of Mg^{2+} excess or in chronic renal failure, excretion can be as high as 50%.

RENAL HANDLING OF Mg^{2+}

Free and nonprotein-bound Mg^{2+} is filtered at the glomerulus. Approximately 2,000 mg of Mg^{2+} are filtered and only 100 mg are excreted in the urine, which implies that 95% of the filtered Mg^{2+} is reabsorbed. The proximal convoluted tubule reabsorbs about 25% of the filtered Mg^{2+}. This amount is relatively low when compared to the reabsorption of Na^+, K^+, Ca^{2+} or phosphate at the proximal convoluted tubule. About 15% of Mg^{2+} is reabsorbed in the proximal straight tubule.

The most important segment for Mg^{2+} reabsorption is the cortical thick ascending limb of Henle's loop. In this segment, about 50% of Mg^{2+} is reabsorbed. The distal convoluted tubule reabsorbs 5% of the filtered Mg^{2+}, and very little reabsorption occurs in the collecting duct. Under steady state conditions, the urinary excretion of Mg^{2+} is about 5% of the filtered load.

CELLULAR MECHANISMS OF Mg^{2+} TRANSPORT

The transport of Mg^{2+} in the proximal tubule is passive and unidirectional down an electrochemical gradient. It is dependent on the concentration of Mg^{2+} in the luminal fluid. Mg^{2+} reabsorption occurs in parallel with Na^+ reabsorption and thus is influenced by changes in extracellular fluid volume.

The transport of Mg^{2+} in the thick ascending limb of Henle's loop is both passive and active. Passive transport is dependent on the lumen-positive voltage difference secondary to Na/K/2Cl cotransport and back-leak of K^+ into the lumen (Figure 15-2). This positive voltage difference facilitates paracellular movement of Mg^{2+}. Inhibition of the Na/K/2Cl cotransport by a loop diuretic diminishes Mg^{2+} reabsorption. A similar decrease in Mg^{2+} reabsorption is also observed with volume expansion. Both these situations lower the potential difference, and thus provide prompt passive transport of Mg^{2+} in this segment of the nephron.

Evidence also exists for active transport of Mg^{2+} in the cortical thick ascending limb of Henle's loop. This mechanism has been suggested based on the observation that Mg^{2+} transport is stimulated by antidiuretic hormone (ADH) and glucagon without any change in the potential difference.

Mg^{2+} ions exit across the basolateral membrane by being actively extruded against their electrochemical gradient. Although the mechanisms have not been studied in epithelial cells, the existence of a Mg-ATPase that extrudes Mg^{2+} has been reported in other cells. Also, a Na/Mg exchanger has been demonstrated in erythrocytes (see Figure 15-2).

The transport of Mg^{2+} in the distal convoluted tubule has not been studied well. In this segment, the lumen has a negative potential difference. Consequently, Mg^{2+} reabsorption is not voltage-dependent and may involve active transport. Fractional reabsorption of Mg^{2+} is about one-third of that of either Na^+ or Ca^{2+}, and any excess delivery of Mg^{2+} to the distal tubule is not reabsorbed.

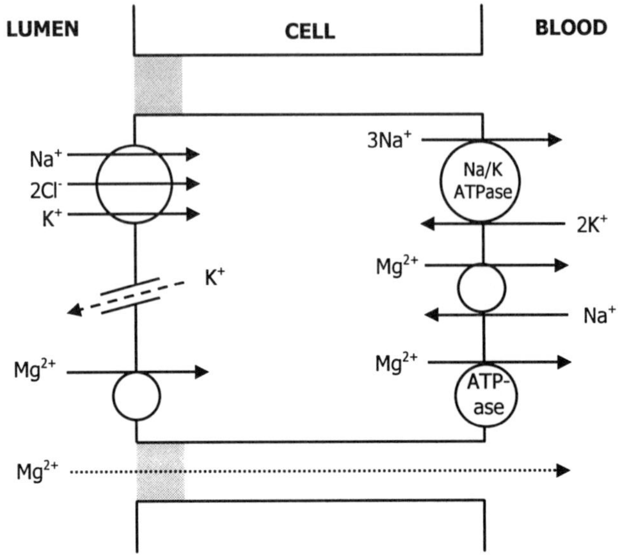

Figure 15-2. Cellular model for Mg^{2+} transport in the cortical thick ascending limb of Henle's loop.

FACTORS THAT ALTER RENAL HANDLING OF Mg^{2+}

Several factors influence the tubular reabsorption of Mg^{2+} and are summarized in Table 15-1. Volume expansion decreases proximal tubular reabsorption of Na^+ and water. As a result, Mg^{2+} reabsorption is also decreased. Conversely, volume depletion causes an increase in Mg^{2+} reabsorption. Hypermagnesemia inhibits Mg^{2+} reabsorption, whereas hypomagnesemia causes renal retention of Mg^{2+}. Hypercalcemia markedly increases Mg^{2+} excretion by inhibiting reabsorption in the proximal tubule and thick ascending limb of Henle. Hypocalcemia has the opposite effect. Phosphate depletion enhances Mg^{2+} excretion by reducing its absorption in the thick ascending limb and distal convoluted tubule. Metabolic acidosis has inconsistent effects on Mg^{2+} handling. Acute acidosis seems to inhibit Mg^{2+} reabsorption in the thick ascending limb, and thus enhance its excretion. On the other hand, metabolic alkalosis decreases urinary excretion of Mg^{2+} probably by enhancing its reabsorption in the proximal straight tubule and distal convoluted tubule. Cyclic AMP-mediated hormones such as parathyroid hormone and ADH enhance Mg^{2+} reabsorption by the thick ascending limb and decrease its urinary excretion. Osmotic diuretics, such as mannitol and urea, promote Mg^{2+} excretion by predominantly inhibiting its reabsorption in the thick ascending limb of Henle's loop and to some extent in the proximal tubule. Loop diuretics, such as furosemide, inhibit Mg^{2+} reabsorption in the thick ascending limb and causes magnesuria. Thiazide diuretics (hydrochlorothiazide) act in the distal tubule and may cause a mild increase in Mg^{2+} excretion. This increase is probably due to a small increase in the delivery of glomerular filtrate to the distal tubule, which has a limited capacity for Mg^{2+} reabsorption. Evidence supporting inhibition of Mg^{2+} reabsorption in the distal tubule is not convincing.

Table 15.1. Factors influencing Mg^{2+} reabsorption and excretion

Factor	PCT	TALH	Urinary excretion
Volume expansion	↓	↓	↑
Volume contraction	↑	↑	↓
Hypermagnesemia	↓	↓	↑
Hypomagnesemia	↑	↑	↓
Hypercalcemia	↓	↓	↑
Hypocalcemia	↑	↑	↓
Hypophosphatemia	NC	↓	↑
Metabolic acidosis	?	NC or ↓	↑
Metabolic alkalosis	↑	NC	↓
PTH	NC	↑	↓
ADH	NC	↑	↓
Glucagon	NC	↑	↓
Osmotic diuretics	↓	↓	↑
Loop diuretics	NC	↓	↑
Thiazide diuretics	NC	NC	↑

↑ = increase; ↓ = decrease; NC = no change; PCT = proximal convoluted tubule; TALH = thick ascending limb of Henle's loop.

DISORDERS OF Mg^{2+}

Hypomagnesemia

As stated earlier, the normal plasma [Mg^{2+}] ranges from 1.7 to 2.7 mg/dL. Hypomagnesemia is defined as a plasma [Mg^{2+}] < 1.7 mg/dL. The prevalence of hypomagnesemia in outpatient and hospitalized patient population is 6 to 12%. The causes of hypomagnesemia fall into three major categories: (1) decreased intake of Mg^{2+}; (2) decreased intestinal absorption; and (3) excessive urinary losses (see At a Glance Box 15-1). In addition to these causes, transcellular transport of Mg^{2+} into the cell is caused by infusion of glucose or epinephrine.

About 30% of alcoholic patients admitted to the hospital present with hypomagnesemia, and the causes are multifactorial: (1) poor dietary intake of Mg^{2+}; (2) increase in renal excretion of Mg^{2+} by alcohol; (3) diarrhea; and (4) starvation ketosis causing increased renal Mg^{2+} loss.

Renal loss of Mg^{2+} is frequently caused by diuretics, aminoglycoside antibiotics, and chemotherapeutic agents such as cis-platinum or cyclosporine. Cis-platinum is used in the treatment of epithelial neoplasma. It causes renal Mg^{2+} loss possibly by inhibiting tubular reabsorption and also by tubular damage due to interstitial nephritis.

At a Glance Box 15-1
Some causes of hypomagnesemia

Decreased intake
- Starvation
- Chronic alcoholism
- Protein-calorie malnutrition
- Prolonged intravenous therapy without Mg^{2+}

Decreased intestinal absorption
- Prolonged nasogastric suction
- Severe diarrhea including malabsorption
- Excessive use of laxatives
- Intestinal and biliary fistulas
- Resection of small intestine

Excessive urinary losses
- Diuretics
- Chronic alcoholism
- Renal Mg^{2+} wasting
- Renal tubular acidosis
- Diabetic ketoacidosis during treatment
- Chronic renal failure with Mg^{2+} wastage
- Hypercalcemia
- Hyperthyroidism
- Hypophosphatemia
- Bartter's syndrome
- Primary aldosteronism
- Aminoglycosides
- Cis-platinum
- Amphotericin B
- Cyclosporine
- Pentamidine

The signs and symptoms of hypomagnesemia are listed in the accompanying At a Glance Box 15-2. The clinical manifestations of hypomagnesemia are often difficult to differentiate from those of hypocalcemia. This difficulty is due to the following reason. Hypomagnesemia impairs the secretion of parathyroid hormone. It also causes skeletal resistance to the action of parathyroid hormone to release Ca^{2+}. As a result, hypocalcemia develops, which causes many signs and symptoms similar to those of hypomagnesemia. Hypomagnesemia can also cause hypokalemia due to the release of renin by low levels of Mg^{2+}. The resultant hyperreninemic hyperaldosteronism causes hypokalemia and associated symptoms. Replacing Mg^{2+} largely abolishes hypocalcemia and prevents K^+ wasting.

At a Glance Box 15-2
Signs and symptoms of hypomagnesemia

Signs	Symptoms
Chvostek's sign*	Nausea
Trousseau's sign*	Vomiting
Tremors	Apathy
Muscle fasciculations	Weakness
Hyperreflexia	Anorexia
Seizures	
Depression	
Psychosis	
Cardiac conduction disturbances	
Hypertension	
Decreased myocardial contractility	
Sudden death	

* see Chapter 13

Hypomagnesemic patients can be treated with both oral and parenteral supplementation of Mg^{2+}. If the patient is asymptomatic, oral supplementation in the form of milk or Mg^{2+} as sulfate, oxide, or chloride salt may be given. For a symptomatic patient, intravenous administration of $MgSO_4$ as a 50% solution in 100 to 500 ml of normal saline may be given over a 15 minute period.

Hypermagnesemia

Hypermagnesemia, which is characterized by a plasma $[Mg^{2+}] > 2.7$ mg/dL, is not a common electrolyte disorder in individuals with normal renal function. As stated earlier, the kidney is able to maintain plasma $[Mg^{2+}]$ within normal range by enhancing its excretion in situations of excess Mg^{2+} intake. Therefore, a decrease in glomerular filtration rate, as seen in chronic renal failure, seems to be the most common cause of hypermagnesemia. The other major cause is an exogenous load of Mg^{2+}. Excess intake of Mg^{2+} can occur when a patient with preeclampsia (a condition characterized by edema, proteinuria and hypertension during third trimester of pregnancy) is treated with $MgSO_4$ or when individuals take Mg^{2+}-containing antacids or enemas. Elderly individuals are particularly susceptible to Mg^{2+} toxicity because of decreased renal function with aging and excessive use of Mg^{2+}-containing medications and vitamins. The clinical manifestations of hypermagnesemia are related to the plasma $[Mg^{2+}]$, as shown in the At a Glance Box 15-3. Two organ systems are greatly affected by hypermagnesemia: the neuromuscular and cardiovascular systems.

If the patient is asymptomatic, removal of the cause will normalize plasma [Mg^{2+}]. If the plasma concentrations do not return to normal, volume expansion and a loop diuretic promote Mg^{2+} excretion by inhibiting its reabsorption in the thick ascending limb of Henle's loop. If the patient is symptomatic, intravenous calcium gluconate (15 mg/kg) should be given over a 4-hour period. Ca^{2+} antagonizes the neuromuscular and cardiovascular effects of hypermagnesemia. For a patient with renal insufficiency, hemodialysis using a Mg^{2+}-free dialysate is the treatment of choice. Since Mg^{2+} is removed by hemodialysis, this treatment provides an efficient means of lowering plasma [Mg^{2+}] within a short period of time.

At a Glance Box 15-3.
Signs and symptoms of hypermagnesemia

Signs/Symptoms	Plasma [Mg^{2+}] (mg/dL)
Nausea and vomiting	3.6 - 6.0
Sedation, hyporeflexia, muscle weakness	4.8 - 8.4
Bradycardia, hypotension	6.0 - 12.0
Absence of reflexes, respiratory paralysis or coma	12.0 - 18.0
Cardiac arrest	> 18.0

SUMMARY

1. Magnesium (Mg^{2+}) is the second most common intracellular cation, and plays an important role in enzyme activation, ion-pump activities, protein synthesis and cell volume regulation. Most of the Mg^{2+} is found in the bone, and only 1-2% is present in the extracellular space.
2. Mg^{2+} homeostasis is regulated by the gastrointestinal tract, bone, and kidneys. About 60% of the plasma Mg^{2+} is free, and is filtered at the glomerulus. Only 20 to 30% of the filtered Mg^{2+} is reabsorbed in the proximal tubule by passive movement through the paracellular pathway. The major site for Mg^{2+} reabsorption is the cortical thick ascending limb of Henle's loop. About 50% of Mg^{2+} is reabsorbed in this segment by passive diffusion through the paracellular pathway. This passive movement is due to lumen-positive potential gradient generated by active Na/K/2Cl cotransport and back-leak of K^+ into the lumen. Active transport of Mg^{2+} has also been demonstrated, which occurs independent of any potential difference.
3. Parathyroid hormone, hypomagnesemia, and volume contraction increase, whereas hypercalcemia, hypermagnesemia and volume expansion decrease the transport of Mg^{2+} in the thick ascending limb of Henle's loop.
4. The distal convoluted tubule and collecting duct play only a minor role in

Mg^{2+} reabsorption. In a steady state condition, about 5% of the filtered load of Mg^{2+} is excreted. This percentage increases substantially in conditions of high Mg^{2+} intake, and decreases in conditions of low Mg^{2+} intake.

5. Hypomagnesemia is caused by either poor dietary intake of Mg^{2+}, excessive gastrointestinal or renal loss of Mg^{2+}. It is associated with biochemical abnormalities, such as hypocalcemia, hypokalemia, and hypophosphatemia. The signs and symptoms of hypomagnesemia include tetany, positive Chvostek's and Trousseau's signs, seizures, EKG changes, weakness and anorexia. Treatment includes oral $MgSO_4$ in asymptomatic patient and intravenous administration of $MgSO_4$ in symptomatic patients.
6. Hypermagnesemia results from decreased renal excretion of Mg^{2+} or excessive intake of Mg^{2+}. The signs and symptoms of hypermagnesemia are related to plasma $[Mg^{2+}]$, and reflect Mg^{2+} ion action on the central nervous and cardiovascular systems. Decreased or absent deep tendon reflexes, cardiac conduction abnormalities, respiratory paralysis, hypotension and cardiac death occur with plasma $[Mg^{2+}] > 6.0$ mEq/L. For a symptomatic patient, intravenous calcium gluconate is the drug of choice.

STUDY QUESTIONS

Case 1

A 62-year-old male was admitted for chemotherapy of small cell (oat cell) cancer of the lung with cis-platinum. The patient was hydrated with 3 L of normal saline prior to the initiation of chemotherapy. He subsequently developed shortness of breath for which he received furosemide 80 mg intravenously. He excreted 4 L of urine in 24-hours. Seven days later, the patient started feeling weak. Physical examination revealed tetany, Chvostek's and Trouasseau's signs. The laboratory data were:

Na^+ = 135 mEq/L
K^+ = 2.9 mEq/L
Cl^- = 100 mEq/L
HCO_3^- = 26 mEq/L
BUN = 30 mg/dL
Creatinine = 1.6 mg/dL
Ca^{2+} = 7.0 mg/dL
Phosphate = 3.0 mg/dL
Albumin = 3.5 mg/dL
Mg^{2+} = 0.7 mEq/L

Question 1. What is the most likely cause of Chvostek's and Trousseau's signs?

Answer: Both hypocalcemia and hypomagnesemia cause tetany, carpopedal spasm and positive Chvostek's and Trousseau's signs. However, in this patient Mg^{2+} depletion is more severe than Ca^{2+} depletion.

Question 2. What precipitated this patient's hypomagnesemia?

Answer: Although loop diuretics (furosemide) cause significant magnesuria, it is the cis-platinum that caused profound hypomagnesemia secondary to excess urinary losses of Mg^{2+}. The mechanism seems to be cis-platinum's inhibition of Mg^{2+} absorption by the loop of Henle or the destruction of loop of Henle due to interstitial nephritis caused by cis-platinum. Hypokalemia and hypocalcemia also result from cis-platinum therapy.

Question 3. How would you treat this patient?

Answer: Replacement of K^+ and Ca^{2+} would not prevent tetany. The appropriate treatment is the intravenous administration of $MgSO_4$. One gram of $MgSO_4.7H_2O$ provides 97.6 mg of elemental or 8 mEq/L Mg^{2+}. It is available in 2 ml quantity as 50% solution, which can be added to 100 ml of normal saline and given in 30-60 minutes. This treatment can be continued until plasma [Mg^{2+}] returns to normal. Normalization of plasma [Mg^{2+}] corrects Ca^{2+}, K^+, and phosphate deficiency can be corrected by potassium phosphate.

Case 2

A 22-year-old pregnant woman in her third trimester was admitted for severe hypertension (180/110 mm Hg) and proteinuria. She was started on $MgSO_4$ and methyldopa (an antihypertensive agent). Her blood pressure was controlled at 140/90 mm Hg. Four days later, she developed nausea and vomiting and progressively became lethargic. Her blood pressure dropped to 100/70 mm Hg. Deep tendon reflexes were decreased. Her serum creatinine was 2.0 mg/dL and Mg^{2+} was 6 mEq/L.

Question 1. Why did the patient develop hypermagnesemia?

Answer: The causes for this patient's elevated plasma [Mg^{2+}] were increased exogenous load and reduced excretion by the kidney. $MgSO_4$ is given to reduce blood pressure in a pregnant woman. A creatinine value of 2.0 mg/dL in this patient represents moderate renal failure, because the serum creatinine is usually < 0.8 mg/dL in a normal pregnant woman.

Question 2. How would you recognize Mg^{2+} intoxication at the bed side?

Answer: Besides hypotension and central nervous system depression, decreased deep tendon reflexes should alert the physician for Mg^{2+} intoxication.

Question 3. How would you treat this patient?

Answer: First, $MgSO_4$ administration should be discontinued. Second, calcium gluconate (20 ml of 10% solution) should be given intravenously over a 10-minute period to counteract the manifestations of hypermagenesemia. Third, if the symptoms persist, hemodialysis with a dialysate containing low Mg^{2+} concentration should be done to remove Mg^{2+}.

SUGGESTED READING

1. Suki, W.N. and Rouse, D. Renal transport of calcium, magnesium, and phosphorus. In: The Kidney. 5th edition. B.M. Brenner (ed.). W.B. Saunders Company, Philadelphia, 1996; pp. 472-515 (*see Suggested Reading in Chapter 13*).
2. Hruska, K. A. and Slatopolsky, E. Disorders of phosphorus, calcium, and magnesium metabolism. In: Disease of the Kidney. 6th edition. R.W. Schrier and C.W. Gottschalk (eds.). Little, Brown and Company, Boston, 1997; pp. 2477-2526 (*see Suggested Reading in Chapter 13*).

CHAPTER 16

DIURETICS

Objectives

After reading this chapter, the student should be able to:

1. Define the terms diuretics, diuresis, and natriuresis.
2. Describe how diuretics are classified.
3. Discuss how diuretics inhibit transport mechanisms.
4. Explain the way diuretics alter renal hemodynamics, water and electrolyte excretion.
5. List the electrolyte and acid-base disorders caused by diuretics.
6. Discuss the clinical uses of diuretics in edematous and nonedematous conditions.

Diuretics are chemical substances that promote urine flow rate. Water and alcoholic beverages also cause an increase in urine output, which is mostly water. Conversely, diuretics promote both water and solute excretion. The major function of diuretics is to inhibit NaCl reabsorption in renal tubules and enhance its excretion. Excretion of Na^+ in the urine is called **natriuresis**, whereas **diuresis** refers to increased urine flow rate.

In clinical medicine, two types of diuresis are recognized: solute diuresis and water diuresis. Solute diuresis results from a decrease in the renal tubular reabsorption of solute. Since water reabsorption follows solute reabsorption, inhibition of solute reabsorption generally diminishes water transport. However, water diuresis can be promoted without solute diuresis by drugs, such as lithium, which impair the action of antidiuretic hormone.

In this chapter, we briefly review the various groups of diuretics, their physiology of action, and their clinical use, including their complications.

CLASSIFICATION OF DIURETICS

Diuretics can be classified according to their chemical structure (e.g., thiazides), site of their action (e.g., loop diuretics), or their effect on electrolyte excretion (e.g., potassium-sparing diuretics). Accordingly, they are divided into the following groups:

1. Osmotic diuretics
2. Carbonic anhydrase inhibitors
3. Loop diuretics
4. Thiazides or distal tubule diuretics
5. Potassium-sparing diuretics

Table 16-1 summarizes various groups of diuretics according to their chemical nature, site of action and relative natriuretic potency.

Table 16-1. Classification of diuretics

Group	Chemical nature	Prototype drug(s)	Site of action	Relative natriuretic potency
Osmotic diuretics	Polysaccharide	Mannitol	Predominantly proximal tubule and loop of Henle	Dose-dependent (> 10%)
Carbonic anhydrase inhibitors	Sulfonamide	Acetazolamide	Proximal tubule	1-3%
Loop diuretics	Sulfonamide Phenoxyacetic acid-derivative	Furosemide Bumetanide Ethacrynic acid	Thick ascending Henle's loop	20-25%
Distal tubule diuretics	Benzothiadiazine or its derivatives	Chlorothiazide Hydrochlorothiazide Chlorthalidone Metolazone Indapamide	Early distal convoluted tubule	5%
Potassium-sparing diuretics	Steroid Pyrazine carboxamides Pteridine derivative	Spironolactone Amiloride Triamterene	Cortical collecting duct	1-3%

RENAL HANDLING OF DIURETICS

Except for mannitol, most diuretics are bound to serum proteins and are not freely filtered at the glomerulus. Instead, they are secreted into the lumen of the proximal tubule by specific transport systems located in the basolateral membrane of the cell. At physiologic pH, diuretics (except for mannitol and spironolactone) exist either as organic anions or cations. Amiloride and triameterene are organic cations, while the remaining diuretics are organic anions. In order to be effective and achieve high urinary concentrations, these diuretics must be secreted into the tubular lumen. Any compound, either endogenous or exogenous, that competes for the specific site where the diuretic is secreted may impair the diuretic action. For example, probenecid competes for the same secretory site as furosemide and diminishes its diuretic action. Similarly, hypoalbuminemia diminishes the effect of furosemide due to less binding of the drug to albumin and decreased tubular secretion of the drug. In patients with nephrotic syndrome, the effect of furosemide is also diminished because the secreted diuretic combines with the filtered protein and becomes less effective. Inhibitors of prostaglandin synthesis, such as indomethacin, may also diminish the efficacy of diuretics. The mechanisms for this diminished efficacy are not completely understood. However, various possibilities have been demonstrated: (1) prostaglandin synthesis inhibitors are organic acids which may compete for the secretory sites of the diuretics, and thus block their secretion; (2) diuretics such as furosemide stimulate prostaglandin synthesis, and these inhibitors may blunt this synthesis; and, (3) prostaglandin inhibitors reduce the renal blood flow and glomerular filtration rate so that the delivery of the filtrate to the site of diuretic action is diminished.

CELLULAR MECHANISMS OF DIURETIC ACTION

Because diuretics inhibit the reabsorption of Na^+ and water, the reader should be familiar with the renal handling of these substances, which are discussed in Chapters 7 and 9.

Osmotic Diuretics

Osmotic diuretics, such as mannitol (Osmitrol) are freely filtered at the glomerulus. They are poorly reabsorbed by the tubules, and thus remain in high concentrations in the tubular lumen. Besides mannitol, urea, glucose, and radiocontrast agents act as osmotic diuretics. However, only mannitol is extensively used as an osmotic diuretic in clinical practice.

The major sites of action for mannitol are the proximal tubule and the loop of Henle. By remaining in the tubular lumen, mannitol exerts an osmotic pressure that inhibits the tubular reabsorption of solute and water. The mechanism of inhibition in the proximal tubule is as follows: normally, as the filtered Na^+ is isomotically reabsorbed, a small osmotic pressure difference develops between the tubular lumen fluid and the interstitial fluid. This pressure difference causes water to move from the slightly hypotonic lumen to the hypertonic interstitium. However, the presence of mannitol in the tubular lumen causes an increase in the osmotic pressure that opposes water reabsorption. The ongoing Na^+ reabsorption progressively diminishes its tubular concentration steadily until a gradient for backflux of reabsorbed Na^+ is established. This results in no further net movement of Na^+. Thus, mannitol inhibits both water and Na^+ reabsorption.

Because reabsorption of Na^+ and water is inhibited in the proximal tubule, more Na^+ and water is delivered to the loop of Henle, which cannot reabsorb this increased load. Also, mannitol increases medullary blood flow, causing a reduction in medullary hypertonicity. This medullary "washout" decreases water and Na^+ reabsorption. Similar to the loop of Henle, the distal tubule and the collecting duct cannot handle this large delivery of Na^+ and water. As a result, both are eliminated in the urine. Deep, rather than superficial, nephrons play an important role in the inhibition of Na^+ and water reabsorption in response to mannitol.

Carbonic Anhydrase Inhibitors

As the name implies, carbonic anhydrase inhibitors inhibit carbonic anhydrase. This enzyme is required for generation of HCO_3^- and H^+ ions (see Chapter 11 and Fig. 16-1). The prototypical carbonic anhydrase inhibitor is acetazolamide (Diamox), which is not routinely used as a diuretic. Rather, it is used to treat

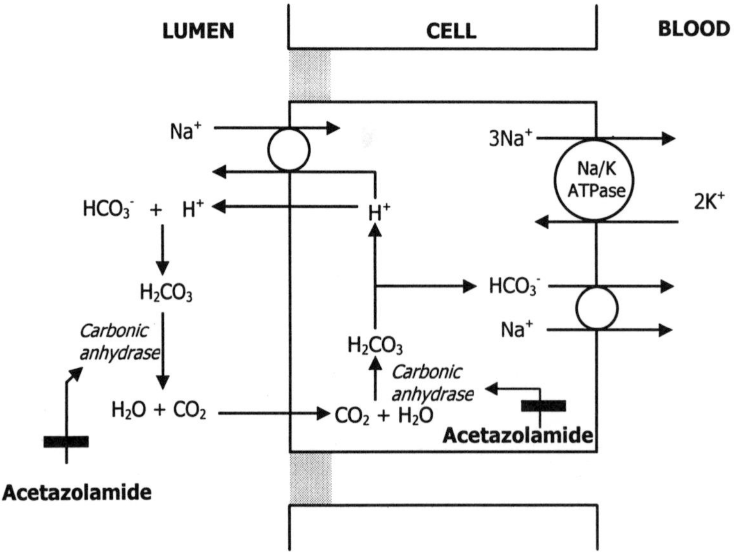

Figure 16-1. Inhibition of carbonic anhydrase by acetazolamide in the proximal tubule.

glaucoma. Because formation of aqueous humor in the eye is dependent on the carbonic anhydrase, inhibition of this enzyme by acetazolamide prevents increase in aqueous humor formation and thus intraocular pressure. By blocking carbonic anhydrase, acetazolamide inhibits proximal H^+ ion secretion at the luminal membrane as well as proximal HCO_3^- reabsorption at the basolateral membrane. Acetazolamide may also indirectly inhibit Na^+-proton exchange. The net result of these inhibitory effects is an increase in urinary excretion of HCO_3^-, which causes metabolic acidosis.

Loop Diuretics

As shown in Table 16-1, furosemide (Lasix), bumetanide (Bumex) and ethacrynic acid (Edecrin) are loop diuretics that act in the thick ascending limb of Henle's loop. In this segment, Na^+ is reabsorbed along with one K^+ and two Cl^-, therefore, this cotransporter is electroneutral. Loop diuretics inhibit this Na/K/2Cl cotransporter (Figure 16-2). As a result of this inhibition, water reabsorption is also inhibited. Furosemide has a weak inhibitory action on carbonic anhydrase in the proximal tubule. Loop diuretics are the most potent diuretics in clinical use today.

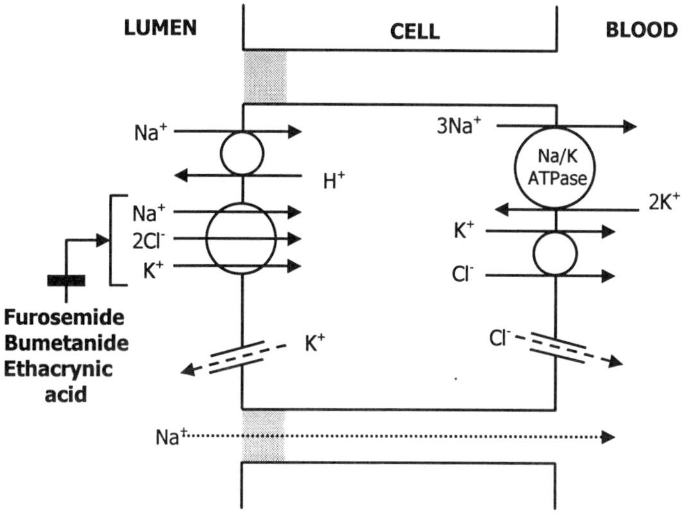

Figure 16-2. Representation of the Na/K/2Cl cotransporter in the thick ascending limb of Henle's loop and its inhibition by loop diuretics.

Thiazide Diuretics

Thiazide and related drugs act primarily in the early distal tubule (cortical diluting segment) and bind to the Cl^- site on the Na/Cl cotransporter. Thus, thiazides inhibit the coupled reabsorption of Na^+ and Cl^- (Figure 16-3). This inhibition causes enhanced urinary excretion of NaCl. Thiazides, such as chlorothiazide (diuril) and hydrochlorothiazide (hydrodiuril), also inhibit carbonic anhydrase in the proximal tubule, and thus enhance NaCl and HCO_3^- excretion. An additional site of thiazide action is the medullary collecting duct, where hydrochlorothiazide inhibits NaCl and fluid reabsorption.

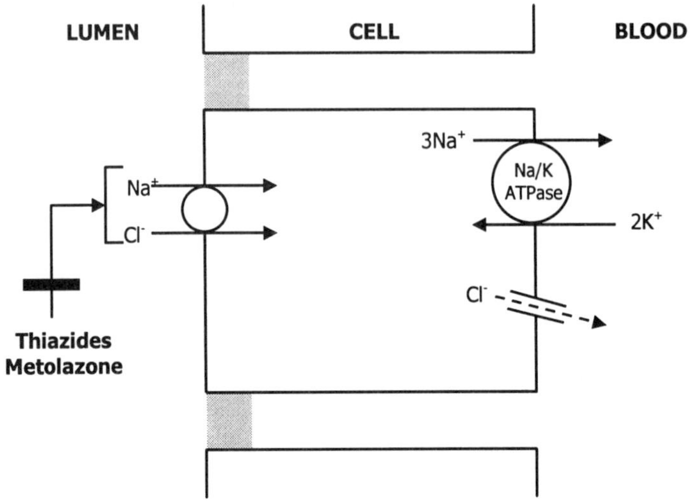

Figure 16-3. Reabsorption of NaCl in the early distal convoluted tubule and its inhibition by thiazide diuretics.

Potassium-sparing Diuretics

As shown in Table 16-1, there are three chemically distinct classes of potassium-sparing diuretics: spironolactone (Aldactone), amiloride (Midamor) and triamterene (Dyrenium). The major site of action for these drugs is the cortical collecting duct. They also seem to act in the late distal tubule (connecting tubule). Amiloride and triamterene inhibit the Na^+ channel in the principal cell (Figure 16-4), whereas spironolactone is a competitive inhibitor of aldosterone. Thus, spironolactone binds to the cytosolic aldosterone receptor from the basolateral membrane and inhibits the actions of aldosterone (see Figure 16-4). Although the principal site for amiloride action is the cortical collecting duct, it also acts in the proximal tubule and inhibits Na/H exchanger at higher concentrations. Potassium-sparing diuretics are used in combination with thiazide diuretics in the treatment of hypertension, or alone in a cirrhotic patient with ascites to prevent K^+ loss.

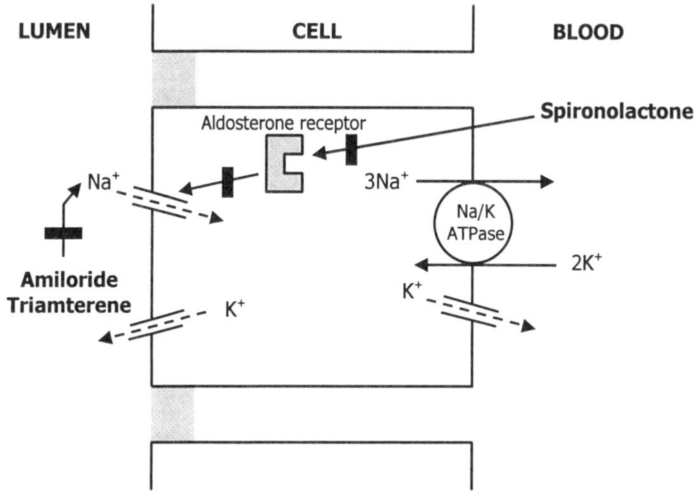

Figure 16-4. Reabsorption of Na^+ and secretion of K^+ in a principal cell of the collecting duct. Amiloride and triamterene inhibit Na^+ channels, whereas spironolactone binds to the aldosterone receptor in the cytoplasm and inhibits aldosterone-mediated effects (i.e., Na^+ reabsorption at the luminal side).

Although the different potassium-sparing diuretics are chemically and functionally unique, they all share the common property of inhibiting Na^+ entry and diminishing K^+ and H^+ ion secretion. By blocking Na^+ uptake, these drugs reduce the intracellular Na^+ and K^+ concentration by reducing the activity of Na/K-ATPase. This action may partly explain the reduction in K^+ secretion. Also, potassium-sparing diuretics abolish the transepithelial lumen-negative potential difference by inhibiting Na^+ uptake, causing a decrease in K^+ as well as H^+ ion secretion.

PHYSIOLOGICAL EFFECTS OF DIURETICS

In addition to their actions on Na^+ and water, diuretics exert several other physiologic effects in the kidney. These include changes in renal blood flow, glomerular filtration rate (GFR), concentration and dilution of urine, and excretion of several other electrolytes. The physiologic effects of diuretics are summarized in Table 16-2.

Renal Blood Flow (RBF) and GFR

Osmotic diuretics cause an increase in RBF due to the extracellular fluid volume expansion and decreased blood viscosity. Expansion of this extracellular fluid volume is caused by water abstraction from cells. Also, osmotic diuretics cause vasodilation of the afferent arteriole, and an increase in the glomerular capillary pressure (P_{GC}). GFR is modestly increased in humans taking these diuretics. Conversely, carbonic anhydrase inhibitors decrease both GFR and RBF secondary to increases in afferent and efferent arteriolar resistance. Furosemide and ethacrynic acid have been shown to cause renal vasodilatation and an increase in RBF. The GFR is not affected. Renal vasodilatation caused by loop diuretics is due to the production of vasodilatory prostaglandins (PGE_2 and PGI_2). Thiazides, like carbonic anhydrase inhibitors, cause an increase in renal vascular resistance, and thus decrease both RBF and GFR. Aldactone and triamterene may either slightly decrease or have no significant change on RBF and GFR. Amiloride seems to have no consistent effect on this renal hemodynamics.

Table 16-2. Physiologic effects of diuretics

	Osmotic diuretics	CA-inhibitors	Loop diuretics	Thiazide diuretics	K^+-sparing diuretics
Hemodynamics					
RBF	↑↑	↓	↑	↓	NC
GFR	↑	↓	NC	↓	NC
Urinary excretion					
Na	↑↑	↑	↑↑	↑↑	↑
K	↑	↑	↑↑	↑	↓↓
Cl	↑	↓	↑	↑	↑
HCO_3	↑	↑↑	NC	NC	↑
Ca	↑	NC	↑↑	↓	NC
PO_4	↑	↑↑	↑	↑	NC
Mg	↑	NC	↑↑	↑	NC
Urine volume	↑↑	↑	↑↑	↑↑	↑
Urine pH	>6.0	>7.0	6.0	>7.0	>7.0
C_{H_2O}	↑	↑	↓	↓	NC
T^cH_2O	↑	↑	↓	NC	NC

↑ = slight increase; ↑↑ = moderate increase; ↓ = slight decrease; NC = no change; ↓↓ = moderate decrease

Urine Concentration and Dilution

For a detailed description of the mechanisms of urine concentration and dilution, see Chapter 9. Osmotic diuretics, such as mannitol, increase the medullary blood flow, and thus "wash out" the medullary hypertonicity, preventing urinary concentration. Similarly, loop diuretics reduce the medullary hypertonicity by inhibiting the Na/K/2Cl cotransporter, and thereby prevent urinary concentration. Thiazides, on the other hand, act in the early distal convoluted tubule and inhibit NaCl reabsorption. The osmolality of the tubular fluid in this segment is hypotonic due to the impermeability of water. By inhibiting NaCl reabsorption, thiazide diuretics impair urinary dilution and not concentration.

As discussed in Chapter 9, the urine is composed of an osmolar (C_{osm}) component and a solute-free water (C_{H_2O}) component. When the urine is hypoosmotic to plasma (i.e., dilute urine), C_{H_2O} exceeds C_{osm}. Conversely, when the urine is concentrated C_{osm} exceeds C_{H_2O}. The urine becomes concentrated when more free water than solute has been reabsorbed. This process is called negative C_{H_2O} clearance and is denoted conventionally by T^cH_2O. A change either in T^cH_2O or C_{H_2O} causes a change in urine concentration or dilution. Accordingly, diuretics can influence either T^cH_2O or C_{H_2O}, and thus affect the kidney's ability either to concentrate or dilute the urine.

Osmotic diuretics and carbonic anhydrase inhibitors increase both C_{H_2O} and T^cH_2O, whereas loop diuretics inhibit both. Thiazides have been shown to reduce C_{H_2O} but not T^cH_2O. Potassium-sparing diuretics seem to have no effect on either C_{H_2O} or T^cH_2O.

Excretion of Electrolytes

In addition to Na^+ excretion, diuretics promote excretion of several other electrolytes. The effects of diuretics on the excretion of electrolytes are summarized in Table 16-2.

COMPLICATIONS OF DIURETICS

Chronic use of diuretics cause several complications, which can be considered under three categories (see At a Glance Box 16-1). Only those related to fluid, electrolyte, and acid-base disorders are discussed here.

Extracellular Volume Depletion

All diuretics cause a depletion in extracellular fluid volume. This effect is due to increased excretions of Na^+ and one of its attendant anions, either Cl^- or HCO_3^-, along with the obligatory water loss. Patients with normal renal function develop an increase in blood urea nitrogen (BUN) and creatinine while taking diuretics, a condition called prerenal azotemia. Patients also develop hypotension and increased pulse rate.

However, volume contraction does not continue even if the diuretic use is continued. Intrarenal compensatory mechanisms limit the diuretic response and prevent further volume contraction, a process called the breaking phenomenon. Chronic volume contraction promotes Na^+ and water reabsorption in those segments of the nephron not inhibited by the diuretic, thus limiting the excretion of Na^+ and water and preventing further volume depletion.

At a Glance Box 16-1
Complications of diuretic use

Fluid, electrolyte, and acid-base disorders
- Extracellular fluid volume depletion
- Hyponatremia
- Hypokalemia and hyperkalemia
- Hypocalcemia and hypercalcemia
- Hypomagnesemia
- Hypophosphatemia
- Metabolic acidosis and metabolic alkalosis

Metabolic disorders
- Hyperuricemia
- Hyperglycemia
- Hyperlipidemia
- Gynecomastia
- Sexual dysfunction

Toxicities
- Hypersensitivity reactions
- Deafness
- Pancreatitis
- Renal calculi

Hypo- and Hyperkalemia

Both hypokalemia and hyperkalemia occur with diuretic use. All diuretics, except potassium-sparing diuretics, cause hypokalemia. Several mechanisms are involved in the induction of hypokalemia: (1) increased delivery of filtrate to more distal sites where K^+ secretion is dependent on Na^+ reabsorption; (2) increased aldosterone production due to volume contraction; (3) increased delivery of HCO_3^--containing filtrate (as in the case of carbonic anhydrase inhibitors) which makes the distal tubule more lumen-negative and thus favorable to K^+ secretion; and (4) reduced K^+ intake while on diuretics. Hypokalemia may also result from high salt intake due to increased delivery of Na^+ to the distal tubule where Na^+ and K^+ exchange occurs.

Potassium-sparing diuretics inhibit K^+ secretion, and thus cause hyperkalemia. Patients who are prone to develop hyperkalemia are those with moderate renal insufficiency; diabetics; the elderly; and those receiving concomitant angiotensin converting enzyme (ACE)-inhibitors, nonsteroidal anti-inflammatory drugs (NSAIDs), β-blockers, and potassium supplements.

Hyponatremia

Hyponatremia is a common problem with diuretic use. Hyponatremia may be due to one or a combination of these mechanisms: (1) an increase in total body water; (2) loss of Na^+ and K^+; and (3) the kidney's inability to dilute urine. As discussed above, diuretics cause volume contraction, which promotes water reabsorption by the proximal tubule. Fluid delivery to the diluting segment is also decreased. In addition, volume contraction increases antidiuretic hormone (ADH) secretion, which promotes water reabsorption by the collecting tubule. Volume contraction also stimulates the thirst mechanism, and therefore water intake exceeds its removal. All of these processes lead to the kidney's inability to dilute urine and excrete free water. Severe loss of either Na^+ or K^+ can cause hyponatremia. Of particular importance is the loss of intracellular K^+, which causes hypokalemia and triggers Na^+ to move into the cell to replace K^+ loss.

Most cases of hyponatremia are caused by thiazides. Loop diuretics rarely cause hyponatremia because they "wash out" medullary hypertonicity and interfere with urine concentration. This medullary hypotonicity diminishes ADH-induced free water reabsorption by the collecting duct. This effect is the rationale behind the use of furosemide for the treatment of hyponatremia in patients with syndrome of inappropriate ADH secretion.

Hypo- and Hypercalcemia

Hypocalcemia and hypercalciuria can be induced acutely by loop diuretics in patients with euvolemia. Chronic use of loop diuretics does not cause hypocalcemia because the resultant volume contraction promotes Ca^{2+} reabsorption by the proximal tubule and reduces Ca^{2+} delivery to the thick ascending limb. In contrast, hypercalcemia is frequently seen with thiazide diuretics that promote Ca^{2+} reabsorption in the distal tubule. As a result, Ca^{2+} excretion is decreased. Amiloride also decreases Ca^{2+} excretion. Because of their hypocalciuric effect, thiazides are used to treat patients with renal calcium stones.

Hypomagnesemia

Chronic administration of loop and thiazide diuretics promote Mg^{2+} excretion and cause hypomagnesemia. Loop diuretics increase Mg^{2+} excretion more than they increase excretion of Ca^{2+}, Na^+ and K^+. Hypomagnesemia is accompanied by hypocalcemia and hypokalemia, and these abnormalities can be corrected with Mg^{2+} supplements.

Hypophosphatemia

All diuretics except potassium-sparing diuretics cause phosphaturia. However, carbonic anhydrase inhibitors cause the highest phosphaturic effect and result in hypophosphatemia. Metabolic alkalosis due to loop and thiazide diuretics may also cause hypophosphatemia due to the intracellular shift of this ion.

Acid-base Disturbance

Diuretics cause acid-base disturbance by altering renal handling of HCO_3^-. Carbonic anhydrase inhibitors reduce HCO_3^- reabsorption and increase its excretion. As a result, the plasma HCO_3^- concentration is decreased, and a metabolic acidosis develops. With the development of metabolic acidosis, the filtered load of HCO_3^- is decreased, which eventually causes the carbonic anhydrase inhibitors to lose their effectiveness. Other diuretics that cause metabolic acidosis are potassium-sparing diuretics, particularly amiloride. Amiloride inhibits Na^+ channels in the cortical collecting duct, and thus maintains a lumen-positive instead of negative potential difference. Since H^+ ion secretion depends on the a lumen-negative potential difference. Amiloride therapy causes a decrease in H^+ ion secretion, which leads to metabolic acidosis. Spironolactone also inhibits H^+ ion secretion, and thus induces metabolic acidosis.

In contrast, loop and thiazide diuretics induce metabolic alkalosis. There are several mechanisms through which these diuretics cause this acid-base disorder. First, these diuretics cause volume contraction, which promotes Na^+ reabsorption in the proximal tubule. Since HCO_3^- reabsorption follows Na^+ reabsorption, the plasma HCO_3^- concentration increases. Second, volume contraction stimulates aldosterone secretion, which in turn stimulates H^+ and K^+ secretion. Third, in addition to aldosterone, furosemide promotes H^+ secretion in the cortical collecting duct and also enhances titratable acidity as well as NH_4^+ excretion. New HCO_3^- is added to the body whenever titratable acidity and NH_4^+ excretion is enhanced. Fourth, K^+ secretion and hypokalemia develop with loop and thiazide diuretics. Hypokalemia promotes NH_4^+ synthesis and enhances HCO_3^- reabsorption. Hypokalemia and volume contraction with decreased GFR maintain metabolic alkalosis.

CLINICAL USES OF DIURETICS

The primary action of diuretics is to increase Na^+ and water excretion in patients with edema of variable causes. Diuretics are also used to treat hypertension and other nonedematous conditions. Table 16-3 summarizes the disease conditions that are treated with diuretics.

Table 16.3. Clinical uses of diuretics

Disease condition	Diuretics commonly used	Mechanism/Effect
Generalized edema states		
Congestive heart failure	Furosemide Metolazone or both	↑ excretion of Na^+ and water to reduce edema
Liver cirrhosis with ascites	Spironolactone Furosemide or both	↑ excretion of Na^+ and water Prevention of hypokalemia ↓ edema
Nephrotic syndrome	Furosemide	↑ excretion of Na^+ and water ↓ edema
Idiopathic edema	Hydrochlorothiazide Furosemide	↓ edema by promoting Na^+ and H_20 excretion
Localized edema		
Pulmonary edema	Furosemide Bumetanide	↓ pulmonary congestion by removing Na^+ and water
Cerebral edema	Mannitol	↓ intracranial pressure
Nonedematous states		
Acute renal failure	Furosemide Mannitol	Improve urine flow and convert oliguric (< 400ml urine) to nonoliguric (> 400ml urine) failure
Chronic renal failure (GFR < 30 ml/min)	Furosemide Metolazone	↑ excretion of Na^+ and water Thiazides do not work at this GFR
Hypertension	Thiazides	↓ plasma volume and cardiac output
Renal calcium stones	Hydrochlorothiazide	↓ Ca^{2+} excretion
Nephrogenic diabetes insipidus	Hydrochlorothiazide	↓ plasma volume and polyuria
Acute hypercalcemia	Furosemide	↓ Ca^{2+} absorption in thick ascending limb and promotes calciuria
Glaucoma	Acetazolamide	↓ HCO_3^- and Na^+ transport and ↓ aqueous humor formation

SUMMARY

1. Diuretics promote NaCl and water excretion, and are classified into 5 groups: (1) osmotic diuretics (e.g., mannitol); (2) carbonic anhydrase inhibitors (e.g., acetazolamide); (3) loop diuretics (e.g., furosemide); (4) thiazide diuretics (e.g., hydrochlorothiazide); and, (5) potassium-sparing diuretics (e.g., spironolactone). Except for mannitol, most diuretics are bound to plasma proteins and are not filtered at the glomerulus. Instead, they are secreted into the tubular lumen.
2. Osmotic diuretics act in the proximal tubule and the loop of Henle and promote almost all electrolyte and water excretion. Carbonic anhydrase inhibitors act in the proximal tubule and inhibit HCO_3^- reabsorption, causing metabolic acidosis. Loop diuretics inhibit the Na/K/2Cl cotransporter in the

thick ascending limb of Henle's loop. The primary site of action for thiazide diuretics is the early distal tubule where they bind to the Cl^- on the Na/Cl cotransporter, and inhibit NaCl reabsorption. Potassium-sparing diuretics act in the cortical collecting duct, and inhibit either Na^+ channel or the action of aldosterone.

3. Most diuretics exert several other physiologic effects besides their effects on NaCl and water excretion. These include changes in RBF, GFR, volume status, concentration and dilution of urine, acid-base balance, and excretion of several other electrolytes.
4. Clinically, diuretics are used to treat edema of variable causes, hypertension, acute renal failure, chronic renal failure, glaucoma, renal stones, and acute hypercalcemia.

STUDY QUESTIONS

Case 1

A 60-year-old female was brought to the emergency room by her husband for progressive shortness of breath. She had hypertension for 20 years and was on a thiazide diuretic hydrochlorothiazide (hydrodiuril). Physical examination revealed a moderately built woman in acute respiratory distress. Her blood pressure was 180/110 mm Hg with a pulse rate of 96 per minute. Lungs had crackles. Heart examination revealed an S_3. She had 2-3 mm pitting edema in lower extremities. Chest x-ray showed pulmonary edema.

Question 1. Based on physical findings and the chest x-ray, what type of diuretic would you use to relieve this patient's pulmonary congestion?

Answer: The appropriate diuretic to use is a loop diuretic. The most commonly used loop diuretic is furosemide (40-80 mg). It promotes Na^+ and water diuresis within 30-60 minutes, if given intravenously. Furosemide also causes vasodilation of the pulmonary vasculature in patients with congestive heart failure. By decreasing ventricular filling pressure and cardiac oxygen consumption, furosemide improves cardiac output as well. Bumetanide (1-2 mg) can also induce natriuresis and diuresis.

Question 2. What would happen if mannitol were given to this patient?

Answer: Although mannitol promotes Na^+ and water diuresis, it increases extracellular fluid volume, and would thus worsen her pulmonary congestion.

Question 3. What would you expect the patient's urine osmolality to be after administration of furosemide?

Answer: Furosemide acts in the medullary thick ascending limb and inhibits the Na/K/2Cl cotransporter. As a result, the medullary hypertonicity is abolished, thereby preventing the urine concentrating ability of the kidney. The patient, therefore, urinates a dilute urine whose osmolality approximates plasma osmolality (isosthenuria).

Case 2

A 30-year-old female was admitted for nausea, vomiting, headache, and blurred vision for 1 week. Examination of the eyes revealed papilledema, and CT scan of the head revealed hydrocephalus (increased intracranial fluid). The patient was started on mannitol to decrease the intracranial pressure.

Question 1. Discuss the effect of mannitol on RBF and GFR.

Answer: Mannitol is an osmotic diuretic. It extracts water from the intracellular compartment to the extracellular compartment, and expands the extracellular fluid volume. Also, mannitol and other osmotic diuretics dilate the afferent arteriole. As a result of these effects, the RBF is increased. A slight increase in GFR is also observed due to an increase in P_{GC}.

Question 2. What would happen to the urinary excretion of electrolytes in this patient?

Answer: In general, osmotic diuretics cause an increase in the urinary excretion of all electrolytes, including Na^+, K^+, Cl^-, HCO_3^-,Ca^{2+},Mg^{2+}, and phosphate.

Case 3

A 50-year-old man with cirrhosis of the liver was admitted for altered mental status (confusion, irritability, etc.). Physical examination revealed ascites and pitting edema in both lower extremities. He was started on several medications, including spironolactone (aldactone).

Question 1. What effect does aldactone have on serum [K^+] and acid-base balance?

Answer: Spironolactone is a competitive antagonist of aldosterone. By counteracting the effect of aldosterone, spironolactone inhibits K^+ secretion in the cortical collecting duct, causing hyperkalemia. Spironolactone also inhibits H^+ secretion at the same site, causing metabolic acidosis in cirrhotic patients.

SUGGESTED READING

1. Puschett, J.B. and Winaver, J. Effects of diuretics on renal function. In: Handbook of Physiology, Section 8. E.E. Windhager (ed.). Oxford University Press, New York, 1992; pp. 2335-2406 (*An excellent discussion on physiologic actions of diuretics*).
2. Jackson, E.K. Diuretics. In: The Pharmacological Basis of Therapeutics. J.C. Hardman, L.E. Limbird, P.B. Molinoff, R.W. Ruddon and A.G. Gilman (eds.). Mc Graw-Hill, New York, 1996, pp. 685-713 (*A review of physiologic and pharmacologic actions of diuretics*).
3. Seldin, D. and Giebisch, G. (eds.). Diuretic Agents. Clinical Physiology and Pharmacology. Academic Press, San Diego, 1997 (*An authoritative multi-authored volume dealing with various aspects of physiology, pharmacology, and clinical uses of diuretics*).

APPENDIX A

BOARD REVIEW QUESTIONS

Chapter 1

1. Which of the following markers is used to determine the plasma volume:

A. Antipyrine
B. Inulin
C. Tritiated water
D. Mannitol
E. ^{131}I- Albumin

The answer is E. ^{131}I - albumin is used to measure plasma volume. Note that ^{131}I - albumin leaks into the interstitium, and causes an overestimation of plasma volume. Antipyrine and tritiated water are used for total body water measurement, whereas inulin and mannitol are used for quantitation of extracellular fluid volume.

2. In a patient who has been vomiting and no fluid intake, the volume of all the body fluid compartments:

A. Increases proportionately
B. Does not change
C. Decreases proportionately
D. Decreases only in the extracellular fluid compartment
E. Increases only in the intracellular fluid compartment

The answer is C. This patient is volume depleted or simply dehydrated. In dehydration, water is lost initially from the extracellular fluid compartment. This causes an increase in plasma [Na^+], and thus osmolality. As a result, water moves from the intracellular to extracellular fluid compartment to maintain isotonicity between the two compartments. The net result is a decrease in the volume of both intracellular and extracellular compartments.

3. Infusion of 1 L of normal (0.9%) saline into the body would cause:

A. No change in extracellular fluid volume
B. An increase in extracellular fluid volume
C. Equal distribution of saline in all body fluid compartments
D. An increase in intracellular fluid volume
E. Equal increase in body fluid osmolality

The answer is B. Normal saline is isotonic to plasma. Therefore, no change in plasma osmolality occurs. However, normal saline remains in the extracellular fluid compartment, and causes its expansion.

4. What would happen to the size of the body fluid compartments if 1 L of D5W (5% dextrose in water) is infused:

A. All body fluid compartments expand
B. No change in fluid compartments
C. Expansion of extracellular fluid compartment (ECF) only
D. Expansion of intracellular fluid compartment (ICF) only
E. All body fluid compartments decrease

The answer is A. Glucose (dextrose) is metabolized to CO_2 and water. Since water diffuses easily, it is distributed throughout the total body water proportionate to compartment size. This means that 1/3 of D5W remains in the ECF and 2/3 in the ICF and both compartments expand.

Chapter 2

5. Which of the following statements is true regarding the juxtamedullary nephrons:

A. They represent 75% of the kidney
B. They originate from the superficial cortex
C. They have short loops of Henle
D. They have long loops which extend deep into the inner medulla
E. They have loops that never enter the medulla

The answer is D. The juxtamedullary nephrons originate from the corticomedullary boundary that have long loops of Henle extending into the inner medulla. Functionally, they are more efficient in concentrating urine and reabsorbing Na^+.

6. The juxtaglomerular apparatus (JGA) contains cells that secrete:

A. Angiotensin II
B. Renin
C. Aldosterone
D. Angiotensin converting enzyme
E. Bradykinin

The answer is B. The JGA is located at the vascular pole of the glomerulus, which contains tubular and vascular components. The tubular component is the macula densa, which is a specialized cellular structure of the cortical thick ascending limb. The vascular component contains the terminal portion of the afferent arteriole, the initial portion of the efferent arteriole, and the extraglomerular mesangial region between the two arterioles. The macula densa is in contact with the vascular component. The wall of the afferent arterioles contains modified smooth muscle cells called juxtaglomerular granular cells, which secrete renin.

7. Regarding principal cells:

A. They are the major cell type in the collecting duct
B. They have a light-staining cytoplasm with few mitochondria
C. Their luminal surface is covered with short microvilli and a cilium
D. In the connecting segment and the cortical collecting duct, they are primarily responsible for K^+ secretion
E. All of the above

The answer is E. The principal cells possess all of the above morphologic and functional characteristics.

8. Regarding intercalated cells:

A. They are of two types
B. They have dense-staining cytoplasm
C. Type B cells have more mitochondria than Type A cells
D. Type A cells are involved in H^+ ion secretion and HCO_3^- reabsorption, whereas Type B cells are involved in HCO_3^- secretion
E. All of the above

The answer is E. Type A and Type B cells are distributed in the connecting and the collecting ducts. All of the above mentioned morphologic and physiologic functions are the characteristics of intercalated cells.

9. Which of the following aquaporins (AQPs) is regulated by the antidiuretic hormone (ADH):

A. AQP-1
B. AQP-2
C. AQP-4
D. AQP-6
E. AQP-7

The answer is B. Of all the AQPs, only AQP-2 is regulated by ADH.

Chapter 3

10. Renin secretion is stimulated by:

A. An increase in catecholamine production
B. Prostaglandin E_2
C. Decrease in blood pressure
D. Decreased delivery of NaCl to macula densa
E. All of the above

The answer is E. All of the above stimulate renin production.

11. Which of the following inhibits renin secretion:

A. Nonsteroidal anti-inflammatory drugs
B. Bradykinin
C. Angiotensin converting enzyme-inhibitors (ACE-inhibitors)
D. Decrease in effective circulating volume
E. None of the above

The answer is A. Vasodilatory prostaglandins stimulate the production of renin by the juxtaglomerular granular cells located in the terminal portion of the afferent and the initial portion of the efferent arteriole. Nonsteroidal anti-inflammatory drugs, such as indomethacin and ibuprofen, inhibit prostaglandin synthesis, and thereby decrease renin production. Bradykinin, ACE-Inhibitors and a decrease in effective circulating volume increase renin production.

12. A 70-year-old man was brought to the emergency room with altered mental status. He had low blood pressure and increased pulse rate. He was afebrile. Which of the following hormones is elevated in his blood:

A. Atrial natriuretic peptide
B. Insulin
C. Renin
D. Parathyroid hormone
E. None of the above

The answer is C. The patient has clinical evidence of volume contraction (also called dehydration) because of low blood pressure and increased pulse rate in the absence of fever. The hormone system that is stimulated by dehydration is the renin-angiotensin II-aldosterone system. Circulating levels of atrial natriuretic peptide are decreased in volume contraction, whereas those of insulin and parathyroid hormone are least affected.

13. Which of the following regarding angiotensin II (AII) is false:

A. Stimulation of aldosterone secretion
B. Lowering of blood pressure
C. Decrease in renal blood flow
D. Constriction of efferent arteriole
E. Decrease in glomerular filtration rate

The answer is B. AII stimulates aldosterone secretion. It is also a potent vasoconstrictor. As a result, the blood pressure is increased. AII primarily causes vasoconstriction of the efferent arteriole, although it may have some effect on the afferent arteriole at higher concentrations. In addition, AII is involved in the autoregulation of renal blood flow and glomerular filtration rate.

14. Aldosterone secretion is regulated by:

A. Atrial natriuretic peptide (ANP)
B. Circulating [K^+]
C. Angiotensin II (AII)
D. Adrenocorticotrophic hormone (ACTH)
E. All of the above

The answer is E. Aldosterone secretion is stimulated by an increase in plasma [K^+], AII, and ACTH. The effect of ACTH is transient because chronic administration of ACTH does not increase aldosterone secretion. ANP decreases aldosterone secretion indirectly by decreasing renin production and directly by acting on glomerulosa cells. Hypokalemia lowers aldosterone levels by inhibiting its secretion as well by enhancing its metabolic clearance rate.

15. With respect to endothelin:

A. It raises blood pressure
B. It increases contraction of the heart
C. It decreases renal blood flow
D. It is stimulated by thrombin
E. All of the above

The answer is E. Endothelin is a 21-amino acid peptide, which is released by vascular endothelial cells in response to thrombin. All the functions mentioned above are characteristics of endothelin.

16. The major stimulus for parathyroid hormone (PTH) secretion is:

A. Low ionized serum [Ca^{2+}]
B. Low total serum [Ca^{2+}]
C. Low serum [Mg^{2+}]
D. Low serum phosphate concentration
E. High serum [K^+]

The answer is A. It is the ionized Ca^{2+} that stimulates PTH secretion. High but not low serum Mg^{2+} levels also stimulate PTH secretion. Hypophosphatemia and hyperkalemia do not have any direct effect on PTH secretion.

17. With respect to atrial natriuretic peptide (ANP):

A. It is synthesized by atrial muscle cells
B. Its levels are increased in states of volume expansion
C. It reduces systemic blood pressure
D. It increases glomerular filtration rate and Na^+ excretion
E. All are correct

The answer is E. Active ANP is a 28-amino acid polypeptide. All of the above physiologic processes are mediated by activation of guanylate cyclase and increased production of cGMP.

Chapters 4 & 5

18. Which of the following forces favor glomerular ultrafiltration:

A. Hydraulic pressure within the glomerulus
B. Colloid osmotic pressure within the glomerulus
C. Hydraulic pressure within the Bowman's space

D. Hydraulic pressure in the efferent arterioles
E. A and B are correct

The answer is A. It is the hydraulic pressure within the glomerular capillaries that tends to push the fluid, whereas the forces mentioned in B and C oppose the ultrafiltration.

19. Regarding renal blood flow (RBF):

A. The kidneys receive about 20% of the cardiac output
B. The O_2 consumption rate per gram is less than that of heart
C. The O_2 consumption is directly proportional to the amount of Na^+ reabsorbed
D. About 10% of RBF goes to the medulla
E. All of the above

The answer is E. The cortex receives about 90% of RBF, where most of the Na^+ is reabsorbed. For each mmol oxygen consumed, about 25 mEq of Na^+ are reabsorbed.

20. The following pressures for the Starling forces were obtained:

Hydraulic pressure within the glomerulus (P_{Gc}) = 50 mm Hg
Hydraulic pressure within the Bowman's space (P_{Bs}) = 10 mm Hg
Colloid oncotic pressure within the glomerulus (π_{Gc}) = 25 mm Hg

What would the net filtration pressure (P_f) be:

A. 20 mm Hg
B. 15 mm Hg
C. 10 mm Hg
D. 35 mm Hg
E. 25 mm Hg

The answer is B. P_f is defined as that amount of pressure needed to push the fluid across the glomerular capillary. It is calculated as follows:

$$P_f = P_{Gc} - P_{Bs} - \pi_{Gc}$$

Substituting the values:

$$P_f = 50 - 10 - 25 = 15 \text{ mm Hg}$$

21. At filtration equilibrium, the glomerular ultrafiltration rate is:

A. Increased
B. Decreased
C. Zero
D. Normal
E. B and C are correct

The answer is C. The net filtration pressure (P_f) at the afferent end is about 15 mm Hg; however, at the efferent end it becomes zero. This is due to the progressive increase in the colloid oncotic pressure (π_{GC}). In the rat, the π_{GC} is 20 mm Hg at the beginning of the afferent arteriole, and it gradually increases to 35 mm Hg at the end of the efferent arteriole. Because of this, the P_f decreases to a point where filtration does not occur anymore. This is called the filtration equilibrium.

22. The RBF and the ultrafiltration coefficient (K_f) are decreased by which of the following:

A. Atrial natriuretic peptide (ANP)
B. Prostaglandin E_2
C. Histamine
D. Angiotensin II (AII)
E. Vasopressin

The answer is D. AII, norepinephrine, and thromboxane A_2 reduce both RBF and K_f, the latter is the product of the hydraulic water permeability and the total filtering surface area of the glomerular capillary. Vasopressin decreases, whereas ANP increases the K_f without affecting the RBF. Prostaglandin E_2 and histamine increase RBF, but decrease the K_f.

23. In a patient with congestive heart failure, the renal plasma flow (RPF) and glomerular filtration rate (GFR):

A. Both are decreased
B. Both are increased
C. Both are unaffected
D. Only RPF is decreased
E. Only GFR is decreased

The answer is D. It has been shown that in patients with congestive heart failure only RPF is decreased and GFR is maintained near normal. This results in an increase in filtration fraction (GFR/RPF x 100).

24. Vasodilation of the efferent arteriole by an angiotensin converting enzyme - inhibitor (ACE-inhibitor) causes GFR to:

A. Decrease
B. Increase
C. Remain normal
D. Decrease RBF but not GFR
E. C and D are correct

The answer is A. Angiotensin II (AII) preferentially causes vasoconstriction of the efferent arteriole to maintain normal GFR. When the production of AII is decreased by ACE-inhibitors, the blood flowing through the glomerular capillaries escapes through the dilated efferent arteriole. This results in a reduction in GFR, which is reflected by an increase in serum creatinine concentration. Since the beneficial effects of ACE-inhibitors outweigh this decrease in GFR, they are commonly used in patients with hypertension, congestive heart failure, and proteinuria.

25. Autoregulation of RBF and GFR is dependent upon:

A. Sympathetic neurons
B. Vasopressin
C. Wall tension of the afferent arteriole and preservation of macula densa
D. Water flow to the distal nephron
E. Osmolality of the tubular fluid

The answer is C. Both RBF and GFR are maintained constant over a wide range (80-180 mm Hg) of systemic blood pressure and not affected by denervation of the kidney. This property, called autoregulation, is therefore intrinsic to the kidney. Two theories have been suggested to explain the phenomenon of autoregulation. They are myogenic and tubuloglomerular feedback theories. Myogenic theory relates to appropriate changes in wall tension of the afferent arteriole, whereas the tubuloglomerular feedback theory relates to the macula densa which responds appropriately to the delivery of NaCl. Autoregulation does not require either vasopressin, water flow to the distal nephron or osmolality of the tubular fluid.

26. If the renal plasma flow (RPF) is 600 ml/min and the hematocrit (Hct) is 45%, what is the renal blood flow (RBF):

A. 1200 ml/min
B. 1091 ml/min
C. 1250 ml/min
D. 750 ml/min
E. 1000 ml/min

The answer is B. The RBF is calculated from RPF and Hct by the following formula:

$$RBF = \frac{RPF}{1 - Hct}$$

Substituting the values;

$$RBF = \frac{600}{1-0.45} \text{ or } \frac{600}{0.55} = 1091 \text{ ml/min}$$

27. The following values were obtained during a 2-hour clearance period from a female subject:

Source	PAH (mg/ml)	Inulin (mg/ml)	Urine flow rate (ml/min)
Arterial plasma	0.05	0.5	2
Urine	15	25	2

The effective renal plasma flow (ml/min) is:

A. 600
B. 700
C. 650
D. 550
E. 800

The answer is A. To calculate the effective renal plasma flow, one must use the following clearance formula for PAH:

$$C = UV/P$$

where C is the clearance (ml/min), U is the urinary concentration of PAH (mg/ml), V is the urine flow rate (ml/min), and P is the plasma concentration of PAH (mg/ml).

Substituting the values, we obtain:

$$C = 15 \times 2/0.05 = 600 \text{ ml/min}$$

The actual renal plasma flow would be:

$$\frac{\text{Effective renal plasma flow}}{\text{PAH extraction*}} = \frac{600}{0.9} = 667 \text{ ml/min}$$

*Total PAH extraction is generally 90%, and therefore should be corrected for 100% to obtain the actual renal plasma flow.

28. From the data given in the above table, the GFR (ml/min) is:

A. 125
B. 100
C. 110
D. 120
E. 115

The answer is B. Again the clearance formula should be used.

Substituting the values for inulin, we obtain:

$$\text{GFR} = \frac{25 \times 2}{0.5} = 100 \text{ ml/min}$$

29. The following values were obtained in a normal individual following glucose infusion:

Plasma glucose = 500 mg/dL
Glomerular filtration rate = 100 ml/min
Urine glucose = 65 mg/ml
Urine flow rate = 2 ml/min

The Tm (mg/min) for glucose is:

A. 350
B. 370
C. 400
D. 320
E. 375

The answer is B. Tm, which is defined as the maximal rate of transport of a substance, is expressed as amount per minute. It is calculated as the difference between the filtered load and the rate of excretion of a solute. The Tm for glucose is:

Tm = Amount filtered - Amount excreted

where amount filtered is equal to the plasma concentration multiplied by glomerular filtration rate. Substituting the values, we obtain:

(5 mg/ml x 100 ml/min) - (65 mg/ml x 2 ml/min)
= 500 mg/min - 130 mg/min = 370 mg/min

30. Match the following clearance data shown in the figure with the following statements:

A. Substance filtered but its clearance is less than inulin clearance
B. Substance filtered but its clearance exceeds that of inulin clearance
C. Substance filtered and its clearance is equal to that of inulin clearance

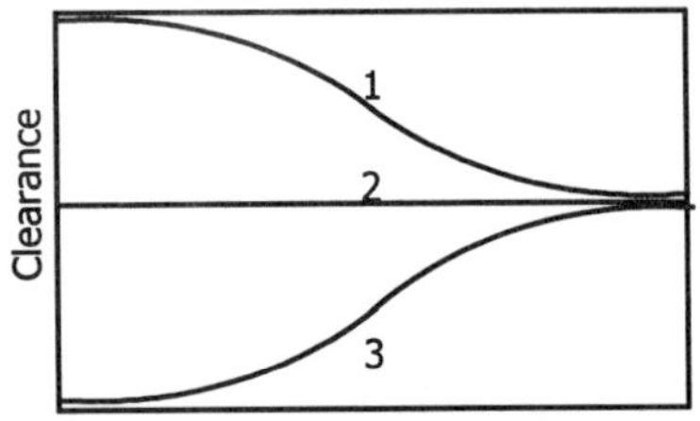

The answers: A = 3; B = 1; C = 2.
Statement A is consistent with reabsorption. As the filtered load of a reabsorbed substance such as glucose is increased, the transport processes become saturated, and the excess filtered load is excreted. Because of a significant reabsorption, the clearance of glucose is always less than that of inulin. Statement B is consistent with secretion. PAH is both filtered and secreted. At lower plasma concentrations, PAH secretion increases, and all plasma is cleared of PAH. As the plasma concentration increases, the transport systems become saturated and the volume of plasma cleared of PAH declines. Statement C is consistent with a substance that is filtered only but not reabsorbed or secreted. Inulin is an example of such a substance. As the plasma concentration of inulin increases, its excretion also rises, and the volume of plasma filtered and cleared will not change. Therefore, the clearance remains constant and independent of plasma concentration.

31. Which of the following substances increases serum creatinine levels:

A. Cimetidine
B. Trimethoprim
C. Cephalosporins
D. Acetoacetate
E. All of the above

The answer is E. Cimetidine and trimethoprim decrease the proximal tubular secretion of creatinine, whereas cephalosporine antibiotics, particularly, cefoxitin, increases the noncreatinine chromogen levels which are measured as creatinine. Acetoacetate is a ketone that interferes with the color reaction of creatinine, and rises serum creatinine concentration.

32. A 70-year-old malnourished male is admitted for urinary tract infection. His urine culture grew E. coli which is sensitive to gentamicin. He weighs 72 kg and his serum creatinine concentration is 1.5 mg/dL. Since gentamicin is excreted by the kidney, the dose should be adjusted according to his creatinine clearance. His calculated creatinine clearance (ml/min) is:

A. 100
B. 47
C. 60
D. 110
E. 80

The answer is B. Since gentamicin should be started immediately, there is no time for a 24-hour urine collection for determination of creatinine clearance, using the formula UV/P. However, at bedside approximate value of creatinine clearance can be obtained by using the following formula:

$$\text{Creatinine clearance (ml/min)} = \frac{(140 - \text{age})\ (\text{wt. in kg})}{72 \times \text{serum creatinine}}$$

Substituting the values, we obtain:

$$\text{Creatinine clearance} = \frac{(140-70)\ (72)}{72 \times 1.5} = 47 \text{ ml/min}$$

33. In a healthy subject, what percentage of the renal plasma flow would be filtered:

A. 50%
B. 40%
C. 10%
D. 20%
E. 100%

The answer is D. The percentage of RPF that is filtered is called the filtration fraction (FF). It is derived from the following formula:

$$FF (\%) = \frac{GFR}{RPF} \times 100$$

If the GFR is 120 ml/min and RPF is 600 ml/min, the FF is 20%. This means that only 20% of the plasma entering the glomerulus is filtered.

Chapter 7

34. Na^+ transport at the apical membrane occurs by all of the following mechanisms, except:

A. Paracellular pathway
B. Na/K-ATPase
C. Na/K/2Cl cotransport
D. Na^+ channel
E. Na/H antiport

The answer is B. Na^+ reabsorption at the apical membrane occurs by all of the above mentioned mechanisms except Na/K-ATPase, which is located at the basolateral membrane. This enzyme system transports 3 Na^+ out and 2 K^+ into the cell.

35. Increase in Na^+ excretion is promoted by:

A. A decrease in serum albumin concentration
B. An increase in GFR
C. An increase in medullary blood flow
D. Acute elevation in blood pressure
E. All are correct

The answer is E. A decrease in albumin concentration causes a decrease in peritubular oncotic pressure, which diminishes Na^+ reabsorption. An increase in GFR increases the filtered load of Na^+, which causes natriuresis and diuresis to maintain Na^+ and water balance. An increase in medullary blood flow diminshes the medullary concentration of solutes and water because of their removal. This causes a decrease in reabsorption of water in the descending limb. As a result, more NaCl is delivered to the thick ascending limb. However, the thick ascending limb cannot handle this additional delivery of NaCl load. Consequently, the reabsorption of NaCl decreases, resulting in increased excretion. Acute elevation in blood pressure causes natriuresis (called pressure natriuresis), and thereby maintains normal blood pressure.

36. Bartter's syndrome is characterized by a mutation in which of the following transporters:

A. Na/Cl cotransporter
B. Na/K/2Cl cotransporter
C. Na^+ channel
D. K^+ channel
E. Na/K-ATPase

The answer is B. Bartter's syndrome, which is characterized by hypokalemia, hypomagnesemia, high plasma renin and aldosterone levels with normal blood pressure, is due to a mutation in the Na/K/2Cl cotransporter. A mutation in the Na/Cl cotransporter causes Gitelman's syndrome, and a mutation in the Na^+ channel causes Liddle's syndrome (see Chapter 7). No clinical syndromes have yet been attributed to mutations either in K^+ channel or Na/K-ATPase genes.

37. Which of the following hormones inhibits NaCl and water reabsorption in the proximal tubule:

A. Glucocorticoids
B. Angiotensin II
C. Atrial natriuretic peptide (ANP)
D. Parathyroid hormone
E. A and D

The answer is C. Of all the hormones listed above, only ANP inhibits NaCl and water reabsorption in the proximal tubule.

38. Which of the following segments of the nephron is impermeable to water:

A. Proximal tubule
B. Distal tubule
C. Thin ascending limb of Henle's loop
D. Thin descending limb of Henle's loop
E. Collecting duct

The answer is C. Of the listed segments of the nephron, only the thin ascending limb of Henle's loop is impermeable to water.

Chapter 8

39. Denervation of carotid sinus receptors causes:

A. An increase in renin production
B. An increase in sympathetic tone
C. An increase in renal vasoconstriction
D. A, B, and C are true
E. None of the above

The answer is D. Receptors that sense the expansion of the extracellular fluid volume are located within the vasculature. Some of these sensing receptors are present in the carotid sinus. Volume expansion stimulates these receptors which then send signals to the appropriate afferent (response) mechanisms to cause natriuresis. Denervation of carotid sinus receptors causes activation of all the aforementioned mechanisms, resulting in Na^+ retention.

40. An increase in filtration fraction (FF) causes:

A. An increase in peritubular capillary colloid osmotic pressure (π_{cap})
B. A decrease in peritubular capillary hydrostatic pressure (P_{cap})
C. An increase in Na^+ reabsorption
D. A decrease in Na^+ reabsorption
E. A, B, and C are true

The answer is E. When FF (GFR/RPF) is increased, the postglomerular albumin concentration is increased. This raises π_{cap}. Also, an increase in FF results in a fall in P_{cap}. Both of these changes favor Na^+ reabsorption.

41. Patients with cardiac failure and cirrhosis of the liver exhibit edema. Which of the following is most responsible for edema formation:

A. Glucose reabsorption
B. Water reabsorption
C. Decreased expression of aquaporin-2 (AQP-2) water channels
D. Na^+ retention
E. Increased plasma ANP levels

The answer is D. Edema is due to retention of Na^+ and water in the interstitium. Either glucose or water reabsorption from the kidney or intestine does not cause edema. Increased rather than decreased expression of AQP-2 has been demonstrated in both cardiac and liver failure. Increased plasma ANP levels promote Na^+ and water diuresis.

42. A patient was brought to the emergency room for weakness, easy fatiguability, and dizziness. Physical examination is consistent with volume contraction. Which of the following statements is false:

A. Decreased effective circulating volume (ECV)
B. Increase in plasma ADH levels
C. Increase in urine osmolality
D. Urinary Na^+ >50 mEq/L
E. Urinary Na^+ <10 mEq/L

The answer is D. In a patient with volume contraction (also called dehydration), the ECV is reduced. As a result, the neurohypophysis releases ADH, which stimulates water reabsorption by the collecting duct. The urine osmolality is thus increased. The filtered load of Na^+ is reduced, which then causes an increase in Na^+ reabsorption by the proximal and other tubular segments. As a result, the urinary excretion of Na^+ is decreased (usually <10 mEq/L). Whenever, urinary Na^+ exceeds 50 mEq/L in the presence of dehydration, one should think of salt-losing nephropathy, or Addison's disease as possible causes.

Chapter 9

43. With regard to free-water clearance (C_{H_2O}), which of the following statements is true:

A. C_{H_2O} is positive when urine osmolality (U_{osm}) is equal to plasma osmolality (P_{osm})
B. C_{H_2O} is positive when U_{osm} is greater than P_{osm}
C. C_{H_2O} is negative when U_{osm} is less than P_{osm}
D. C_{H_2O} is positive when osmolar clearance (C_{osm}) is less than urinary volume
E. B and D are true

The answer is D. C_{H_2O} defines the kidney's ability to excrete or conserve solute-free water. In order to calculate C_{H_2O}, two additional variables are needed: U_{osm} and urinary volume (V). C_{H_2O} is calculated as follows:

$$C_{H_2O} = V - C_{osm}$$

If urinary volume is greater than C_{osm}, the C_{H_2O} is positive. This means that more water has been added to the urine. On the other hand, if C_{osm} is greater than urinary volume, the C_{H_2O} is negative. This means that less water has been added to the urine. In isosmotic urine (i.e., urine osmolality similar to plasma osmolality), the C_{H_2O} is zero.

44. Which of the following diuretic agents increases free-water clearance (C_{H_2O}):

A. Acetazolamide
B. Furosemide
C. Spironolactone

D. Hydrochlorothiazide
E. Amiloride

The answer is A. Any diuretic that inhibits proximal tubular reabsorption of water enhances C_{H_2O}. On the other hand, diuretics that act more distally decrease C_{H_2O}.

Chapter 10

45. Which of the following stimulus increases thirst:

A. Increase in serum glucose
B. Increase in serum urea nitrogen
C. Alcohol
D. Decrease in serum [Na^+]
E. None of the above

The answer is A. Thirst is a desire to drink water. An increase in plasma osmolality due to severe dehydration, hyperglycemia, or hypernatremia stimulates thirst by causing shrinkage of the osmoreceptors located in the anterolateral hypothalamus. On the other hand, an increase in plasma osmolality due to urea nitrogen or alcohol intake does not cause shrinkage of osmoreceptors, and therefore does not stimulate thirst.

46. Which of the following is the major stimulus for ADH release:

A. Decrease in plama osmolality by 1-2%
B. Increase in plasma osmolality by 1-2%
C. Increase in serum urea nitrogen
D. Decrease in serum urea nitrogen
E. Decrease in serum glucose

The answer is B. The most important stimulus for ADH release is an increase in plama osmolality. The osmoreceptors, located in the wall of the third ventricle, sense even 1-2% increase in plasma osmolality, and send impulses to the supraoptic and paraventricular nuclei which synthesize ADH. The ADH is stored in the neurohypophysis and subsequently released. A decrease in plasma osmolality inhibits ADH release. An increase in serum urea nitrogen may not generally cause release of ADH. Although glucose may stimulate ADH release, its effect is not as stimulatory as hypertonic saline.

47. Match the following laboratory data in Column A with the clinical diagnosis in Column B.

Column A

	Plasma $[Na^+]$ (mEq/L)	Plasma ADH Level	Plasma osmolality ($mOsm/kg\ H_2O$)	Urine osmolality ($mOsm/kg\ H_2O$)
A.	140	Normal	285	400
B.	150	Absent or low	310	100
C.	150	High	310	1000
D.	126	High	264	340

Column B
1. Central diabetes insipidus (CDI)
2. Syndrome of inappropriate ADH (SIADH)
3. Volume contraction

The answers: 1 = B; 2 = D; 3 = C. In CDI, the plasma ADH levels are either low or absent. Therefore, the patients with CDI do not concentrate their urine, and their plasma osmolality is low. If these patients fail to drink water, their plasma osmolality becomes elevated. As a result, hypernatremia develops. In patients with SIADH, the plasma ADH levels are high because of its inappropriate secretion by cerebral or non-cerebral (pulmonary disease or tumors) disease. As a result, the kidneys conserve water, which dilutes plasma $[Na^+]$ to hyponatremic level. Urine osmolality is higher than plasma osmolality because of water abstraction by ADH. In some patients with volume contraction, hypernatremia develops because of water loss in excess or Na^+ loss. Plasma osmolality rises, which stimulates the production of ADH. Water reabsorption by the collecting duct is enhanced, resulting in the excretion of concentrated urine with high osmolality. Option A corresponds to the normal condition.

48. All of the following substances inhibit ADH release, except:

A. Ethanol
B. Phenytoin
C. Atrial natriuretic peptide
D. α-adrenergic agents
E. β-adrenergic agents

The answer is E. All of the above mentioned agents except β-adrenergic agents inhibit ADH release.

49. ADH exerts its actions through:

A. Binding to V2 receptors on the epithelial cells of the collecting duct
B. Stimulation of G-protein coupled adenylate cyclase
C. Translocation of aquaporin-2 (AQP-2) toward luminal membrane
D. Stimulation of cAMP-dependent protein kinase A
E. All of the above

The answer is E. ADH binds to V2 receptors and stimulates the production of cAMP through the activation of G-protein coupled adenylate cyclase. The cAMP thus formed activates protein kinase A, which in turn translocates AQP-2 water channels toward the luminal membrane. These water channels fuse with the luminal membrane, and allow entry of water into the cell. Water then leaves the basolateral membrane via AQP-3 and AQP-4 water channels.

Chapter 11

50. Which amino acids contribute to the production of fixed acids:

A. Sulfur-containing amino acids
B. Arginine and histidine-containing amino acids
C. Phosphorus-containing amino acids
D. Glutamate and aspartate-containing amino acids
E. A, B, and C are correct

The answer is E. Sulfur-containing, phosphorus-containing and arginine, histidine and lysine-containing amino acids generate sulfuric acid, phosphoric acid and HCl, respectively. On the other hand, glutamate and aspartate - containing amino acids yield HCO_3^-.

51. Carbonic anhydrase is present in:

A. Apical membrane of the proximal tubule
B. Apical membrane of the collecting duct
C. Apical membrane of the papilla
D. Apical and basolateral membranes of the thin ascending limb
E. A and B are true

The answer is A. Carbonic anhydrase, which catalyzes the formation of carbonic acid from H_2O and CO_2, is present in the cytoplasm and brush borders of the apical membrane of the proximal convoluted tubule. This apical membrane enzyme has a functional contact with the luminal fluid, and plays an important role in the acidification process. Carbonic anhydrase is totally absent in the papilla and thin ascending limb. In the collecting duct, carbonic anhydrase is present in the cytoplasm, but the enzyme is absent in the apical membrane.

52. The mechanisms for reabsorption of HCO_3^- in the proximal tubule include all of the following, except:

A. H^+ ion secretion occurs by Na/H antiporter and H-ATPase
B. The presence of carbonic anhydrase in the apical membrane
C. Exit across the basolateral membrane occurs by Na/HCO_3^- symporter and Cl/HCO_3 antiporter
D. HCO_3^- crosses the apical membrane by simple diffusion
E. A, B, and C are true

The answer is D. Reabsorption of HCO_3^- in the proximal tubule depends on the H^+ ion secretion, presence of carbonic anhydrase in the apical membrane and tubular fluid. HCO_3^- exit occurs via Na/HCO_3 symporter where 2-3 HCO_3^- ions are transported for each Na^+ ion. Also, HCO_3^- is transported across the basolateral membrane via Cl/HCO_3 antiporter.

53. Which of the following factors or conditions increases HCO_3^- reabsorption in the proximal tubule:

A. Volume contraction
B. Chloride depletion
C. Hypokalemia
D. Metabolic acidosis
E. All of the above

The answer is E. Volume contraction and chloride depletion decrease GFR, and thus enhance the proximal tubular reabsorption of HCO_3^-. Also, hypokalemia and metabolic acidosis promote HCO_3^- reabsorption possibly by stimulating H^+ ion secretion via Na/H antiporter.

54. Distal tubular reabsorption of HCO_3^- is enhanced by:

A. Aldosterone
B. Hypokalemia
C. Increase in plasma [H^+]
D. Adrenalectomy
E. A, B, and C are true

The answer is E. Aldosterone promotes HCO_3^- reabsorption by secreting H^+ ions. This occurs by three mechanisms. First, aldosterone stimulates Na^+ reabsorption, and creates a lumen-negative potential difference. Second, aldosterone directly stimulates H^+ ion secretion independent of Na^+ reabsorption. Third, aldosterone causes hypokalemia, which in turn stimulates NH_3 synthesis and delivering excess urinary buffer to the collecting duct. Conversely, adrenalectomy inhibits H^+ ion secretion and thus HCO_3^- reabsorption. Hypokalemia decreases GFR, and thus enhances HCO_3^- reabsorption. Increase in plasma $[H^+]$ also promotes HCO_3^- reabsorption by raising intracellular $[H^+]$.

55. Renal handling of NH_4^+ includes:

A. Secretion into the proximal tubule
B. Reabsorption by the medullary thick ascending limb
C. Accumulation in the medulla
D. Secretion of NH_3 and not NH_4^+ into the collecting tubule
E. All of the above

The answer is E. The general pathway for NH_4^+ handling from its production in the proximal tubule to its secretion in the collecting duct follows all of the options given above. NH_4^+ is secreted into the proximal tubule via Na/H antiporter where NH_4^+ replaces H^+ ion. It is then transported into the medullary thick ascending limb via Na/K/2Cl cotransporter. Here NH_4^+ replaces K^+. In the medulla, NH_4^+ is split into NH_3^+ and H^+ ion. NH_3 diffuses into the collecting tubular lumen where it combines with the H^+ ions secreted via H-ATPase to form NH_4^+ and then excreted as urinary buffer.

56. Factors that increase both synthesis and excretion of NH_4^+ include all of the following, except:

A. Aldosterone
B. Hypokalemia
C. Hyperkalemia
D. Metabolic acidosis
E. Glucocorticoids

The answer is C. Hyperkalemia inhibits, whereas the other factors stimulate both the synthesis and excretion of NH_4^+.

57. The net acid excretion (NAE) is increased in all of the following conditions, except:

A. Metabolic acidosis
B. Acidic urine pH
C. Hypokalemia
D. Aldosterone
E. Decreased phosphate intake

The answer is E. The NAE is the sum of urine titratable acid (TA) and NH_4^+ concentration minus the urine HCO_3^- concentration, and can be expressed as follows:

$$NAE = TA + NH_4^+ - HCO_3^-$$

In a normal individual, the excretion of HCO_3^- is negligible. Thus, the major components of NAE are TA and NH_4^+. TA is the excretion of phosphate as $H_2PO_4^-$, since the major source of phosphate is the diet. Low dietary intake causes a decrease in TA, and thus decreases NAE. Metabolic acidosis, hypokalemia, and aldosterone stimulate NH_3 synthesis, and thus elevate NAE. Low urine pH promotes trapping mechanism for NH_4^+ in the tubular lumen more effectively than slightly alkaline urine pH. This causes more NH_4^+ excretion and NAE production.

58. A 50-year-old man was admitted to the intensive care unit with anterior wall myocardial infarction. Six hours later, he developed shortness of breath. Physical examination and chest x-ray are consistent with pulmonary edema. Electrolytes and arterial blood gas (ABG) values showed:

Electrolytes	ABG
Na^+ = 140 mEq/L	pH = 7.36
K^+ = 5.2 mEq/L	PCO_2 = 34 mm Hg
Cl^- = 94 mEq/L	PO_2 = 80 mm Hg
HCO_3^- = 16 mEq/L	HCO_3^- = 22 mEq/L
BUN = 30 mg/dL	
Creatinine = 1.4 mg/dL	
Glucose = 200 mg/dL	

The acid-base disturbance is:

A. Metabolic acidosis
B. Metabolic alkalosis
C. Respiratory acidosis
D. Respiratory alkalosis
E. None of the above

The answer is E. The acid-base disorder should be analyzed systematically. The first step in this analysis is to check whether the pH is correct or not. One must use the Henderson equation to obtain the $[H^+]$ and then the pH. The Henderson equation is:

$$[H^+] = 24 \times \frac{PCO_2}{[HCO_3^-]}$$

Substituting the values, we obtain:

$$[H^+] = 24 \times \frac{34}{16} = 51$$

The $[H^+]$ of 51 corresponds to the pH of 7.30. Therefore, the pH reported from the laboratory is incorrect. In view of this, it is difficult to interpret the ABG.

59. Match the laboratory values shown in Column A with clinical findings shown in Column B:

Column A

	Electrolytes (mEq/L)			Arterial blood gases (ABG) (mm Hg)		
	Na^+	Cl^-	HCO_3^-	pH	PCO_2	PO_2
A.	140	90	16	7.32	32	90
B.	136	112	14	7.30	29	94
C.	132	88	30	7.46	44	89
D.	134	103	16	7.50	20	92
E.	140	90	30	7.36	55	89

Column B

1. A 60-year-old man with long history of smoking and emphysema
2. An 18-year-old female with insulin-dependent diabetes mellitus and acetone breath
3. A 50-year-old man with peptic ulcer disease and vomiting
4. A 30 year-old man with diarrhea for four days
5. A 26-year-old female with splenectomy and pneumonia

The answers: 1 = E; 2 = A; 3 = C; 4 = B; 5 = D. The patient described in option 1 is a CO_2 retainer due to emphysema and has chronic respiratory acidosis. Values shown in E are consistent with this acid-base disturbance.

Values shown in A and B represent metabolic acidosis. However, the anion gap (AG), which is calculated as (Na^+ - (Cl^- + HCO_3^-), is increased in option A and normal in option B. The clinical history of patient 2 with insulin-dependent diabetes and acetone breath indicates diabetic ketoacidosis, which gives a high AG. Values given in option A are consistent with this patient. Diarrhea causes hyperchloremic metabolic acidosis with normal AG. The patient described in option 4 developed normal AG metabolic acidosis due to diarrhea, and the values given in option B substantiate this diagnosis. The patient with peptic ulcer disease and vomiting (option 3) has metabolic alkalosis, and the values shown in C are consistent with this. The patient with pneumonia (option 5) develops respiratory alkalosis due to hyperventilation, and the values shown in D represent this acid-base disorder.

60-64. For each set of laboratory data, select the appropriate acid-base disturbance:

	Electrolytes				ABG	
	Na^+	Cl^- (mEq/L)	HCO_3^-	pH	PCO_2 (mm Hg)	PO_2
A.	130	95	10	7.34	19	92
B.	136	94	24	7.39	39	90
C.	130	85	29	7.50	36	94
D.	140	100	20	7.27	44	91
E.	142	100	32	7.41	52.	90

60. Metabolic alkalosis and respiratory acidosis
61. Metabolic acidosis and respiratory alkalosis
62. Metabolic acidosis and respiratory acidosis
63. Metabolic acidosis and metabolic alkalosis
64. Metabolic alkalosis and respiratory alkalosis

The answers: 60 = E; 61 = A; 62 = D; 63 = B; 64 = C. A systematic approach to the acid-base disturbance is again in order. The steps include: 1) checking the validity of pH; 2) identifying the primary disorder; 3) calculating the anion gap (AG); 4) identifying the pathogenesis of acid-base disorders; and 5) evaluation of appropriate compensation. The reported pH values are all correct using the Henderson equation. The primary disorders are all given in questions 60 to 64. The AG and the pathogenesis of the above mixed acid-base disorders are important clues for their identification. The AG for the values shown in options A to E are 25, 18, 16, 20 and 10 mEq/L, respectively. Regarding the pathogenesis of the acid-base disorder in question 60, either vomiting or diuretic (thiazide or loop diuretic) use generally causes metabolic alkalosis and emphysema or any disorder causing retention of CO_2 results in respiratory acidosis. Laboratory data shown in option E are consistent with metabolic alkalosis and respiratory acidosis. Both disorders cause a normal to high pH, elevated HCO_3^- and PCO_2. The AG is usually normal or slightly elevated if metabolic alkalosis predominates.

The acid-base disturbance given in question 61 may be caused by diseases such as renal failure, lactic acidosis, ketoacidosis or ingestion of toxins such as methyl alcohol or ethylene glycol, which lower serum [HCO_3^-] and elevate AG. The appropriate response for metabolic acidosis is hyperventilation. This results in low PCO_2. Data shown in option A are consistent with metabolic acidosis and respiratory alkalosis. Metabolic acidosis may exist alone (pure) or may exist with another primary disorder (mixed). In order to distinguish between the two disorders, one needs to calculate the expected PCO_2 using the following formula:

$$PCO_2 = 1.5 \times HCO_3^- + 8 \pm 2$$

Using [HCO_3^-] from option A,

$$PCO_2 = 1.5 \times 10 + 8 \pm 2$$
$$= 23 \text{ with a range from 21 to 25}$$

If the ABG shown in option A were a pure metabolic acidosis, the PCO_2 would have been between 21 and 25. Instead, the PCO_2 was 19. Therefore, respiratory alkalosis is superimposed on metabolic acidosis.

The acid-base disturbance given in question 62 is generally caused by a condition that generates lactic acid acutely such as sudden cardiac arrest or severe hypotension superimposed on a patient with underlying emphysema with CO_2 retention. The combination of metabolic acidosis and respiratory acidosis lowers pH below 7.40 and [HCO_3^-] below 24 mEq/L with normal to slightly elevated PCO_2. The AG is usually elevated because of accumulation of lactic acid or a similar anion. Laboratory data shown in option D are consistent with both metabolic and respiratory acidosis.

The acid-base disorder given in question 63 occurs in a patient with renal failure who develops vomiting or whose hypertension is treated with a thiazide diuretic. Renal failure causes high AG metabolic acidosis with low pH, low [HCO_3^-] and low PCO_2. On the other hand, metabolic alkalosis results in a high pH, elevated [HCO_3^-] and a high PCO_2 due to hypoventilation. When both disorders are combined, the pH, [HCO_3^-] and PCO_2 are normalized. The only clue to this acid-base disorder is elevated AG, because both metabolic acidosis and metabolic alkalosis cause elevated AG. However, metabolic acidosis due to diarrhea or renal tubular acidosis does not elevate AG. The combination of normal AG metabolic acidosis and metabolic alkalosis generally causes slight elevation in AG because of the latter acid-base disorder. Metabolic alkalosis increases AG because of two mechanisms: 1) serum albumin concentration increases as a result of volume contraction, which releases H^+ ions and becomes anionic; and 2) alkaline pH generates lactic acid production in the glycolysis pathway by enhancing the rate-limiting enzyme phosphofructokinase. Laboratory data shown in option B are consistent with metabolic acidosis and metabolic alkalosis.

The acid-base disturbance given in question 64 is seen in a patient who has liver failure with hyperventilation. This causes respiratory alkalosis. If this patient is also being treated with a diuretic, such as furosemide, the patient develops metabolic alkalosis. In such a patient, the pH is usually >7.40, the [HCO_3^-] is normal to high, and PCO_2 is normal to slightly low. Laboratory data shown in option C are consistent with respiratory and metabolic alkalosis. A similar acid-base disorder can be seen in a normal pregnant woman with severe vomiting.

Chapter 12

65. Renal handling of K^+ involves:

A. Reabsorption in the proximal tubule
B. Reabsorption and secretion in the thick ascending limb
C. Secretion occurs mostly in the cortical collecting duct
D. A, B, and C are true
E. A and C are true

The answer is D. About 50-70% of the filtered K^+ is reabsorbed in the proximal tubule. In the thick ascending limb of Henle's loop, about 25% of K^+ is reabsorbed with Na^+ and Cl^-. K^+ secretion also occurs in this segment through K^+ conductance channels. This back-leak of K^+ is indeed necessary to provide continuous supply of K^+ ions for cotransport with Na^+ and Cl^-. The major secretory site for K^+ is the cortical collecting duct, which is sensitive to aldosterone. Although the connecting tubule secretes K^+ at a low rate, this secretion is not stimulated by aldosterone.

66. Hormones and drugs that promote transcellular K^+ uptake include all of the following, except:

A. Insulin
B. Epinephrine
C. Phentolamine
D. Glucagon and propranolol
E. A, B, and C are true

The answer is E. Insulin increases the cellular uptake of K^+ by muscle and hepatic cells, and the mechanism of this uptake is not completely understood. However, some studies demonstrated stimulation of Na/K-ATPase by insulin, and other studies reported a physiologic negative control loop between insulin and K^+. Administration of epinephrine has also been shown to stimulate K^+ uptake by skeletal and heart muscle cells. The mechanism appears to be the formation of cAMP, leading to the activation of Na/K-ATPase. In contrast, administration of an α-adrenergic agonist, such as phenylephrine, induces hyperkalemia by decreasing cellular uptake or enhancing cellular efflux of K^+. This effect is abolished by α-adrenergic blockers, such as phentolamine, which promotes cellular uptake of K^+. Glucagon seems to elevate serum K^+ levels probably by its efflux from the liver. Propranolol is a β-adrenergic blocker, and therefore it counteracts the actions of epinephrine. This causes an increase in serum $[K^+]$ slightly in an individual with normal renal function. However, propranolol may cause greater increases in serum $[K^+]$ in patients with renal failure, diabetes mellitus, and hypoaldosteronism.

67. Cellular mechanisms for K^+ transport include:

A. Transcellular and paracellular pathways in the proximal tubule
B. A Na/K/2Cl cotransporter in the thick ascending limb
C. A K/Cl cotransporter in the distal tubule
D. A K/Cl cotransporter and K^+ conductance channel in the cortical collecting duct
E. All of the above

The answer is E. Mechanisms A and B are related to K^+ reabsorption, whereas mechanisms C and D are concerned with K^+ secretion.

68. K^+ excretion is increased by all of the following, except:

A. Acute metabolic acidosis
B. Increased distal delivery of fluid
C. Loop diuretics (furosemide and bumetanide)
D. An increase in K^+ intake
E. Metabolic alkalosis

The answer is A. All of the above factors except acute metabolic acidosis promote K^+ excretion. The mechanism for increased K^+ excretion in chronic metabolic acidosis appars to be an increase in fluid delivery to the cortical collecting duct.

69. All of the following EKG changes are characteristic of mild to severe hyperkalemia, except:

A. Peaked T waves
B. Shortened Q-T interval
C. Prolonged Q-T interval
D. Absence of P waves
E. Presence of a sine wave

The answer is C. The magnitude of EKG changes is related to serum [K^+]. Mild hyperkalemia may cause only peaked (tented) T waves with shortened Q-T interval. Severe hyperkalemia causes absence of P waves and widened QRS complex. All of these changes finally lead to a sine wave. Prolonged Q-T interval is usually caused by hypokalemia, hypocalcemia, and hypomagnesemia.

70. A 30-year-old man, on maintenance hemodialysis three times a week, came to the emergency room with a complaint of weakness. He was not dialyzed for one week. His serum [K^+] was 7.2 mEq/L. EKG showed peaked T waves and widened QRS complex. The initial treatment of choice for his hyperkalemia is:

A. Glucose and insulin
B. Calcium gluconate
C. $NaHCO_3$
D. Kayexalate
E. Hemodialysis

The answer is B. All treatment modalities are indicated in this patient. However, the EKG changes warrant the intravenous administration of calcium in the form of either gluconate or chloride, which immediately counteracts the membrane effects of hyperkalemia. Following this, the patient can receive intravenous administration of glucose and insulin, and $NaHCO_3$. These treatment modalities do not decrease total body K^+. Only kayexalate and hemodialysis reduce the total body K^+ content. Kayexalate is a K^+-binding resin, and can be given orally or in the form of enema. In this patient, hemodialysis has to be done initially using a dialysate without K^+ and then a dialysate containing low [K^+].

Chapter 13

71. A 32-old-male was admitted for weakness due to extensive diarrhea. An arterial blood gas showed metabolic acidosis with a pH of 7.18. Correction of this pH to 7.45 over a six-hour period would cause ionized Ca^{2+} to:

A. Increase
B. Decrease
C. Remain unchanged
D. A and C are true
E. None of the above

The answer is B. In plasma, Ca^{2+} exists in three forms: about 50% as free or ionized form, about 40% is bound to albumin and 10% is complexed with citrate, phosphate or HCO_3^-. It is only the ionized form that is physiologically active. Severe metabolic acidosis increases the concentration of ionized Ca^{2+} because the binding of Ca^{2+} to albumin is decreased. Overcorrection of metabolic acidosis results in increased binding of Ca^{2+} to albumin, and thus decreases ionized Ca^{2+}. Occasionally this may precipitate tetany.

72. Regarding Ca^{2+} homeostasis:

A. It is the most abundant divalent cation in the body
B. Plasma [Ca^{2+}] is maintained within narrow limits by coordinated actions of the intestine, bone, and kidney
C. About 98% of the filtered Ca^{2+} is reabsorbed
D. About 99% is stored in bone
E. All of the above

The answer is E. About 1.2 to 1.3 kg of Ca^{2+} is present in a 70-kg man. Of this, 99% is present in bone. The plasma [Ca^{2+}] is maintained around 10 mg/dL because of the coordinated interaction of several factors that regulate the intestinal absorption, bone turnover, and renal reabsorption. About 98% of the filtered Ca^{2+} is reabsorbed and only 2% (< 200 mg) is excreted in the urine.

73. Ca^{2+} excretion is enhanced by which of the following agents:

A. Parathyroid hormone (PTH)
B. Hydrochlorothiazide (HCTZ)
C. Furosemide
D. Amiloride
E. None of the above

The answer is C. All other agents except furosemide decrease Ca^{2+} excretion. PTH is an important regulator of Ca^{2+} homeostasis. It promotes Ca^{2+} reabsorption by the thick ascending limb and the distal convoluted tubule. Because of this, Ca^{2+} excretion is reduced. The effect of PTH on Ca^{2+} reabsorption is variable in the proximal tubule. HCTZ, if chronically administered, causes hypocalciuria because of enhanced reabsorption in the proximal tubule. Amiloride also causes reduced excretion of Ca^{2+} because of augmented Ca^{2+} reabsorption in the distal convoluted tubule.

74. Which of the following statements is false regarding the cellular transport of Ca^{2+}:

A. Both transcellular and paracellular pathways occur in the proximal tubule
B. Passive diffusion is the major transport process in the thin ascending limb
C. Paracellular route is the major transport process in the thick ascending limb
D. Active transport is the predominant mode of transport system in the distal convoluted tubule
E. Unlike in other segments, the transport of Ca^{2+} and Na^+ are not interdependent in the distal convoluted tubule

The answer is B. About 70% of the filtered Ca^{2+} is reabsorbed in the proximal tubule by transcellular and paracellular pathways. Most of this reabsorption is passive. About 20% of Ca^{2+} is reabsorbed in the thick ascending limb via the paracellular pathway. Approximately 5 to 10% of filtered Ca^{2+} is reabsorbed in the thick ascending limb of Henle's loop mostly by an active process. In the proximal tubule and thick ascending limb, Ca^{2+} reabsorption is dependent on Na^+ reabsorption. However, in the distal convoluted tubule both are dissociated. Ca^{2+} transport does not occur in thin limbs of the Henle's loop.

75. The immediate treatment of acute hypercalcemia is:

A. Glucocorticoids
B. Normal (0.9%) saline and furosemide
C. Biphosphonates
D. Mithramycin
E. Hemodialysis

The answer is B. Hydration followed by furosemide administration is the treatment of choice for acute hypercalcemia. This treatment promotes Ca^{2+} excretion and lowers serum [Ca^{2+}] to an acceptable level. Except hemodialysis, prednisone, biphosphonates, and mithramycin take hours to days for action and should be considered following hydration and furosemide.

76. An alcoholic patient with liver cirrhosis was admitted for abdominal pain. His serum chemistry was as follows: Ca^{2+} = 6 mg/dL; Mg^{2+} = mEq/L; K^+ = 2.6 mEq/dL and albumin 2.5 g/dL. The causes for his hypocalcemia include all of the following, except:

A. Hypoalbuminemia
B. Hypomagnesemia
C. Hyperparathyroidism
D. Decreased production of 25-hydroxycholecalciferol
E. Hypoparathyroidism

The answer is C. Except for hyperparathyroidism, the remaining conditions cause hypocalcemia. Hypoalbuminemia decreases total serum [Ca^{2+}] by 0.8 mg/dL per gram decrease of albumin. Hypomagnesemia causes hypocalcemia by two mechanisms: 1) by inhibiting parathyroid hormone (PTH) secretion; and 2) by causing PTH resistance to bone resorption of Ca^{2+}. Patients with liver disease produce less 25–hydroxycholecalciferol, which is the substrate for the production of active vitamin D_3 in the kidney. Hypoparathyroidism is a known cause of hypocalcemia in a subject with normal renal function.

Chapter 14

77. Which of the following is true regarding the plasma phosphorus:

A. Phosphate is measured as phosphorus in plasma
B. It is the phosphate that is filtered at the glomerulus
C. Only the inorganic form of phosphate is biologically active
D. No relationship between plasma phosphate and albumin concentration
E. All of the above

The answer is E. Although phosphate and phosphorus are used interchangeably, it is the phosphate that is measured as elemental phosphorus in various biologic fluids. Also, it is the phosphate that is filtered at the glomerulus and transported across the tubular membranes. In plasma, phosphate exists as organic (70%) and inorganic (30%) forms. It is the inorganic form that is physiologically active and only 10% of it is bound to albumin. Therefore, phosphate concentration is not altered by changes in plasma albumin concentration.

78. Renal phosphate handling includes all of the following, except:

A. About 80% of filtered phosphate is reabsorbed by the proximal tubule
B. Phosphate excretion increases with excess phosphate intake
C. The transport in the proximal tubule is unidirectional
D. Excreted phosphate is derived mostly from the thick ascending limb
E. The transport in the proximal tubule is dependent upon luminal [Na^+]

The answer is D. The proximal tubule reabsorbs about 80% of the filtered phosphate. The transport is generally unidirectional and active with no secretion of phosphate into the tubular lumen. It is dependent upon the luminal availability of [Na^+], and one phosphate ion is coupled to 2 Na^+ ions at the apical membrane for transport. The other segment of the nephron that reabsorbs approximately 10% of phosphate is the distal convoluted tubule. The remaining 10% of phosphate is excreted in the urine. There is little or no phosphate transport in the loop of Henle or collecting duct.

79. All of the following factors promote phosphate excretion, except:

A. Chronic metabolic alkalosis
B. Volume expansion
C. Parathyroid hormone (PTH)
D. Glucose
E. Chronic metabolic acidosis

The answer is A. Volume expansion inhibits phosphate reabsorption by the proximal tubule and promotes phosphate excretion. PTH is the major regulator of phosphate reabsorption in the proximal tubule. Infusion of PTH causes enhanced excretion, whereas parathyroidectomy decreases phosphate excretion. This phosphaturic effect is mediated by cAMP. At physiologic concentrations, PTH causes phosphaturia through the activation of protein kinase C signaling mechanism. Glucose is also phosphaturic. Part of this effect is due to osmotic diuresis, and part is related to its competition with phosphate for Na^+-mediated cotransport. Only chronic but not acute metabolic acidosis decreases phosphate reabsorption, and promotes phosphate excretion. This decrease in phosphate reabsorption appears to be due to diminished turnover of Na^+-dependent transporters. Conversely, chronic metabolic alkalosis decreases phosphate excretion by promoting its reabsorption through activation of Na^+-dependent transporters.

80. The biochemical abnormalities resulting from hypophosphatemia include all of the following, except:

A. Depletion of ATP
B. Reduction of 2,3-diphosphoglycerate (2,3-DPG)
C. Increase in plasma creatinine concentration
D. Decrease in plasma [K^+]
E. Increase in plasma uric acid concentration

The answer is D. Hypophosphatemia results in a decrease in intracellular ATP and erythrocyte 2,3-DPG levels, which lead to altered cellular function and hypoxia. The latter is due to increased affinity between 2,3-DPG and O_2, causing less delivery of O_2 to tissues. Persistent hypophosphatemia causes muscle injury resulting in acute renal failure as manifested by an increase in plamsa creatinine and BUN (blood urea nitrogen) concentrations. This mechanism of acute renal failure is called rhabdomyolysis. Because of cellular necrosis, all of the intracellular contents are released into the circulation and thus elevate plasma or serum concentrations of K^+ and uric acid.

81. Which of the following is NOT the treatment for hyperphosphatemia:

A. Calcium acetate
B. Glucose and insulin
C. Calcium carbonate
D. High-flux hemodialysis
E. Vitamin D_3

The answer is E. Treatment of hyperphosphatemia depends upon the symptoms. Acute symptomatic hyperphosphatemia can be treated with volume expansion by normal (0.9%) saline if the patient has adequate renal function. Also, high-flux hemodialysis is useful in lowering serum phosphate and simultaneously elevating Ca^{2+} concentration, because tetany is due to hypocalcemia induced by hyperphosphatemia. Glucose with insulin may be given to promote cellular uptake of phosphate until hemodialysis is begun. Treatment of chronic asymptomatic hyperphosphatemia includes restriction of dietary phosphate intake and phosphate-binders, such as calcium acetate. These binders decrease gastrointestinal absorption of phosphorus. Active vitamin D_3 causes hyperphosphatemia.

Chapter 15

82. Reabsorption of Mg^{2+} occurs most in which of the following nephron segments:

A. Proximal convoluted tubule
B. Thick ascending limb
C. Distal convoluted tubule
D. Connecting tubule
E. Collecting duct

The answer is B. About 2,000 mg of nonprotein-bound Mg^{2+} is filtered at the glomerulus. Of this, 95% is reabsorbed by various segments of the nephron. The proximal convoluted tubule reabsorbs approximately 25% of the filtered Mg^{2+}. The most important segment for Mg^{2+} reabsorption is the thick ascending limb of Henle's loop. Approximately 50% of Mg^{2+} is reabsorbed in this segment.

The distal convoluted tubule reabsorbs about 5% of Mg^{2+}, and very little Mg^{2+} is reabsorbed in the collecting duct.

83. Cellular mechanisms of Mg^{2+} transport include all of the following, except:

A. In the proximal tubule, Mg^{2+} transport is dependent on Na^+ transport
B. Inhibition of Na/K/2Cl transport inhibits Mg^{2+} transport
C. Mg^{2+} transport depends on the lumen-positive potential difference in the thick ascending limb
D. Mg^{2+} transport is dependent on the lumen-positive potential difference in the distal convoluted tubule
E. Mg^{2+} exit across the basolateral membrane occurs against its electrochemical gradient

The answer is D. Mg^{2+} reabsorption in the proximal tubule closely follows that of NaCl, but at a lower fractional rate. In the thick ascending limb, Mg^{2+} reabsorption also follows NaCl reabsorption because inhibition of Na/K/2Cl transporter by a loop diuretic (furosemide) inhibits Mg^{2+} reabsorption. Because of Cl^- reabsorption, the tubular lumen has a positive potential difference which promotes passive reabsorption of Mg^{2+}. However, in the distal convoluted tubule the lumen is voltage-negative, and therefore, Mg^{2+} reabsorption is not voltage-dependent. There is evidence for an active transport of Mg^{2+} in this segment. Unlike Ca^{2+} or Na^+, Mg^{2+} transport reaches saturation, and thus its transport dissociates from that of Ca^{2+} or Na^+. Transfer of Mg^{2+} across the basolateral membrane occurs against its electrochemical gradient, and thus involves an active or secondary active transport process.

84. All of the following factors increase Mg^{2+} excretion, except:

A. Volume expansion
B. Hypermagnesemia
C. Antidiuretic hormone (ADH)
D. Loop diuretics
E. Hypercalcemia

The answer is C. Expansion of intravascular volume by the administration of normal saline increases the excretion of Mg^{2+} by an increase in the delivery of filtrate to the thick ascending limb. This delivery of filtrate decreases the positive potential difference, resulting in less passive reabsorption of Mg^{2+}. Consequently, the distal delivery of Mg^{2+} is enhanced. Thus, all of the Mg^{2+} delivered from the loop of Henle is excreted. Hypermagnesemia inhibits Mg^{2+} reabsorption in the proximal tubule and the thick ascending limb, resulting in Mg^{2+} wastage. Loop diuretics, such as furosemide, inhibit Na/K/2Cl cotransporter, and thus dissipate lumen-positive voltage. This inhibits Mg^{2+} reabsorption, and promotes Mg^{2+} excretion. The effect of metabolic acidosis on Mg^{2+} excretion is inconsistent. However, acute metabolic acidosis in animals causes Mg^{2+} wastage; the site of action is the thick ascending limb of Henle's loop. cAMP-mediated hormones, such as ADH and parathyroid hormone, promote Mg^{2+} reabsorption in the thick ascending limb, and decrease its excretion. ADH creates a lumen-positive potential difference by stimulating Na/K/2Cl cotransporter, and promotes Mg^{2+} transport passively.

85. Which of the following causes hypomagnesemia:

A. Chronic alcoholism
B. Diarrhea
C. Hypercalcemia
D. Cis-platinum
E. All of the above

The answer is E. Chronic alcoholism causes hypomagnesemia because of decreaed dietary intake. Diarrhea or malabsorption results in decreased gastrointestinal absorption of Mg^{2+}, and thus causes hypomagnesemia. Hypercalcemia and cis-platinum promote renal excretion of Mg^{2+}, resulting in hypomagnesemia.

86. Which of the clinical manifestations is suggestive of hypermagnesemia:

A. Hypertension
B. Tremors
C. Absent deep tendon reflexes
D. Increase in heart rate
E. Increase in deep tendon reflexes

The answer is C. The clinical manifestations of hypermagnesemia are related to the serum $[Mg^{2+}]$. Absence of reflexes is typically seen when serum $[Mg^{2+}]$ reaches 12 mg/dL. All other manifestations listed are related to low serum $[Mg^{2+}]$.

Chapter 16

87. A 30-year-old male with renal failure (creatinine clearance of 20 ml/min) has hypertension and bilateral leg edema. The appropriate diuretic that works in this patient is:

A. Hydrochlorothiazide (HCTZ)
B. Furosemide
C. Acetazolamide
D. Spironolactone
E. Amiloride

The answer is B. HCTZ is effective only in a patient with a creatinine clearance above 30 ml/min. Therefore, this is not a suitable diuretic in this patient. Acetazolamide causes metabolic acidosis, and is relatively contraindicated in renal failure patients who develop metabolic acidosis because of decreased excretion of H^+ ions by the kidney. Spironolactone and amiloride are K^+ -sparing diuretics and cause hyperkalemia. Since patients with renal failure retain K^+ because of decreased secretion by the kidney, these K^+-sparing diuretics are relatively contraindicated. Loop diuretics such as furosemide can work at low creatinine clearances, and are frequently used to treat edema in renal failure patients before maintenance dialysis is started.

88. A patient with rheumatoid arthritis develops congestive heart failure with bilateral leg edema. He is on indomethacin (nonsteroidal anti-inflammatory drug) for his arthritis. His physician starts him on furosemide for edema which improved in a week. However, the patient comes back to the physician's office with a claim that his legs are getting swollen despite salt and water restriction. He also says that he is taking one extra tablet of indomethacin for leg pain for the last three days. The reason for re-accumulation of edema is:

A. The heart disease is worsening
B. Inadequate dose of furosemide
C. Decreased efficacy of furosemide in the presence of indomethacin
D. Inadequate control of salt and water intake
E. None of the above

The answer is C. Inhibitors of prostaglandin (PG) synthesis, such as indomethacin, diminish the efficacy of diuretics. The patient is on both indomethacin and furosemide, and therefore the efficacy of furosemide was diminished. The mechanisms for this interaction are incompletely understood. However, three possibilities have been suggested: 1) PG inhibitors are generally organic anions, and may compete for the same secretory site of the furosemide; 2) furosemide stimulates vasodilatory PG synthesis, which is suppressed by concomitant administration of indomethacin; 3) PG inhibitors reduce RBF and GFR so that the delivery of the filtrate to the site of diuretic is decreased. In this patient, decreasing the dose or discontinuation of indomethacin may be helpful in preventing excess edema.

89. Regarding spironolactone, which of the following statements is false:

A. K^+ is an inhibitor of aldosterone
B. It inhibits K^+ secretion
C. It causes metabolic acidosis, particularly in patients with decompensated liver disease
D. It interferes with urinary concentrating ability
E. Unlike other diuretics, it does not act at the luminal side

The answer is D. Spironolactone binds to the cytosolic aldosterone receptor from the basolateral membrane in the cortical collecting duct, and inhibits the actions of aldosterone. Because of its anti-aldosterone effects, spironolactone is used to treat ascites in patients with liver cirrhosis. One of the complications of this drug in these patients is the production of a non-anion gap metabolic acidosis because of its inhibition of H^+ ion secretion. Spironolactone does not interfere with the urinary concentrating ability of the kidney.

90. Regarding mannitol:

A. It is freely filtered at the glomerulus
B. It increases both RBF and GFR
C. It increases free-water clearance (C_{H_2O})
D. It is clinically used to treat brain edema
E. All of the above

The answer is E. Mannitol is less bound to albumin, and is filtered at the glomerulus. It is poorly reabsorbed by the tubules, and therefore it is concentrated in the proximal tubule. Because of its increased osmotic concentration, reabsorption of water is decreased. This causes an increase in C_{H_2O}. Maninitol increases both RBF and GFR. It is used prophylactically to prevent acute renal failure in a high risk patient. Mannitol is also used in the management of cerebral edema. A clinical trial has demonstrated higher survival rate in those treated with mannitol compared to a control group.

91. Acetazolamide causes all of the following, except:

A. Metabolic alkalosis
B. Metabolic acidosis
C. Increase in free-water clearance (C_{H_2O})
D. Decrease in serum [HCO_3^-]
E. Alkaline urine pH

The answer is A. Acetazolamide is a carbonic anhydrase inhibitor. By inhibiting this enzyme, acetazolamide inhibits H^+ ion secretion and HCO_3^- reabsorption in the proximal tubule. This results in low serum [HCO_3^-] and metabolic acidosis. Any diuretic that acts in the proximal tubule and inhibits Na^+ reabsorption also inhibits water reabsorption. As a result, C_{H_2O} is increased. Since HCO_3^- reabsorption is inhibited, it escapes into the urine and increases the urine pH above 6.5.

92. Which of the following diuretic agents does NOT cause hypercalcemia:

A. Hydrochlorothiazide (HCTZ)
B. Amiloride
C. Furosemide
D. Metolazone
E. None of the above

The answer is C. Loop diuretics, such as furosemide and bumetanide, promote Ca^{2+} excretion, and therefore are used to treat hypercalcemia. HCTZ, metolazone, and amiloride promote reabsorption, and cause an elevation in serum [Ca^{2+}]. Because of hypocalciuric effect, HCTZ is used to treat calcium stones in the kidney.

APPENDIX B

NORMAL LABORATORY VALUES

	Conventional Units	SI Units
Serum Chemistry		
Sodium	135-145 mEq/L	135-145 mmol/L
Potassium	3.5-5.0 mEq/L	3.5-5.0 mmol/L
Chloride	95-105 mEq/L	95-105 mmol/L
Total carbon dioxide content or [HCO_3^-]	22-30 mEq/L	22-30 mmol/L
Creatinine	0.8-1.4 mg/dL (male)	71-124 umol/L
	0.7-1.2 mg/dL (female)	62-106 umol/L
Urea nitrogen (BUN)	8-20 mg/dL	2.8-7.1 mmol/L
Glucose (fasting)	70-110 mg/dL	3.9-6.1 mmol/L
Calcium	8.5-10.5 mg/dL	2.1-2.6 mmol/L
Phosphorus	2.5-4.5 mg/dL	0.8-1.45 mmol/L
Magnesium	1.8-2.1 mEq/dL	0.75-1.05 mmol/L
Uric acid	3.5-7.2 mg/dL (male)	0.21-0.42 mmol/L
	2.6-6.0 mg/dL (female)	0.15-0.35 mmol/L
Albumin	3.5-5.0 g/dL	35-50 g/L
Arterial Blood Gas		
pH	7.38-7.42 (arterial)	[H^+] 38-42 nmol/L
PCO_2	32-48 mm Hg	4.16-6.24 kPa*
PO_2	83-108 mm Hg	10.79-14.04 kPa
Plasma osmolality	280-295 mOsm/kg H_2O	280-295 mOsm/kg H_2O
Urine specific gravity	1.002-1.030	
Urine osmolality	50-1200 mOsm/kg H_2O	50-1200 mOsm/kg H_2O
Urine pH	4.5-8.0	
Creatinine clearance	90-140 ml/min (male)	90-140 ml/min(Male)
	130-202 L/day	130-202 L/day
	87-130 ml/min (female)	87-130 ml/min (female)
	125-187 L/day	125-187 L/day

*Pressure is expressed as kPa (kilopascals) rather than mm Hg.

GLOSSARY

Acid: a molecule that donates a proton (H^+ ion).
Acidemia: an increase in blood [H^+]
Acidosis: a pathophysiologic process that tends to acidify body fluids
Active transport: movement of electrolytes against a concentration gradient, requiring expenditure of cellular energy. Active transport can be either primary, in which the energy is derived from the hydrolysis of ATP, or secondary, in which the energy is derived from ionic concentration gradients that have been established by the primary active transport system.
Aldosterone: a steroid hormone synthesized by the glomerulosa cells of the adrenal cortex. This hormone promotes Na^+ reabsorption and K^+ secretion in principal cells of the cortical collecting duct. Aldosterone also stimulates secretion of H^+ ions in Type A intercalated cells.
Alkalemia: a decrease in blood [H^+]
Alkalosis: a pathophysiologic process that tends to alkalanize body fluids
Angiotensin II: a vasoactive peptide that is formed from angiotensin I by angiotensin converting enzyme. It causes vasoconstriction of blood vessels, and stimulates the secretion of aldosterone.
Anion gap (AG): a reflection of unmeasured anions in plasma, such as sulfates, phosphates, albumin and organic acids. AG is calculated as the difference between Na^+ and the sum of Cl^- and HCO_3^-, as follows:

$$AG\ (mEq/L) = Na^+ - (Cl^- + HCO_3^-)$$

The normal AG ranges between 8 and 12. AG is useful in classifying metabolic acidosis and evaluating mixed-acid base disorders.
Anions: negatively charged ions.
Antidiuretic hormone (ADH): a hormone synthesized by supraoptic and paraventricular nuclei of the hypothalamus, and stored in the posterior pituary gland. ADH is also called arginine vasopressin. The major physiologic stimulus for ADH release is plasma osmolality. ADH increases water permeability in the cortical and medullary collecting ducts and plays an important role in urinary concentration and dilution. Thus, ADH is an important regulator of water metabolism and plasma osmolality.
Antiport: transport of solutes in opposite direction. Antiport is also called countertransport.
Aquaporins: water channel proteins that are resposible for water transport across water-permeable epithelial cells in the nephron.
Arterial blood gas (ABG): includes pH, PCO_2 and plasma [HCO_3^-]
Atrial natriuretic peptide (ANP): a hormone released from cardiac atria in response to volume overload or stretch. It increases GFR, and promotes Na^+

as well as water excretion. ANP also lowers systemic blood pressure, and inhibits the secretion of ADH.

Autoregulation: a process by which the kidneys maintain a constant renal blood flow and GFR over a wide range of systemic blood pressure, usually between 80 and 180 mm Hg.

Baroreceptors: pressure-sensitive nerve endings located in the aortic arch, carotid sinus, cardiac atria, pulmonary veins, the kidneys, and liver. These baroreceptors respond to changes in blood pressure and cause changes in cardiac output, and renal handling of Na^+ and water. Since pressure and volume are directly related, these receptors are also called volume regulatory receptors.

Base: a molecule that accepts a proton (H^+ ion).

Buffer: a substance that combines with an excess acid or a base to minimize changes in pH.

Calcitriol: the active form of vitamin D_3. It is also called 1,25-dihydroxycholecalciferol.

Cations: positively charged ions.

Chvostek's sign: a sign of tetany due to hypocalcemia and hypomagnesemia. Chvostek's sign is positive when tapping over the facial nerve produces contraction of facial muscles.

Clearance: a volume of plasma that has been cleared of a particular substance per minute. The clearance of any substance is calculated by using the formula: UV/P, where U is the urine concentration of a substance (mg/ml), V is the urine volume (ml/min), and P is the plasma concentration of a substance (mg/ml). Inulin clearance approximates GFR, whereas para-aminohippurate clearance approximates renal plasma flow.

Compensation: a physiologic process that minimizes changes in $[H^+]$ brought about by a primary acid-base change. Metabolic acid-base disorders involve a respiratory compensation, whereas respiratory acid-base disorders involve a renal compensation.

Concentrating ability: the kidney's ability to produce urine hypertonic to plasma. A normal individual is able to concentrate urine up to 1200 mOsm/kg H_2O.

Countercurrent multiplication: a process that maintains an osmotic or solute gradient along the length of two streams flowing in opposite directions, as in loop of Henle.

Diffusion (simple): passive movement of a solute from a higher to a lower concentration until equilibrium is established. Diffusion arises from random molecular motion of solutes (see passive transport).

Diluting ability: the kidney's ability to produce urine hypotonic to plasma. A normal individual is able to dilute urine up to 50 mOsm/kg H_20.

Diuresis: an increased urine flow rate of solute and water.

Diuretics: chemical substances that promote urinary solute and water excretion

Edema: a condition in which excess salt and water accumulate in the interstitium. Edema can be either generalized as in congestive heart failure or cirrhosis of the liver or localized as in lungs or brain.
Effective circulating volume (ECV): a component of the intravascular volume that is perfusing the tissues. ECV is different from extracellular fluid volume.
Electrolyte: a substance that dissociates in water into charged particles called ions.
Endothelin: a hormone released by vascular endothelial cells. It is a vasoconstricter of vascular smooth muscle cells and mesangial cells. Endothelin increases renal vascular resistance and thereby reduces RBF and GFR.
Eryrthropoietin: a glycoprotein hormone, which acts on the colony-forming units of erythroid cells to stimulate red blood cell production. This hormone is synthesized by the peritubular interstitial cells of the corticomedullary junction.
Extracellular fluid volume (ECF): a volume that is found outside the cells. ECF comprises one-third of the total body volume.
Facilitated diffusion: a transport mechanism that is facilitated by specific carrier proteins residing in the cell membrane (see passive transport).
Filtration equilibrium: the point where filtration across the glomerular capillary ceases due to progressive increase in colloid oncotic pressure.
Filtration fraction: the amount of plasma that is filtered at the glomerulus. It is calculated as the ratio of the glomerular filtration rate (GFR) to the renal plasma flow (RPF). The normal filtration fraction is 20%.
Free-water clearance: a volume of solute-free water, excreted per minute, to make urine isosmotic with plasma. It is expressed as C_{H_2O}. If the urine osmolality is less than the plasma osmolality, the C_{H_2O} is positive, whereas the C_{H_2O} is negative if the urine osmolality is greater than the plasma osmolality.
Gibbs-Donnan equilibrium: a principle that explains the unequal distribution of ions between two compartments. It states that at eqilibrium the distribution of ions between two compartments separated by a semipermeable membrane is such that the product of the diffusible ions in one compartment must equal the product of the diffusible ions in the other compartment.
Glomerular filtration: a process where a portion of blood flows through the glomerular capillaries into the Bowman's space to form an ultrafiltrate. The rate at which ultrafiltration occurs per unit time is called the glomerular filtration rate (GFR). The GFR is usually 125 ml/min or 180 L/day.
Glomerulo-tubular balance (G-T balance): a relationship between GFR and renal tubules for Na^+ and water handling. Whenever changes in GFR occur, a constant fraction rather than a constant volume of the filtered load of Na^+ is reabsorbed by the renal tubules (mostly by the proximal tubule) to maintain Na^+ and water homeostasis.

Glomerulus: a part of the renal corpuscle consisting of blood capillaries derived from the afferent arteriole. Each glomerular capillary is composed of an inner layer of endothelial cells; an outer layer of epithelial cells, and a central region of mesangial cells surrounded by a collagen-like mesangial matrix. The endothelial and epithelial cells are separated by the glomerular basement membrane. Plasma is filtered at the glomerulus to form an ultrafiltrate.

Henderson equation: an equation that relates $[H^+]$ to pH. Henderson equation is expressed as:

$$[H^+]\ (\text{nmol/L}) = 24 \times \frac{PCO_2}{[HCO_3^-]}$$

Henderson-Hasselbalch equation: an equation that is used to calculate the pH of a solution:

$$pH = pKa + \log\ [HCO_3^-]/\ [H_2CO_3]$$

Hyperbicarbonatemia: an increase in plasma $[HCO_3^-]$.

Hypercalcemia: serum $[Ca^{2+}] > 11.0$ mg/dL.

Hypercapnia: an increase in arterial PCO_2.

Hyperkalemia: serum $[K^+] > 5.5$ mEq/L.

Hypermagnesemia: serum $[Mg^{2+}] > 2.7$ mg/dL.

Hypernatremia: serum $[Na^+] > 145$ mEq/L, which is due to water deficit.

Hyperphosphatemia: serum $[Pi] > 4.5$ mg/dL.

Hypertonic: fluids that cause shrinkage of red blood cells suspended in them. Hypertonicity decribes the osmolality that is higher than that of body fluids.

Hypobicarbonatemia: a decrease in serum $[HCO_3^-]$.

Hypocalcemia: serum $[Ca^{2+}] < 8.5$ mg/dL.

Hypocapnia: a decrease in arterial PCO_2.

Hypokalemia: serum $[K^+] < 3.5$ mEq/L.

Hypomagnesemia: serum $[Mg^{2+}] < 1.7$ mg/dL.

Hyponatremia: serum $[Na^+] < 135$ mEq/L, which is due to water excess.

Hypophosphatemia: serum $[Pi] < 2.5$ mg/dL.

Hypotonic: fluids that cause swelling of red blood cells suspended in them. Hypotonicity describes the osmolality that is lower than that of body fluids.

Insensible loss: water loss from organs other than the kidney, and amounts to approximately 10 ml/kg/day.

Intracellular fluid volume (ICF): the amount of volume that is found inside the cells. ICF comprises two-thirds of total body volume.

Isosmotic: similar osmolal concentration.

Isotonic: fluids that do not change the volume of red blood cells suspended in them. Isotonicity describes the osmolality that is identical to that of body fluids.

Juxtaglomerular apparatus (JGA): a specialized structure that includes the macula densa, the terminal portion of the afferent arteriole with its renin-producing granular cells, and the extraglomerular mesangial cells. The JGA is located at the vascular pole of the glomerulus.

Loop diuretics: diuretics that act in the thick ascending limb of loop of Henle..
Metabolic acid-base disorders: are those that result primarily from changes in serum [HCO_3^-]. In metabolic acidosis, the serum [HCO_3^-] is < 24 mEq/L, whereas in metabolic alkalosis the serum [HCO_3^-] is > 24 mEq/L.
Micturition: a process of voiding urine.
Mixed acid-base disorder: refers to the simultaneous occurrence of two or more primary acid-base disorders.
Natriuresis: excretion of Na^+ in the urine.
Nephron: the fundamental structural unit of the kidney. Each kidney consists of approximately 600,000 nephrons. The nephron consists of a renal corpuscle, the proximal tubule, the loop of Henle, and the distal tubule. Although the collecting duct is not a part of the nephron, it is included in the nephron because of its related function.
Nephrotic syndrome: defined as proteinuria > 3.5 g/day, hypoalbuminemia, hyperlipidemia, edema and lipiduria.
Net acid excretion (NAE): defined as the sum of titratable acidity (TA) and NH_4^+ minus any H^+ ion that is added to the body because of urinary loss of HCO_3^-. It is calculated as:

$$NAE = TA + NH_4^+ - HCO_3^-$$

Nonvolatile acids: acids produced from sulfur-containing amino acids and phosphoproteins, and are excreted in the urine as urinary buffers.
Normobicarbonatemia: normal serum [HCO_3^-].
Normocapnia: normal arterial PCO_2.
Oncotic pressure: the osmotic force generated by relatively impermeable solutes such as proteins, which are confined to the plasma. Oncotic pressure is also called colloid osmotic pressure.
Osmolality: the number of mOsm in one kg of water.
Osmolar clearance: the volume of water, excreted per minute, containing all the solute that is isosmotic to plasma. It is expressed as C_{osm}, which is defined by the clearance formula as $U_{osm} \times V / P_{osm}$, where V is the urine volume in ml/min, U_{osm} and P_{osm} refer to urinary and plasma osmolalities, respectively.
Osmolarity: the number of mOsm in 1 L of solution.
Osmosis: defined as water movement through the cell membrane from a lower to a higher concentration solution until the two solutions reach equal concentration.
Osmotic pressure: the pressure developed when two solutions of different concentrations are separated by a semipermeable membrane during the osmotic flow.
Osmotic diuresis: defined as increased urine flow rate of solute and water due to osmotic agents, such as mannitol and glucose.
Paracellular transport: movement of small substances other than large macromolecules, such as proteins, through the tight junctions of epithelial cells.
Parathyroid hormone (PTH): a hormone that is secreted by the parathyroid

gland in response to hypocalcemia. It acts on the kidney and bone. In the kidney, PTH stimulates Ca^{2+} reabsorption in the distal nephron, and stimulates the synthesis of 1,25-dihydroxycholecalciferol in the proximal tubule. In the bone, PTH causes bone resorption. In the intestine, PTH promotes Ca^{2+} reabsorption through 1,25-dihydroxycholecalciferol.

Passive transport: a form of transport that does not require an expenditure of metabolic or cellular energy. Examples of passive transport include simple diffusion, facilitated diffusion, and solvent drag.

pH: defined as the negative logarithm of $[H^+]$.

pKa: a constant for the Henderson-Hasselbalch equation relating to the degree of dissociation of $[H^+]$ at a given temperature.

Poluria: a condition of excess urination, usually 3-5 L/day.

Potassium-sparing diuretics: diuretics that retain K^+.

Primary change: an abnormality in either the $[HCO_3^-]$ or PCO_2 resulting from a primary change in body function/metabolism or additions to/losses from the body fluids.

Prostaglandins (PGs): hormones that participate in renal hemodynamics. Vasodilatory PGs (PGE_2 and PGI_2) increase the RBF and GFR, whereas vasoconstrictory PGs (thromboxane A_2) decrease both RBF and GFR. PGE_2 also increases Na^+ and water excretion.

Renin: a hormone secreted by the juxtaglomerular cells of the afferent arteriole of the JGA. Renin converts angiotensinogen to angiotensin I (AI).

Respiratory acid-base disorders: are those that result primarily from changes in arterial PCO_2. In respiratory acidosis, there is an increase in arterial PCO_2, whereas in respiratory alkalosis, there is a decrease in arterial PCO_2.

Secondary change: a compensatory response that minimizes alterations in blood pH.

Simple acid-base disorder: the occurance of one primary disturbance with appropriate secondary response.

Solvent drag: a process in which the osmotic flow of water (solvent) drags certain solutes across the cell membrane through channels or paracellular pathways (see passive transport).

Specific gravity: defined as the ratio of the weight of a solution to the weight of an equal volume of water.

Symport: transport of solutes in the same direction. Symport is also called cotransport.

Syndrome of inappropriate secretion of ADH (SIADH): a clinical condition of hyponatremia due to inappropriate hypothalamic or nonhypothalamic production of ADH. Certain drugs may potentiate the action of endogenous ADH, and cause SIADH.

Titratable acidity: defined as the number of equivalents of hydroxyl ions to titrate a unit volume of acidic urine to the pH of the blood (i.e., pH of 7.40). The excretion of phosphate in the form of $H_2PO_4^-$ is called titratable acid excretion.

Tonicity: refers to the effective osmolality of a solution, and is determined by the concentration of those solutes that cannot pass through the cell membrane.
Transcellular transport: movement of substances through the cell membranes.
Trousseau's sign: a sign of tetany due to hypocalcemia and hypomagnesemia. Trousseau's sign induces carpal spasm when a blood pressure cuff is inflated above the systolic blood pressure for 2-3 minutes.
Tubuloglomerular feedback (TGF): a mechanism by whch the GFR and RPF are autoregulated. The macula densa of the JGA plays an important role in the TGF mechanism. Note that TGF is different from G-T balance.
Volatile acid: an acid (H_2CO_3) that is dehydrated to CO_2 and water, and is expelled by the lungs.

INDEX